D1251248

"You know anything about mushrooms, Joe?..."

"Grin and Bear It," by George Lichty
Courtesy of Publishers-Hall Syndicate

Soil Biochemistry

Volume 4

BOOKS IN SOILS AND THE ENVIRONMENT

edited by

A. Douglas McLaren

College of Natural Resources
University of California
Berkeley, California

Soil Biochemistry, Volume 1, edited by A. D. McLaren and G. H. Peterson

Soil Biochemistry, Volume 2, edited by A. D. McLaren and J. Skujiņš

Soil Biochemistry, Volume 3, edited by E. A. Paul and A. D. McLaren

Soil Biochemistry, Volume 4, edited by E. A. Paul and A. D. McLaren

Also in the Series

Organic Chemicals in the Soil Environment, Volume 1, edited by C. A. I. Goring and J. W. Hamaker

Organic Chemicals in the Soil Environment, Volume 2, edited by C. A. I. Goring and J. W. Hamaker

Humic Substances in the Environment, by M. Schnitzer and S. U. Khan

Microbial Life in the Soil: An Introduction, by T. Hattori

Additional Volumes in Preparation

SOIL BIOCHEMISTRY

EDITED BY

E. A. Paul
Department of Soil Science
University of Saskatchewan
Saskatoon, Saskatchewan, Canada

A. Douglas McLaren
College of Natural Resources
University of California
Berkeley, California

Volume 4

MARCEL DEKKER, INC., New York

MARCEL DEKKER, INC.
270 Madison Avenue, New York, New York   10016

LIBRARY OF CONGRESS CATALOG CARD NUMBER: 66-27705

ISBN: 0-8247-6141-3

Current printing (last digit):
10 9 8 7 6 5 4 3 2 1

PRINTED IN THE UNITED STATES OF AMERICA

PREFACE

This volume acknowledges an expanding literature concerning
the transformation of pesticides and hydroxamic acids in soils.
The importance of environmental factors is recognized in discussions
of the microbiology and biochemistry of nitrogen and phosphorus
transfer in ecosystems. Some aspects of humus biochemistry have
been updated, and efforts to mimic soil enzyme systems by means of
artificial polymer-enzyme matrices are described.

In a sense, the content of this volume spirals back on
Volume 1 of this series, but it does not circle back because one
can see steady progress. That humus is now better understood can
be realized if one considers that model building of humus and
humus-enzyme systems is being taken seriously. Furthermore, since
the first volume appeared in 1967, entire monographs, *Humic
Substances*, by M. Schnitzer and S. U. Khan, and *Microbial Life in
the Soil*, by T. Hattori, have appeared with a rigor of approaches
unknown and only hoped for at that time. The volume *Organic
Chemicals in the Soil Environment*, by C. A. Goring and J. W. Hamaker,
has been expanded to two volumes. Finally, the new journal *Soil
Biology and Biochemistry* is making a major contribution to the
field. Our subject is manifesting an excitement heretofore found
only among animal and plant biochemists. To the extent that
environmentalists have fanned an interest, we are grateful. It
is our hope that the study of the underlying principles of the
biochemistry of the soil and related systems, such as sediments,
will in turn be a meeting ground of the numerous environmental
disciplines.

E. A. Paul
A. D. McLaren

iii

CONTRIBUTORS TO THIS VOLUME

R. G. BURNS, Biological Laboratory, University of Kent, Canterbury, Kent, England

J. H. A. BUTLER, Division of Soils, CSIRO, Glen Osmond, South Australia

Z. FILIP, Department of Microbiology, Agricultural University, Prague, CSSR

K. HAIDER, Institut für Biochemie des Bodens, Forschungsanstalt für Landwirtschaft, Braunschweig-Völkenrode, Germany

R. L. HALSTEAD, Soil Research Institute, Canada Department of Agriculture, Ottawa, Ontario, Canada

J. N. LADD, Division of Soils, CSIRO, Glen Osmond, South Australia

R. B. McKERCHER, Department of Soil Science, University of Saskatchewan, Saskatoon, Saskatchewan, Canada

J. P. MARTIN, Department of Soil Science and Agricultural Engineering, University of California, Riverside, California

LYNN K. PORTER, United States Department of Agriculture, Agricultural Research Service, Fort Collins, Colorado

J. S. WAID, Department of Botany, University of Canterbury, Christchurch, New Zealand

CONTENTS

CONTENTS OF OTHER VOLUMES

xi

CHAPTER 1

NITROGEN TRANSFER IN ECOSYSTEMS

Lynn K. Porter[*]
United States Department of Agriculture
Agricultural Research Service
Fort Collins, Colorado

I. INTRODUCTION

On our planet, nitrogen interchanges from one chemical compound
to another and is also transferred from one N pool to another. The
N pools can be thought of in such global terms as atmospheric N,
lithospheric (rock and mineral) N, and biospheric (soil organic matter, plant and animal) N. The biospheric N can also be subdivided
into the N associated with the earth's major ecosystems: forests,
grasslands, deserts, oceans, marshes, lakes, rivers, estuaries, and
tundra, and, of course, many varied ecosystems that would fit under
these broad headings. In each of these ecosystems, N interchanges
from one chemical compound to another by the biochemical reactions
of ammonification, nitrification, nitrogen fixation, and denitrifi-

---

*Research Soil Scientist.

1

cation. In each ecosystem, the rate of the above reactions may be largely controlled by abiotic factors, such as temperature and aeration, etc. Each ecosystem has its own peculiar plant life, animals, soils, and water-movement systems; therefore, N transfer from component to component in each ecosystem will vary. Detailed information for the N transfers in each ecosystem is not available, and in this chapter, only limited information can be given about a few of these ecosystems.

In addition to the N transfers occurring within an ecosystem, many N transfers are between ecosystems or are global transfers. Rivers carry N-rich sediments and inorganic NO_3^- from the forests, grasslands, and deserts to lakes and oceans, or ammonia volatilized from the landscape of one ecosystem is transported via the atmosphere to many other ecosystems. An entire spectrum of N transfers occurs. Many of the transfers are within the framework of a single ecosystem, from soil to plant to animal and then the return of animal and plant back to the soil. However, many of the N transfers must be visualized in terms of regional or global movement of N.

II. GLOBAL DISTRIBUTION AND TRANSFER OF N

An examination of the global distribution of N shows that 98% of the N mass of the earth is contained in the rocks and minerals (Table 1). Stevenson [1, 2] has indicated that it is the general view that this N exists as nitrides of iron, titanium, and other metals, or as NH_4^+ ions held in the lattice structure of primary silicate minerals. No doubt a continuous supply of N (largely as NH_4^+) is being released by the weathering of rocks and minerals. The rate of this release and its magnitude are unknown. Viets and Hageman [3] have discussed the occurrence of nitrate-N in rocks. They state: "Nitrate deposits are not limited to the country rock of a definite geologic series. They have been found in large quantities in the Cretaceous, Tertiary, and Triassic with smaller quantities in the Jurassic."

TABLE 1

Geochemical Distribution of N[a]

N Pool	N Mass geograms = 10^{20} g	Percent of total N mass
Atmosphere	38.0	1.96
Lithosphere		
Igneous rocks	1930.0	97.82
Sedimentary rocks	4.0	
Biosphere		
Living organisms	0.00038 ⎫	
Terrestrial organic N	0.0082 ⎬	0.02
Ocean-bottom organic N	0.0054 ⎭	
Total N Mass	1972	

[a]Reprinted from Ref. [1], page 4, by courtesy of The American Society of Agronomy.

The amount of nitrogen in the biosphere constitutes only 0.02% of the global mass of N (Table 1). Most of the biospheric N is found in humus or partially decayed organic matter. It is the microbial conversion of this dead organic N into mineral forms of N (NH_4^+ and NO_3^-) that largely underlies the active growing biomass (plants and animals) of the earth.

There are 7550 kg of N above each square meter of land or water, or approximately 27,234 metric tons of N in the air above each acre of the earth [4], and this N mass represents 1.96% of the earth's N mass (Table 1). Most of the atmospheric N exists as molecular N_2 and the triple bond (N≡N) of this diatomic molecule is exceedingly stable. The chemistry and modes of reaction of molecular nitrogen, N_2, have been discussed by Leigh [5], Chatt and Richards [6], and Roberts [7]. Symbiotic nitrogen fixers (i.e., microorganisms living in association with plants) and free-living organisms contain an enzyme nitrogenase that is able to activate the triple bond of molecular nitrogen so that it can be reduced to NH_3 (nitrogen fixation: N≡N + nitrogenase → activated 2 N, activated 2 N + 3 H_2 → 2 NH_3). The microorganisms containing nitrogenase are able to convert N_2 to NH_3 at low temperatures (15°C-40°C and atmospheric pressure).

Commercially, N_2 is converted into NH_3 by the Haber process. This reaction proceeds in the presence of an iron catalyst at an elevated temperature, approximately $500^{\circ}C$, and at several hundred atmospheres of N_2. Hardy et al. [8] said, "Recent engineering improvements in the Haber-Bosch process have substantially reduced the cost of chemical fixation. Turbo-compressors capable of operating at extremely high temperatures and pressures have greatly improved the process. In 1000-ton-per-day or larger plants, ammonia can be produced for $30 per ton at the production site. This cost is composed of 40% for raw materials, 33% for utilities, 2.3% for catalysts and chemicals, 0.9% for labor, 3.7% for plant maintenance, and 20% for indirect charges." There is now substantial evidence [5, 6] that it may be possible to synthesize industrial catalysts that would permit N_2 fixation to take place under milder conditions than are now required in the Haber process. No doubt milder conditions would further reduce the cost of $30 per ton at the plant site. However, transportation costs of $25 per ton now nearly equal the cost of reducing N_2 to ammonia [8].

Enormous amounts of energy are expended by both microorganism and man in converting N_2 into NH_3. Delwiche [9] suggests that man expends 6000 kcal of energy in converting 1 kg of N_2 to inorganic NH_4^+ or NO_3^-. He also stated: "The few controlled studies with which I am familiar suggest that the increase in crop yields achieved by the addition of a kilogram of fertilizer N amounts to about the same number of calories. This suggests that one can exchange the calories put into industrial fixation of nitrogen for the calories in food." It is apparent that part of the green revolution (greater crop yields) achieved through N fertilization and mechanization is bought at the expense of our dwindling carbon reserves.

Delwiche [9] pointed out that caution must be used in trying to present worldwide inventories and the annual flows of N from one global N pool to another. This is because so many uncertainties exist in our knowledge and the information we do have that would permit estimates to be made is exceedingly crude. Even so, Delwiche

attempted to assign values to the amounts of N flowing into and out
of the atmosphere (Table 2). The amount of industrially fixed N is
known with a high degree of confidence. Thirty million metric tons

TABLE 2

Estimates of the Annual Amounts of N Leaving
and Returning to the Atmosphere[a]

	10^6 N Mass metric tons
Leaving atmosphere via:	
NH_3 and NO_3^- in precipitation and adsorbed by plants, water, and soils[b]	25
Industrial fixation of N_2	30
Biological fixation of N_2	
Marine organisms 10	
Cultivated legumes (symbiotic organisms) 14	54
Terrestrial organisms (symbiotic and nonsymbiotic) excluding cultivated legumes 30	
Returning to atmosphere via:	
N_2 and N_2O generated in microbial and chemical denitrification	
Terrestrial sources 43	83
Marine sources 40	
NH_3 and N oxides generated by combustion, volatilization, and volcanic sources[b]	17.3

[a]Reprinted from Ref. [5] by courtesy of Scientific American, Inc.
[b]Delwiche estimates 25 metric tons delivered to earth in rainfall
but only 30% is freshly fixed by lightning and ionization phenomena
in the atmosphere. The other 70% is previously fixed N_2 that is
cycling.

of fertilizer N are now being produced annually, and this is expected
to increase to about 50×10^6 metric tons by the mid-1970s [10].
Delwiche estimates that terrestrial organisms other than symbiotic
organisms associated with cultivated legumes fix 30×10^6 metric tons
of N, cultivated symbiotic organisms fix 14×10^6 metric tons of N,
and marine organisms fix 10×10^6 metric tons for an annual global
estimate of 54×10^6 metric tons. However, he readily admits that
his estimates for marine fixation could be off as much as a factor

TABLE 3

Annual Rates of N_2 Fixed by Various Symbiotic and
Nonsymbiotic Organisms in Various Ecological Habitats

Organism and habitat	N fixed (kg/ha/year)	Reference
Bluegreen algae and lichens		
Arid Australian soils	3	[11]
Arizona desert soils	10	[12]
Rice soils (Philippines)	10-55	[13]
Paddy soils of India	13-80	[11]
Mountain meadow soils	26-48	[14]
Tropical oceans during algal blooms	0.32 (kg/ha/day)	[15]
Nonsymbiotic free-living organisms		
Native grassland (Pawnee)	1	[16]
Native grassland (Matador)	1	[17]
Native vegetation (Davis, Calif.)	2.1±0.8	[18]
Fallow soil (Davis, Calif.)	3.5±1.7	[18]
Wheat (Davis, Calif.)	4.0±1.3	[18]
Irrigated turf	4.8±1.9	[18]
Under wheat	24.6-42.5	[18]
Under Pinus	35.8-62.7	[11]
Under mustard	44.8	[18]
Under *Eleusine coracana*	112-145.6	[18]
Under tropical bare soil	123	[18]
Under regenerated African bush	716.8	[18]
Nodulated nonlegumes		
Myrica gale	8.9	[11]
Alnus crispa (alder, Glacier Bay, Alaska)	61.5	[19]
Alnus glutenosa	224	[11]
Hippophae rhamnoides (Britain)	69.5	[20]
Casuraine equisetifolia (Cape Verde Islands)	58	[21]
Nodulated legumes		
Soybean	94	[11]
Sweet clover	104	[11]
Red clover	115	[11]
Mixed legumes	125	[11]
White clover	148	[11]
Lucerne	176	[11]

of ten. Increasing the marine estimate tenfold would increase the total annual global figures to 134 x 10^6 metric tons, or a nearly threefold increase in the global N fixed annually by microorganisms and algae. Good quantitative information on the rate of N_2 fixation in various ecosystems is hard to obtain (Table 3). Stewart [22] probably best summarized our dearth of quantitative information: "Studies on legumes have rightly centered around the 200-odd species commonly used in agriculture, where they contribute, on the average, 100 to 200 kilograms of nitrogen per hectare per year. However, the 12,000-odd species distributed throughout the nonagricultural soils which constitute nine-tenths of the land surface should not be forgotten. Many are bushes and trees which have not yet been examined for nodules, but as 89% of those so far examined are nodule bearing, there is little doubt that they also contribute appreciably to soil fertility."

To illustrate our limited knowledge concerning legumes, we can cite the case of legumes native to the grasslands. In 1952, Whitman and Stevens [23] observed nodules on 27 species of legumes native to the North Dakota grasslands. The legume productivity was usually less than 10% and often less than 1% of the total grassland productivity. In 1969, in an exploratory study (unpublished), I found nodules on 20 species of legumes native to the Montana counties of Rosebud, Custer, Carter, Fallon, and Prairie, and even though sampled under less than ideal conditions, 50% of the nodules from various legume species were capable of fixing $^{15}N_2$. Paul et al. [17] have found nodules on 16 species of legumes native to the Matador (Canada) grassland. Using the C_2H_2 assay for nitrogenase, they found all the nodules tested reduced C_2H_2 to C_2H_4. The C_2H_2 and $^{15}N_2$ assays have provided positive evidence that legumes native to grassland fix N_2, but only meager information exists concerning the magnitude of the symbiont's N contribution to various grasslands. The low legume population on the Matador [17] and Pawnee [16] grassland sites indicates only very low fixation rates. Nitrogen-fixing nodules are found on plant species of the Angiospermae class. These usually scrubby plants

thrive in the foothills and mountains of the temperate and arctic
regions [24]. Becking [25] described the distribution of nodule-
bearing nonlegume plants that are scattered throughout the world.
We have only limited quantitative information concerning these numerous species. Nodules have been observed on sagebrush (*Artemisia*)
and prickly pear (*Opuntia*) [26]. Nodules also have been observed
for the softwood tree of the Coniferales class. These useful trees
are found throughout South America, Mexico, South Africa, the West
Indies, New Zealand, Australia, and the islands of the Pacific [24].

Bluegreen algae (Table 3) are important to the N economy of desert
soils [12], mountain meadow soils [14], rice culture [13], and oceans
and lakes [15, 27, 28]. Also, a symbiosis exists between lichens
and bluegreen algae; yet quantitative information is not available
on the contribution that lichens make to the N economics of various
ecosystems [4]. Considerable literature [4, 11, 22, 24, 25, 29-32]
describes the different plant genera in various habitats that fix N.
In Table 3 are presented estimates that give some idea of the magnitude of the N input in various ecosystems. However, most of the
information presented is based on minimal observations. Hardy et al.
[8, 33] give values obtained by the sensitive C_2H_2-to-C_2H_4 method.
It will probably require a decade using the sensitive C_2H_2-to-C_2H_4
method before we have adequate information for the N-fixation inputs
for various ecosystems.

Besides the fixation of molecular N_2 there are other important
exchanges between the atmosphere and biosphere. Numerous N compounds
are emitted or escape into the air. Oxides of nitrogen are emitted
into the air from combustion engines; electrical and steam plants
utilizing fossil fuels; refineries; industrial retorts such as cement
plants; and, finally, denitrification processes in the soil and
aquatic habitats. Nitric oxide is the major nitrogen oxide emitted
by combustion engines [34]. This oxide is rapidly oxidized by ozone
and slowly by oxygen to form nitrogen dioxide and, finally, nitric
acid [35]. In the United States in 1968, Newell [36] reported that
the following amounts of nitrogen oxide in millions of metric tons

were produced by combustion processes: power and heating, 9.1; vehicles, 7.3; refuse disposal, 0.5; industry, 0.2. This amounts to 17.1 x 10^6 metric tons of nitrogen oxides. Most of these nitrogen oxides were probably converted to nitric acid in the atmosphere. The United States, through incidental combustion processes, produces nitrogen oxides (assuming most as NO) that equal more than one-fourth of the world's industrial production of fertilizer N.

Denitrification processes in soils produce molecular nitrogen and nitrogen oxides [37-49]. Numerous organisms if given an energy source, moderately warm temperatures, nitrate and an anaerobic environment, will reduce nitrate to nitrite and, finally, to the gaseous products nitrous oxide, N_2O, and molecular nitrogen, N_2. Fry [50] gives the following hypothetical scheme for nitrate reduction in microorganisms:

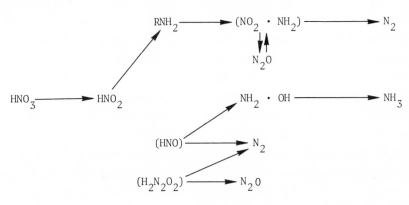

Although most of the N being released by bacterial denitrification is N_2, nitrous oxide (N_2O) is an important product. Stefanson and Greenland [42], in studying nitrous oxide evolution patterns from the Urrbrae red-brown earth (soils representative of major wheat growing areas of southern Australia), found nitrous oxide accounted for two-thirds of the nitrogen appearing in the gaseous phase. Even though evolution of N_2O has been reported from soils in the field [41, 45], the data are only qualitative. Rates of production and diffusion of N_2O from natural ecosystem soils are unknown. Environmental conditions

such as soil temperature, soil volumetric moisture, and the compac-
tion and texture of the soil would affect diffusion and production
rates. Even though we do not know the transfer rates of N_2O between
the biosphere and atmosphere we do know that N_2O escaping from soils
helps to maintain the approximately 0.25 ppm N_2O [34] of the atmospher

Ammonia, amines, and other reduced volatile compounds of nitrogen interchange between the atmosphere and biosphere. Sources of
volatile ammonia and amines are animal wastes [51-56]; ammoniacal
fertilizers [37, 57-67]; sewage streams and impoundments [68, 69];
and combustion processes [70-71]. In 1875, Schloesing [72] proposed
that some of the ammonia in the atmosphere originates from marine
sources. The degree of release of ammonia, or degree of absorption
of ammonia by any water surface, is highly dependent on the pH and
the temperature of the water surface [73]. The pH of ocean water
is about 8.1 ± 0.2 [74] and probably is alkaline enough to release
ammonia, depending on the water temperature. Dugdale [15] has indicated that ocean waters contain only small amounts of ammonium
(0.2-5 µg NH_4^+-N per liter). Apparently the NH_4^+ is rapidly assimilated by phytoplankton, for Dugdale estimated the turnover time for
ammonium in tropical ocean water to be about 40 hrs. If ammonia is
volatilized from ocean surfaces, the concentrations are probably
extremely small, making detection very difficult. However, the atmospheric NH_3 pool could be maintained and buffered easily by only
small amounts of NH_3 escaping from or being absorbed by the vast
ocean surfaces. Our understanding of the biosphere-atmosphere exchange or biosphere NH_4^+-N cycle will depend to a great degree on our
understanding of the equilibrium between the atmosphere's NH_3 and
NH_4^+ and the ocean's NH_4^+-N.

To a lesser degree, NH_3 escaping from or being absorbed by lakes
and streams tends to modify atmospheric NH_3 pools. Some lakes serve
as effective sinks for NH_3 [75], and considerable data exist that
show a tremendous seasonal fluctuation for the NH_4^+ concentration in
lake waters [27, 28, 76]. Part of the variations in NH_4^+ content is
caused by the seasonal stratification and seasonal circulation of
many lake waters, part is caused by the seasonal assimilation by

plant and microbial life. However, we must ask ourselves whether
some of the variation might not be caused by NH_3 volatilization.
Stratton [68, 69] showed that NH_3 is volatilized from sewage streams
and secondary sewage water impoundments.

Soils [75, 77, 78] and plants [79, 80] also serve as sinks for
atmospheric NH_3. Hutchinson et al. [80], from absorption rate data
at very low concentrations (20 ppb NH_3), have suggested that a field
crop might satisfy as much as 10% of its total N requirement by foliar
absorption of NH_3. A committee of the American Chemical Society
[34] indicates that the atmospheric NH_3 concentration is approximately
0.01 ppm. Small amounts of NH_3 may also escape from plants into
the atmosphere [79, 81].

The atmosphere is not only a reservoir but a dynamic system,
where N_2, NO, N_2O, and NH_3 are transformed to other nitrogenous compounds by ionizing radiations and oxidation reactions [82]. Also,
nitrogen compounds move and are dispersed by the atmosphere. These
volatile nitrogenous compounds (NH_3, $R-NH_2$, NO, NO_2, NO_3^-, and N_2O)
react among themselves and with other substances and are absorbed or
utilized by various sinks in the biosphere. But an uncertainty
exists as to the magnitude of the chemical reactions and to the
extent of interchange between the atmosphere and the biosphere.

Perhaps this uncertainty can be illustrated by variations reported for NH_4^+ and NO_3^- in rainfall. Ericksson [83] reported the NH_4^+
and NO_3^- in annual precipitation for various locations in North America.
The total inorganic N values ranged from 1.6 kg N per hectare per
year in Oklahoma to 21.0 in Kentucky. Miller's [84] data from locations all over the world ranged from 1.79 kg N per hectare per year
in New Zealand to 22.2 at Proskau, Germany. The average total inorganic N from rainfall was 9.03 kg/ha/yr, with about one-third as
NO_3^--N, and two-thirds as NH_4^+-N. The NH_4^+ content of spring rainfall
has been reported to be as much as four times higher than rain in other
seasons [85]. Delwiche [9] estimated that the total amount of fixed
N delivered to the earth in rainfall is of the order of 25 million
metric tons per year. He stated: "My own estimate is that 70 percent
of this total is previously fixed nitrogen cycling through the bio-

sphere and that only 30 percent is freshly fixed by lightning and
other atmospheric phenomena." We are far from understanding the fixed
N (NH_4^+ and NO_3^-) cycle of the atmosphere.

The small but persistent amounts of NH_4^+ and NO_3^- in the atmosphere
may be of great ecological significance. For example, Taylor et al.
[86] reported that for a watershed at Coshocton, Ohio, the input of
nitrogen in rain was greater than that lost in runoff and Bormann
et al. [87] found similar information for a forest watershed in New
Hampshire.

III. GLOBAL DISTRIBUTION AND TRANSFER OF BIOSPHERIC N

As mentioned previously, the N in the biosphere constitutes only
0.02% of the N mass of our planet. Table 4 illustrates the distribution of that N between the land and water masses of the earth. On
both the land (39.7%) and the ocean bottoms (47%), most of the N is
associated with fairly inert organic substances. When added together,
inert organic N sources constitute 86.7% of the biosphere N. It is
the slow microbial degradation (ammonification: amino acids and
heterocyclic N compounds + $O_2 \rightarrow CO_2 + H_2O + NH_3$) of these organic

TABLE 4

Global Distribution of Biosphere N[a]

Source	N mass (10^{15} g)	Percent of total
Land		
Soil organic N	760	39.72
Inorganic N (NO_3^- and NH_4^+)	140	7.32
Plants N	12	0.63
Animals N	0.2	0.01
Ocean		
Ocean bottom organic N	900	47.04
Inorganic N (NO_3^- and NH_4^+)	100	5.23
Plants N	0.80	0.04
Animals N	0.17	0.01
Total Biosphere N	1913.17	

[a]Reprinted from Ref. [9] by courtesy of Scientific American, Inc.

substances, with the release of NH_4^+ that provides the majority of N
for terrestrial plants. Although inorganic nitrogen (NH_4^+ and NO_3^-)
makes up only 12% of the biospheric N (Table 4), it plays an exceedingly important part in the movement of nitrogen in ecosystems and
between ecosystems. In most agricultural soils, NH_4^+ is oxidized by
Nitrosomonas (NH_4^+ + 1 1/2 O → HNO_2 + H_2O) and *Nitrobacter* (NO_2^- +
1/2 O_2 → NO_3^- + H_2O). However, plants in the grasslands and forest
probably obtain most of their N in the NH_4^+ form.

The degradation rate of organic N located on ocean bottoms may
be slow and considerably different from that observed for soils.
Jannasch et al. [88] have shown that rates of microbial degradation
for various organic substrates were 10 to 100 times slower at sea
depths of 5300 m than in refrigerated controls at comparable
temperatures.

The oceans contain large quantities of nitrate, with the content
increasing with depth and reaching a maximum at about 1000 m. Pinchot
[89] has an illustration that shows the NO_3^--N concentration at a
depth of 1000 m, in the Atlantic, Pacific and Indian oceans, ranges
from approximately 440 to 590 mg NO_3^--N per cubic meter. The productivity of the ocean's surface is largely dependent upon the upwelling
of nutrients from deep sea depths. One of the best known of these
upwelling areas is 800 miles long and 30 miles wide, along the shores
of Chile and Peru [89]. Most of the oceans are like a desert as
compared with this area. In 1968, in this upwelling area, 9.53 x 10^6
metric tons (399 metric tons per square mile) of fish, mostly an-
chovies, were harvested. The anchovie protein (amine nitrogen) is
transported to the United States and other countries and used largely
as protein in chicken and animal feed. If we assume that this fish
protein has an N content of 16%, then 1.45 x 10^6 metric tons of N
are transferred from this one ocean area to our land masses yearly.

Concern over NO_3^- pollution of ground waters and eutrophication
of lakes and streams has prompted investigation into how extensive
and varied is the transport of nutrients by waters [3, 90-92]. Viets
and Hageman [3] and Frink [91] reviewed studies concerned with NO_3^-
in drainage waters for numerous watersheds and for irrigation and

drainage basins. The estimates are as varied as the land use itself.
Perhaps this complexity can best be illustrated with N data assembled
for the upper Santa Ana basin of California [93]. This basin contains 144,073 ha and has a human population of 630,000. The land
receives about 4201 metric tons N per year from the atmosphere (1939
metric tons as NH_3 and NO_3^-, either absorbed directly by plants and
soils or dissolved in rain, and 2262 metric tons N_2 by symbiotic and
nonsymbiotic fixation). The land also receives 4716 metric tons N
per year (1960 basis) in the water supply (4534 metric tons/year from
pumped ground waters and 182 metric tons/year from stream flow). Although manures and ammoniacal fertilizers are subject to volatile
losses, these investigators calculate that 2896 metric tons N per
year from manure and 7363 metric tons N per year from fertilizers
actually enter the soil. In addition, the land surface receives
3554 metric tons N per year in municipal sewage and solid wastes and
73 metric tons/year from industrial sources. The total N transferred
into the soils of this basin yearly via precipitation, sorption,
sewage, manures, fertilizer, and nitrogen fixation, and in water
sources, amounts to 22,802 metric tons of N. About 12,802 metric
tons N per year are assimilated by plants, and the soil loses 2391
metric tons of N yearly by denitrification. This leaves 7609 metric
tons N per year for leaching or accumulation in soil profiles as
NO_3^- or soil organics.

   In addition to the N transfer mentioned above for N entering or
leaving the soil, the basin loses to the atmosphere 4303 metric tons
N per year emitted by motor vehicles, boilers, incinerators, etc.
Ammonia volatilized from manure and ammoniacal fertilizers accounts
for 1547 metric tons of N yearly transferred to the atmosphere.
Adding these figures to the 2391 metric tons N lost from the soil via
denitrification, a yearly total of 8241 metric tons N are transferred
to the atmosphere in this basin. Because the basin only receives
4201 metric tons N per year from nitrogen fixation and as NH_3^+ and NO_3^-
in rain or by sorption, this leaves a balance of 4040 metric tons N
to be transferred via the atmosphere to other systems.

The hydrology of each watershed, regional basin, or natural ecosystem must be considered in the transfer of N. Maybe this can best
be illustrated by the rate of groundwater recharge and turnover given
by Viets and Hageman [3]. They indicated that Carlson found the mean
residence time of recharged ground water in a Wisconsin drainage basin
as 45 days and in a New Jersey basin as 30 days, whereas the mean
residence time for the Ogallala aquifer under Colorado's northern
high plains was 186 years. They state: "The Ogallala contains very
'old' water. Obviously, on a time-scale, nitrate pollution and de-
pollution of the New Jersey basin can occur 2265 times as fast (186
year/30 day) as the Ogallala formation." The investigators of nitrate
pollution [93] in the upper Santa Ana Basin emphasize the need for
studying hydrological information. They observed that hydrologic
responses in this basin were highly damped in both space and time.
Consequently, seasonal variations in withdrawal and recharge are
reflected in changes in water levels taking place over months and
years. The presence and movement of nitrate must also be associated
with this slow movement of water. Because of the slow horizontal
movement of water (0.0055 to 0.185 km/year), high nitrate levels persisting in ground waters of some areas must be related directly to
a nitrogen source in the soil or ground surface overlying these areas.
Similarly, the slow vertical movement of nitrate through the zone of
aeration suggests that the high nitrate in some wells can be accounted
for only by events that reflect changes in surface nitrogen levels
tens or perhaps even hundreds of years before.

The N in plants and animals constitutes only 0.69% of the N in
the biosphere (Table 4). This amount may seem inconsequential to
the overall picture of global biosphere N. However, the nitrogen in
plants and animals plays a highly important part in the development
of the soils and organic N in the soils of each ecosystem. Jenny [94]
and Stevenson [1] emphasized that the nitrogen content of the soils
in natural ecosystems slowly approaches an equilibrium value (climax
of vegetation succession). Jenny indicated that the magnitude of
this value depends upon such factors as climate, type of vegetation,

nature of terrain, soil physical characteristics, and the activities
of the microflora and microfauna.

The climate usually determines whether a forest, a grassland, a
desert, marsh, or a tundra ecosystem develop. The array of plant
species, the quantity of material they produce (both above and below
ground), and the intensity of the microbial activities all influence
the N content of the soils. Surface soils of deserts may contain
only 0.05% N; grassland may range from 0.1 to 0.3% N; and peat and
muck soils from 0.3 to 0.5% nitrogen [95]. Jenny [94] illustrated
how the nitrogen content in the grassland soils of the semihumid
and semiarid regions of North America may vary between 0.5 and
0.005% N, depending upon the mean annual temperature. His illustra-
tions show a decline in soil N with a rise in mean annual temperature
conforming to the equations

$$N = 1.55/[1 + e^{0.065(t-18.5)}] \tag{1}$$

for the semihumid region, and

$$N = 1.7/[1 + e^{0.45(t-1.5)}] \tag{2}$$

for the semiarid grasslands.

The amount of plant growth and extent of the below-ground root
systems must be very important factors in determining the amount of
N accumulating in any given ecosystem. In the tropics, the largest
addition of organic matter to the soil takes place under forest vegetation and the soil organic matter levels tend to be greater under
forest than under savannah [96]. However, in temperate zones, the
nitrogen content is higher in grassland than in forest soils. In
the temperate forest ecosystems most of the plant debris is in the
form of fallen leaves and woody materials, whereas in temperate grasslands there is extensive root debris.

Sims and Singh [97] have studied the herbage dynamics of various
grassland sites. They observed the average below-ground biomass (excluding litter): Y, in grams per square meter, is related to the

mean annual temperature (X) according to the equation Y = 2358.892 - 89.904X in ungrazed grasslands and Y = 2574 - 107.5X in grazed grass- lands. These equations indicate that as the mean annual temperature of the grassland sites increases, the below-ground biomass decreases. Furthermore, these investigators have shown that the relationship of the amount of root to the amount of shoot also seems to be governed by the temperature. Part of their explanation for the effect of temperature on below-ground biomass production is that as the sites shift from cool temperatures to warmer temperatures there is a shift from cool-season grasses and forbs to warm-season ones. Of course, the effects of temperature, moisture, and nitrogen on plant produc- tion are well known and must be evaluated in each natural community.

IV. DISTRIBUTION, TRANSFER, AND TURNOVER OF N IN NATURAL ECOSYSTEMS

Table 5 shows the major N distribution for a few natural communi- ties. Most of the N is located in the soil of each system, with various amounts in the plant materials. Usually, investigators consider only the total N in the soil to depths of 15.2 or 30.5 cm, because these are the zones of maximum root activity. However, in most ecosystems (natural and agricultural) some N is mineralized and also assimilated at soil depths up to 183 cm. Even though the N content of most soils decreases with depth, extensive amounts of N do exist below the first 30 cm. For example, Smika et al. [98] reported the following amounts of total N by depth for a North Dakota grassland soil: 0-15.2 cm, 6093 kg/ha; 15-30 cm, 3292 kg/ha; 30-45.7 cm, 2396 kg/ha; 45.7-60.9 cm, 1769 kg/ha; 60.9-91 cm, 2464 kg/ha; 91-122 cm, 1478 kg/ha; 122-152 cm, 1209 kg/ha; and 122-183 cm, 1040 kg/ha. In the 0- to 30-cm depth of this soil, there was 9385 kg N per hectare, whereas in the 0- to 183-cm profile, there was 19,824 kg N per hectare. The N profiles representative of several great soil groups have been illustrated by Stevenson [1]. Seldom do scientists study the mineralization and changes that occur in the soil N below 30 cm depth. For most eco- systems, highly detailed plant and soil N data are not available.

It is hoped that such information will be gathered as the Internationa
Biological Programme moves forward.

TABLE 5

Nitrogen Distribution in Various Natural Communities

Description of community	Total N (kg/ha)				Referen
	Soil	Plant	Litter	Roots	
Pine-afforested moor 80 years old	4192	493	470	124	[99]
Moist tropical forest, Ghana, 50 years old	4596	1797	35	214	[100]
Eucalyptus forest or Hawkesbury sandstone 14 years old	2264	392	11.2	--	[101]
Blue grama, Pawnee Grassland, Colo.	2500	10-15	--	120	[16]
Missouri prairie	6000	36	33	60-120	[102]

In the data presented in Table 5, no attempt was made to include
the total N found in the animal life of these communities. In the
Pawnee grassland, Reuss [16] estimates livestock N to represent 1 kg
N per hectare. This amount of animal N for the Pawnee grassland is
insignificant as compared to the soil and plant reserves of N (Table
5). Probably in most natural ecosystems (i.e., uninhabited by colon-
izing man), the amount of N in animal life will be only a very minor
portion of the N in the system considered. However, in urban communities and even in agricultural communities, animal life may contain considerable amounts of N. For example, the investigators [93]
for the upper Santa Ana project mentioned in Section III indicated
that the basin's 630,000 people contained 3.2×10^3 metric tons of
N, cattle (70,122 head) contained 9.5×10^2 metric tons, and poultry
(6.4×10^6) contained 2.6×10^2 metric tons. In the transfer of N
within an ecosystem or between ecosystems animal life plays a highly
important role. Animals consume a high amount of the grain and
roughage produced. This is especially true in modern agriculture
systems. Chickens, hogs, and cattle on United States farms produce
roughly 7.85×10^6 metric tons of N yearly in excrement [55]. The

630,000 human beings in the Santa Ana basin of California produced
municipal sewage containing 3.55 x 10^3 metric tons of N yearly [93].
Assuming that the approximately 200 x 10^6 people in the United States
produced amounts of municipal waste comparable to the people living
in the Santa Ana basin, then the human population of the United
States produces 1.128 x 10^6 metric tons of N yearly.

In natural ecosystems, a small amount of N is transferred from
animal life to the inorganic NO_3^- and NH_4^+ pool. In Reuss' [16] ten-
tative N model for the Pawnee grassland, livestock only transfer 6 kg
N per hectare per year to the NH_4^+ and NO_3^- pool, whereas the soil
organic matter N pool transfers 75 kg N per hectare per year. The
soil organic matter (biomass and humus) N pool receives most of its
N from plant roots (50 kg N per hectare per year) and plant tops (29
kg N per hectare per year).

Any ecosystem is a dynamic system capable of changing both biologically and chemically whenever the environment is altered. The
flux between various N pools or components in an ecosystem is established over long time intervals and may be drastically altered by
new management practices. For example, extensive timber harvesting
in our forests alters the amounts of residue being returned to the
soil and thus alters immobilization of N by microorganisms. Grasslands soils subjected to cultivation decline in N [103-105]. Ulti-
mately any management or climatic change results in a new balance
between the N components of the system. In each ecosystem the major
transfer steps among plants, microflora, and soil are the decomposition of organic materials with the subsequent release of NH_4^+, the
assimilation of NH_4^+ and NO_3^- by microflora and plant life, and the
nitrification of part of the NH_4^+. In grasslands and forest, nitrification probably plays a minor role, whereas in cultivated soil, it
may assume a major role. The nitrification process produces NO_2^- and
NO_3^-, both ions being susceptible to denitrification reactions and
leaching losses. Leaching and/or gaseous losses are a part of each
system and vary from ecosystem to ecosystem, but in most terrestrial
ecosystems, the release of NH_4^+ from soil organic matter and biomass

and the assimilation of N (NH_4^+ and NO_3^-) by newly developing plant
and microbial life plays the dominant role.

Whether we are dealing with a successional (developmental) or a
climax ecosystem, the equilibrium amount of soil organic matter N
is determined by the rate of addition of new biomass and the decomposition rate of humus components or dead biomass. This rate of
change of organic matter N with change of time is described in the
equation: $dN/dt = A - kN$, where N is the weight of organic matter
N per unit mass of soil, A is the yearly addition of N or new biomass per unit mass of soil, and k is the fraction of N decomposed
annually per unit mass of soil. On integrating and transposing
terms, the equation becomes $N = A/k + (N_o - A/k)e^{-kt}$, where N_o is
the weight of N in the soil-plant system initially. When the system
is in a steady-state condition, $dN/dt = 0$ and $A/k = N_s$, where N_s is
the steady-state nitrogen content of the soil-plant system. One
form or another of this equation has been used by various investigators [96, 104-110] in describing past changes in soil organic
matter or soil nitrogen and in predicting future changes, and the
equation often describes closely the total N changes occurring in
a system. However, Jenkinson [111] points out that this model
greatly oversimplifies the picture. The most serious objections
to the above equation are that it assumes (1) that annual addition of
biomass, A, is constant; (2) that the rate of decay of organic matter is independent of the amount added; and (3) that all parts of
the organic matter are equally subjected to decomposition.

In natural ecosystems the annual addition of plant and microflora biomass depends on environmental factors, especially climatic
factors (moisture and temperature), that vary during the year and
from year to year. Thus, an ecosystem's biomass is subjected to
times of feast and plenty and times of drought and famine. Finally,
k, the fraction decomposed annually, is not equal for all parts of
the ecosystem biomass. Carbon dating techniques and ^{14}C studies
have indicated that organic components of the soil differ in their
turnover and residence time in soil. Jenkinson [112], in working

with plant material uniformly labeled with ^{14}C found that about 10%
of the labeled carbon was in microbial tissue after 1 year and about
4% after 4 years. Jenkinson [113] summarized the expected loss of
carbon from plant material added to various soils and from these investigations found that the proportion of added carbon retained in
soils under different climatic conditions is remarkably similar. He
states: "Excluding very acid soils, about one-third of the added
carbon remains after 1 year and about one-fifth after 5 years."
Dahlman and Kucera [114] incorporated ^{14}C into growing grass plants
in a Missouri prairie and found the complete turnover of plant root
carbon to be about 4 years.

Some of the organic carbon in well-aerated mineral soils is extremely stable. Radiocarbon dating of the total carbon and carbon
fractions such as fulvic and humic acids has shown mean residence
times of from hundreds up to thousands of years [113, 115-117].
Clark and Paul [118] have summarized such information by stating:
"Recent work indicates that organic components of soil are composed
of at least three fractions when considered on a dynamic basis: (1)
decomposing plant residues and the associated biomass which turn
over at least once every few years; (2) microbial metabolites and
cell wall constituents that become stabilized in soil and possess a
half-life of 5-25 years; and (3) the resistant fractions, which in
grassland soils are composed of humic components ranging in age from
250 up to 2500 years."

Tracer studies [119-124] with the stable nitrogen isotope ^{15}N
also have shown that soil organic N can be fractionated into fractions
that show varying degrees of biological activity. Most of the above-
cited fractionation work was achieved by acid hydrolysis of the soils
and probably has little meaning as far as being able to relate these
fractions to the dynamic pools mentioned by Clark and Paul [118].
Methods for fractionating soil N into meaningful constituents are
far from perfected but progress is being made. Densimetric fractionation [125-127] of soil N into a humified and nonhumified "light
fraction," although only including 7-23% of the total N in soil,

accounted for 25-60% of the mineral nitrogen formed. Greenland discussed this technique and associated results in an extensive review
[128]. Paul et al. [117] used this technique in studying the distribution of radioactive plant residues in soil separates. By adding
100-mesh ^{14}C oat tissue to soil, moistening, drying, and then fractionating the soil with a density gradient column, they found slightly
more than half of the material was recovered relatively free from
inorganic materials. The remainder, however, appeared to be tightly
adsorbed to the clay-humus complex and could not be separated by
this physical technique. If ground, nondecomposed materials are so
rapidly adsorbed by clay minerals and humus colloids, it can be seen
why both chemical and physical separations are exceedingly difficult
in soils.

Most fractionation procedures disperse the nondecomposed or nonhumified plant material, the microflora biomass, and the humified
organic matter to some extent among all fractions. Thus, fractionation procedures are characterized by producing heterogeneous products that differ from fraction to fraction, depending on the procedure selected. Stanford et al. [129-132] and Smith and Stanford [133]
used hot water and $CaCl_2$ to extract organic N that was correlated
with N mineralization and N uptake by plants. Jenkinson [134], using
0.1 N Ba(OH)$_2$, extracted labeled-C materials from soils that were
directly proportional to the amount of labeled C mineralized by those
soils. Chichester [135] has been able to separate organic mineral
sediments that seem to have biological significance. The susceptibility of each size fraction to mineralization was assessed and the
percent N mineralized showed a severalfold increase in the finer
fractions. In addition, as the particle size of the organic-mineral
sediment decreased, the C:N ratio generally decreased, indicating
that nitrogen-rich substances were being adsorbed by clay minerals.
This focuses attention on the proteinaceous constituents of soil and
how they are stabilized and protected from biodegradation. Paul and
Clark [118] state: "Resistance of proteinaceous constituents of
soil humic materials to degradation by a wide array of microbial

proteases can probably be attributed to a lack of flexibility of the substrate and to mechanical as well as chemical shielding of localized areas of substrate surface." Greenland [136], Mortland [137, McLaren and Peterson [138], Estermann and McLaren [139], Burns et al. [140], and Skujins [141] have reviewed and discussed the many facets of absorption of organics by clays and how such adsorption may influence biochemical reactions. The biodegradation of organic N compounds is influenced by the adsorption of organic substrates and enzymes by clays, polymeric humic acid colloids, and amorphous iron and aluminum hydroxides. That organic compounds including enzymes can be stabilized in soils against biodegradation does point out the necessity of relating any isolated organic N constituent to its dynamic or mean residence time in the soil or ecosystem.

Nearly all of the mathematical treatments [117, 142-144] describing turnover of organic matter N or plant residues utilize the first-order decay equation $-dC/dt = kC$, where C is the concentration of the substance undergoing change, t is the time, and k is a proportionality constant. The differential term, dC/dt, denotes the velocity of the reaction. The differential equation can be integrated between the limits of the concentration C at time $t = 0$ (let this concentration be C_0-p). The quantity p is, therefore, the amount of the substance that has undergone reaction with time. The integrated equation is

$$-\int_{C_0}^{C_a-P} \frac{dC}{C} = K \int_0^t dt \tag{3}$$

which yields $-\ln (C_0- p) - (\ln C_0) = kt$, and solving for k yields

$$k = t^{-1} \ln [C_0/(C_0 - p)] = 2.303t^{-1} \log [C_0/(C_0 - p)] \tag{4}$$

The last equation permits one to calculate, from the measurement of values of p at various time intervals, the value of the first-order velocity constant k. Because the logarithm of the ratio $C_0/(C_0 - p)$

is a pure number, the velocity constant k is in reciprocal time units
(for mineralization of organic nitrogen, k is in terms of months^{-1}
or years^{-1}). Another important consequence of the first-order equation is that it permits the calculation of the time required to trans-
form one-half of a substance, i.e., when $t = t_{\frac{1}{2}}$ then $p = C_o/2$. Substitution of C_o into the integrated equation for p gives

$$t_{\frac{1}{2}} = (\ln 2)k^{-1} = 2.303(\log 2)k^{-1} = 0.693k^{-1} \qquad (5)$$

Russell [144] graphically presents the relationship for k in years
(half-life); his plots illustrate that as k increases, half-life decreases, e.g., for a k of 1%, the half-life is 69 years, whereas for
a k value of 10% the half-life is 6.9 years.

Jansson [143] assumed that the average annual removal rate of
labeled nitrogen for the years 1962-1967 gave good approximations of
the velocity constant k and he calculated the half-lives for the fertilizer nitrogen. The half-lives ranged from 27 to 53 years, depending
on the soil treatment. Fertilizer nitrogen not recovered in the
first year or two of the experiment was incorporated into biological
substances that were slowly mineralized. The half-life of the labeled
nitrogen applied to a soil without any organic matter addition was
49 years, whereas the following half-lives were found when the labeled
nitrogen was applied with various sources of organic matter: digested
sewage sludge, 53 years; leached sewage sludge, 33 years; leached
farm-yard manure, 32 years, farm-yard manure, 27 years; and fresh cow
dung, 33 years. Jansson [142] studied the turnover of residual ^{15}N
in an outdoor pot experiment with oats that were cropped yearly. After 6 years of cropping, he calculated the half-life of residual fertilizer ^{15}N (where nitrate was added) to be 20 years. The corresponding half-life of the residual ^{15}N in ammonium-treated pots was
29 years. Russell [144] found the half-life periods of N in various
pastures ranged from 24 to 280 years.

In natural ecosystems we are interested in describing the N
transfer from component to component. Detailed information is needed

on the k values, residence, or half-life of such N fractions as plant residues, soil microflora biomass, roots or nonhumified biomass, humified or polymerized soil organic N, and mineral-adsorbed NH_4^+ and organic N. To obtain such information, very detailed fractionation studies using tracer N will be needed. Although such studies are time-consuming, and often frustrating, they will eventually provide the information required to model the dynamic transfer of N from component to component in natural ecosystems.

A discussion of the rate constant, k, for turnover of inorganic nitrogen may be found in Chapter 1, Volume 3, and in Chapter 1, Volume 2, of *Soil Biochemistry*. The nitrogen cycle has also been discussed from other points of view by Campbell in Volume 1 and by Jansson in Volume 2 of this treatise.

REFERENCES

1. F. J. Stevenson, in *Soil Nitrogen* (W. V. Bartholomew and F. E. Clark, Eds.), Monograph 10, pp. 1-42, Amer. Soc. Agron., Madison, 1965.
2. F. J. Stevenson, *Science 130*, 221 (1959).
3. F. G. Viets, Jr., and R. H. Hageman, *Agricultural Handbook 413*, 63 pp., US Govt. Printing Off., Washington D.C., 1971.
4. E. F. Henzell and D. O. Norris, in *A Review of Nitrogen in the Tropics with Particular Reference to Pastures. (A Symposium)*, pp. 1-18, Commonwealth Bur. Pastures and Field Crops, Hurley, Berkshire, England *Bull. 46*, 1962.
5. G. J. Leigh, in *The Chemistry and Biochemistry of Nitrogen Fixation* (J. R. Postgate, Ed.), pp. 19-56, Plenum, New York, 1971.
6. J. Chatt and R. L. Richards, in *The Chemistry and Biochemistry of Nitrogen Fixation* (J. R. Postgate, Ed.), pp. 57-103, Plenum, New York, 1971.
7. E. A. Roberts, in *Nitrogen Nutrition of Plants* (E. A. Kirkby, Ed.), pp. 9-21, Wigley, Waverley, 1970.
8. R. W. F. Hardy, R. C. Burns, R. R. Herbert, R. D. Holsten, and E. K. Jackson. *Plant Soil (Special volume)*, p. 561 (1971).
9. C. C. Delwiche, *Sci. Amer. 223*, 137 (1970).
10. E. A. Harre, in *Fertilizer Trends*, p. 20, TVA, Muscle Shoals, Alabama, 1967.
11. W. D. P. Stewart, *Nitrogen Fixation in Plants*, p. 168, Athlone, London, 1966.
12. H. F. Mayland, T. H. McIntosh, and W. H. Fuller, *Soil Sci. Soc. Amer. Proc., 30*, 56 (1966).

13.   I. C. MacRae and T. F. Castro, *Soil Sci.*, *103*, 277 (1967).
14.   L. K. Porter and A. R. Grable, *Agron. J.*, *61*, 521 (1969).
15.   R. C. Dugdale, in *Biology and Ecology of Nitrogen*, Proc. Conf.
      Univ. Calif., Davis, December 1967, pp. 16-18, Natl. Acad.
      Sci., Washington, D. C., 1969.
16.   J. O. Reuss, in *Preliminary Analysis of Structure and Function
      in Grasslands* (N. R. French, Ed.), *Range Sci. Dept. Ser.
      No. 10*, pp. 133-146, Colo. State Univ., Ft. Collins, 1971.
17.   E. A. Paul, R. J. K. Myers, and W. A. Rice, *Plant Soil (Spe-
      cial volume)*, p. 495 (1971).
18.   P. L. Steyn and C. C. Delwiche, *Environ. Sci. Technol.*, *4*,
      1122 (1970).
19.   R. L. Crocker and J. Major, *J. Ecol.*, *43*, 427 (1955).
20.   W. D. P. Stewart and M. Pearson, *Plant Soil*, *26*, 348 (1967).
21.   Y. Dommergues, *Agrochimica*, *7*, 335 (1963).
22.   W. D. P. Stewart, *Science*, *158*, 1426 (1967).
23.   W. C. Whitman and O. A. Stevens, *North Dakota Acad. Sci. Proc.*,
      6, 73 (1952).
24.   E. K. Allen and O. N. Allen, in *Microbiology and Soil Fertility*,
      (C. M. Gilmour and O. N. Allen, Eds.), pp. 77-106, Oregon
      State Univ. Press, Corvallis, 1965.
25.   J. H. Becking, in *Stikstof (Dutch nitrogenous fertilizer review)*
      No. 12, pp. 47-74, issued by Centraal Stikstof Verkoop-
      kantoor (CSV) Central Nitrogen Sales Organization, Ltd.,
      The Hague, Netherlands, 1968.
26.   R. B. Farnsworth and M. W. Hammond, *Agron. Abstr.*, 83 (Novem-
      ber 1968).
27.   G. E. Hutchinson, *The Nitrogen Cycle in Lake Waters*, p. 836,
      Wiley, New York, 1957.
28.   D. R. Keeney, *The Nitrogen Cycle in Sediment-Water Systems*, a
      review presented before Div. S-2, Soil Sci. Soc. Amer.,
      August 1971.
29.   J. H. Becking, in *Nitrogen-15 in Soil-Plant Studies*, pp. 189-
      222, IAEA, Vienna, 1971.
30.   M. F. Jurgensen and C. B. Davey, *Soils Fert.* *33*, 435 (1970).
31.   A. W. Moore, *Soils Fert.* *29*, 113 (1966).
32.   G. Bond, *Ann. Rev. Plant Physiol.*, *18*, 107 (1967).
33.   R. W. F. Hardy, R. C. Burns, and R. D. Holsten, *Soil Biol.
      Biochem.*, *5*, 47 (1973).
34.   A report by the subcommittee on Environmental Improvement,
      Committee on Chemistry and Public Affairs, *Cleaning Our
      Environment, The Chemical Basis for Action*, pp. 35, 53,
      American Chem. Soc., Washington, D.C. 1969.
35.   R. D. Cadle and E. R. Allen, *Science*, *167*, 243 (1970).
36.   R. E. Newell, *Sci. Amer.*, *224*, 243 (1970).
37.   J. W. Woldendorp, in *Stickstoff (Dutch nitrogenous fertilizer
      review) No. 12*, pp. 32-46, issued by Centraal Stikstof
      Verkoopkantoor (CSV) Central Nitrogen Sales Organization,
      Ltd., The Hague, Netherlands, 1968.

38.   F. E. Broadbent and F. E. Clark, in *Soil Nitrogen* (W. V. Bar-
        tholomew and F. E. Clark, Eds.), Monograph *10*, p. 344,
        Amer. Soc. Agron., Madison, 1965.

39.   F. von Führ and J. M. Bremner, *Atompraxis 10* Hef 2, 109 (1964).

40.   D. W. Nelson and J. M. Bremner, *Soil Biol. Biochem.*, *2*, 203
        (1970).

41.   J. R. Burford and R. J. Millington, in *Trans.*, *9th Intl. Congr.
        Soil Sci.*, pp. 505-511, Adelaide, 1968.

42.   R. C. Stefanson and D. J. Greenland, *Soil Sci.*, *109*, 203 (1970).

43.   A. Adel, *Science*, *103*, 280 (1946).

44.   A. Adel, *Astron. J.*, *56*, 33 (1951).

45.   P. W. Arnold, *J. Soil Sci.*, *5*, 116 (1954).

46.   H. Nommik, *Acta Agric. Scand.*, *VI2*, 195 (1956).

47.   F. E. Clark and W. V. Bartholomew, *Soil Sci. Soc. Amer. Proc.*,
        24, 353 (1960).

48.   F. E. Clark and D. H. Smith, *Soil Sci. Soc. Amer. Proc.*, *24*,
        50 (1960).

49.   F. E. Clark, in *Trans. Intl. Congr. Soil Sci.*, Comm. IV and V,
        Palmerston North, N.Z., 1962, p. 173.

50.   B. A. Fry, *The Nitrogen Metabolism of Microorganisms*, p. 166,
        Wiley, New York, 1955.

51.   B. A. Stewart, *Env. Sci. Technol.*, *4*, 579 (1970).

52.   J. R. Simpson, in *9th Intl. Congr. Soil Sci. Trans.* p. 459,
        Adelaide, 1968.

53.   G. L. Hutchinson and F. G. Viets, Jr., *Science*, *166*, 514
        (1969).

54.   L. F. Elliott, G. E. Schuman and F. G. Viets, Jr., *Soil Sci.
        Soc. Amer. Proc.*, *35*, 752 (1971).

55.   R. C. Loehr, *Pollution Implications of Animal Waste--A Forward
        Oriented Review* (Prepared for the Robert S. Kerr Water
        Res. Center, FWPCA), p. 175, US Dept. Interior, Washing-
        ton, D.C., 1968.

56.   W. E. Burnett, *Environ. Sci. Technol*, *3*, 744 (1969).

57.   M. Blasco and A. H. Cornfield, *Nature (London)*, *212*, 1279
        (1966).

58.   J. P. Martin and N. D. Chapman, *Soil Sci.*, *71*, 25 (1951).

59.   G. M. Volk, *Agron. J.*, *51*, 746 (1959).

60.   C. B. Kresge and D. P. Satchell, *Agron. J.*, *52*, 104 (1960).

61.   L. N. Overein and P. G. Mose, *Soil Sci. Soc. Amer. Proc.*, *31*,
        57 (1967).

62.   G. M. Volk, *J. Agri. Food Chem.*, *9*, 280 (1961).

63.   G. H. Wagner and G. E. Smith, *Soil Sci.*, *85* (1958).

64.   R. D. Meyer, R. A. Olson and H. F. Rhodes, *Agron. J.*, *53*,
        241 (1961).

65.   G. M. Volk, *Soil Sci. Soc. Amer.*, *Proc.*, *34*, 513 (1970).

66.   I. C. MacRae and R. Ancajas, *Plant Soil*, *33*, 97 (1970).

67.   S. Larsen and D. Gunary, *J. Sci. Food Agri.*, *13*, 566 (1962).

68.   F. E. Stratton, *J. San. Eng. Div.*, *ASCE No. SA 2* (Proc. Paper
        6495), *95*, 223 (1969).

69. F. E. Stratton, *J. San. Eng. Div.*, *ASCE No. SA 6* (Proc. Paper 6283), *94*, 1085 (1968).

70. J. H. Harkins and S. W. Nicksic, *Environ. Sci. Technol.*, *1*, 751 (1967).

71. E. J. Russell and E. H. Richards, *J. Agri. Sci.*, *9*, 309 (1919).

72. A. Schloesing, *Compt. Rend.*, *80*, 175 (1875).

73. A. Melamed and C. Saliternik, in *Developments in Water Quality Research* (H. I. Shuval, Ed.), p.   , Ann Arbor, Humphrey, 1970.

74. W. W. Kellogg, R. D. Cadle, E. R. Allen, A. L. Lazrus, and E. A. Martell, *Science*, *175*, 587 (1972).

75. B. A. Malo, Ph.D. Thesis, Rutgers University, New Jersey, 1963.

76. C. Serruya and T. Berman, in *Developments in Water Quality Research* (H. I. Shuval, Ed.), p. 73, Ann Arbor, Humphrey, 1970.

77. G. L. Hutchinson and F. G. Viets, Jr., *Science*, *166*, 514 (1969).

78. R. B. Hanwalt, *Soil Sci. Soc. Amer. Proc. 33*, 231 (1969).

79. L. K. Porter, F. G. Viets, Jr., and G. L. Hutchinson, *Science*, *175*, 759 (1972).

80. G. L. Hutchinson, R. J. Millington, and D. B. Peters, *Science*, *175*, 771 (1972).

81. A. E. Martin and P. J. Ross, *Plant Soil*, *28*, 182 (1968).

82. P. Harteck and S. Dondes, *Science*, *146*, 30 (1964).

83. E. Ericksson, *Tellus*, *4*, 214 (1952).

84. N. H. J. Miller, *J. Agri. Sci.*, *1*, 480 (1905); also tabulated in: F. E. Allison, in *Soil Nitrogen* (W. V. Bartholomew and F. E. Clark, Eds.), Monograph 10, p. 573, Amer. Soc. Agron., Madison, 1965.

85. D. H. Yallon, *Tellus*, *16*, 200 (1964).

86. A. W. Taylor, W. M. Edwards, and E. C. Simpson, *Water Res. Res.*, *7*, 81 (1971).

87. F. H. Bormann, G. E. Likens, D. W. Fisher, and R. S. Pierce, *Science*, *159*, 882 (1968).

88. H. W. Jannasch, K. Eihjellen, C. O. Wirsen, and A. Farmanfarmaian, *Science*, *171*, 672 (1971).

89. G. B. Pinchot, *Sci. Amer.*, *223*, 3 (1970).

90. J. W. Biggar and R. B. Corey, in *Eutrophication: causes, consequences, correctives*, p. 404, Nat. Acad. Sci., Washington, D.C., 1969.

91. C. R. Frink, *Agri. Sci. Rev.*, *9*, 11 (1971).

92. United States Department of the Interior, Federal Water Pollution Control Administration, *Characteristics and pollution problems of irrigation return flow*, p. 237, Robert S. Kerr Water Res. Center, Ada, Oklahoma, 1969.

93. R. S. Ayers and R. L. Branson, unpublished work, 1971 *(Calif. Exp. Sta. Bull.*, in press (1973). Nitrates in the upper Santa Ana Basin in relation to groundwater pollution.)

94. H. Jenny, *Missouri Agri. Exp. Sta.*, *Bull.*, *152*, 66 (1930).

95. O. Schreiner and B. E. Brown, in *Soils and Men, Yearbook Agr.*, pp. 361-376, U.S. Govt. Printing Off., Washington, D.C., 1938.

96. D. J. Greenland and P. H. Nye, *J. Soil Sci.*, *10*, 284 (1959).

97. P. L. Sims and J. S. Singh, in *Preliminary analysis of structure and function in grasslands* (N. R. French, Ed.), pp. 59-113, Range Sci. Dept., Sci. Ser. No. 10, Colorado State Univ., Fort Collins, 1971.

98. D. E. Smika, H. J. Haas, G. A. Rogler and R. J. Lorenze, *J. Range Management, 14,* 213 (1961).

99. P. J. Rennie, *Plant Soil, 7,* 49 (1955).

100. D. J. Greenland and J. M. L. Kowal, *Plant Soil, 12,* 154 (1960).

101. N. J. Hannon, *Proc. Limnol. Soc. N. S. W., 83,* 65 (1958).

102. R. C. Dahlman, J. S. Olson, and K. Doxtader, in *Biology and Ecology of Nitrogen,* Nat. Acad. Sci., Washington, D.C., 1969, p. 54, Proc. of a conference, Univ. Calif., Davis, Nov., 1967.

103. H. J. Haas, C. E. Evans, and E. F. Miles, *U. S. Dept. Agr. Tech. Bull. 1164,* 111, 1957.

104. J. A. Hobbs and P. L. Brown, *Kansas Agri. Exp. Sta. Tech. Bull. No. 89,* 48, 1957.

105. J. A. Hobbs and P. L. Brown, *Agron. J., 49,* 257 (1957).

106. H. Jenny, *Missouri Agr. Exp. Sta. Bull. 324,* 10, 1933.

107. H. Jenny, *Factors of Soil Formation,* p. 281, McGraw-Hill, New York, 1941.

108. J. S. Russell and D. L. Harvey, *Austral. J. Agr. Res., 10,* 637 (1959).

109. T. W. Walker, *Trans. 6th Intern. Congr. Soil Sci., Vol. D,* 409, Paris, France, (1956).

110. C. M. Woodruff, *Soil Sci. Soc. Amer. Proc., 14,* 208 (1949).

111. D. S. Jenkinson, in *The Use of Isotopes in Soil Organic Matter Studies,* p. 187, Pergamon, New York, 1963.

112. D. S. Jenkinson, *J. Soil Sci., 17,* 280 (1966).

113. D. S. Jenkinson, *Soil Sci., 111,* 64 (1971).

114. R. C. Dahlman and C. L. Kucera, *Ecology, 49,* 1199 (1968).

115. C. A. Campbell, E. A. Paul, D. A. Rennie, and K. J. McCallum, *Soil Sci., 104,* 81 (1967).

116. E. A. Paul, C. A. Campbell, D. A. Rennie, and K. J. McCallum, in *8th Intern. Congr. Soil Sci., Trans., 2,* 201 (1964).

117. E. A. Paul, V. O. Biederbeck, and N. S. Rosha, in *Methods of Study in Soil Ecology* (J. Phillipson, Ed.), p. 111, UNESCO, Paris, 1970.

118. F. E. Clark and E. A. Paul, in *Advan. Agron.,* Vol. 22, p. 375, Academic Press, New York, 1970.

119. B. A. Stewart, L. K. Porter and D. D. Johnson, *Soil Sci. Soc. Amer. Proc., 27,* 302 (1963).

120. B. A. Stewart, D. D. Johnson, and L. K. Porter, *Soil Sci. Soc. Amer. Proc., 27,* 656 (1963).

121. J. R. Simpson and J. R. Freney, *Austral. J. Agri. Res., 18,* 613 (1967).

122. J. R. Freney and J. R. Simpson, *Soil Biol. Biochem., 1,* 241 (1969).

123. H. H. Cheng and L. T. Kurtz, *Soil Sci. Soc. Amer. Proc., 27,* 312 (1963).

124. J. P. H. Chu and R. Knowles, *Soil Sci. Soc. Amer. Proc., 30,* 210 (1966).

125. D. J. Greenland and G. W. Ford, in *Trans. 8th Int. Congr. Soil Sci.*, *3*, 137 (1964).
126. G. W. Ford, D. J. Greenland, and J. M. Oades, *J. Soil Sci.*, *20*, 291 (1968).
127. G. W. Ford and D. J. Greenland, *Trans. 9th Int. Congr. Soil Sci.*, *2*, 403 (1968).
128. D. J. Greenland, *Soils Fert.*, *34*, 237 (1971).
129. G. Stanford and W. H. DeMar, *Soil Sci.*, *107*, 203 (1969).
130. G. Stanford, *Soil Sci.*, *106*, 345 (1968).
131. G. Stanford and W. H. DeMar, *Soil Sci.*, *109*, 190 (1969).
132. G. Stanford and J. O. Legg, *Soil Sci.*, *105*, 320 (1968).
133. S. J. Smith and G. Stanford, *Soil Sci.*, *111*, 228 (1971).
134. D. S. Jenkinson, *J. Soil Sci.*, *19*, 25 (1968).
135. F. W. Chichester, *Soil Sci.*, *107*, 356 (1969).
136. D. L. Greenland, *Soils Fert.*, *28*, 415, 521 (1965).
137. M. M. Mortland, in *Advan. Agron.*, Vol. 22, p. 75-114, Academic, New York, 1970.
138. A. D. McLaren and G. H. Peterson, in *Soil Nitrogen* (W. V. Bartholomew and F. E. Clark, Eds.), Monograph 10, p. 261, Amer. Soc. Agron., Madison, 1965.
139. E. F. Estermann and A. D. McLaren, *J. Soil Sci.*, *10*, 64 (1959).
140. R. G. Burns, A. H. Pukite and A. D. McLaren, *Soil Sci. Soc. Amer. Proc.*, *36*, 308 (1972).
141. J. J. Skujins, in *Soil Biochemistry* (A. D. McLaren and G. H. Peterson, Eds.), Vol. 1, pp. 371-414, Dekker, New York, 1967.
142. S. L. Jansson, *Soil Sci.*, *95*, 31 (1963).
143. S. L. Jansson, in *Festskrift til Has Laurits Jensen Gadgaard Nielsen Bogtrykkeri*, pp. 49-69, Lemvig, Sweden, 1968.
144. J. S. Russell, in *Intern. Soil Sci. Soc. Trans., Comm. IV, V*, pp. 191-196, New Zealand, 1969.

CHAPTER 2

BIOCHEMISTRY AND CYCLING OF PHOSPHORUS

R. L. Halstead
Soil Research Institute
Canada Department of Agriculture
Ottawa, Ontario, Canada

and

R. B. McKercher
Department of Soil Science
University of Saskatchewan
Saskatoon, Saskatchewan, Canada

I. INTRODUCTION

Soil phosphorus has received much attention and the scientific

literature is abundant; however, the transformations in the soil

which are associated with plant nutrition remain uncertainly defined.
This is particularly true of the specific processes by which phosphorus becomes available for plant uptake. Research on the nature of
soil phosphorus components has characterized the inorganic components
to a greater extent than has yet been possible with the organic
phosphorus. A major asset has been the use of the radioactive isotope ^{32}P, which has become routine in inorganic phosphorus studies.
Its use in organic phosphorus studies is not widespread for several
reasons. Variable and usually large portions of soil organic phosphorus compounds are still unidentified. Laboratory syntheses and
use of many of the known components of soil organic phosphorus are
often both tedious and time consuming. Thus, the usefulness of ^{32}P-
labeled materials for organic phosphorus work is at present limited.
Labeling with ^{33}P seems promising since ^{33}P has a longer half-life
than ^{32}P.

The intent of this chapter is to consider only the phosphorus
associated with or derived from living tissue, that is, with the
organic phosphorus. Our discussion will be restricted for the most
part to "soil" organic phosphorus, the intra- and extracellular phosphorus found within the soil matrix. Phosphorus transformations
that occur within plants as a part of the physiological activities
of the stem, leaf, flower, or seed will not be considered. We recognize that a complete discussion of this subject would involve geochemical as well as biochemical activities, however, the various
aspects of mineral phosphorus reactions occurring both geochemically
and as a result of soil genesis are deserving of independent consid-
eration.

Most of the reliable information on the quantities and characteristics of the soil organic phosphorus has accumulated over the
last two decades. Two review articles have summarized information
before this period [1, 2] and more recent work has been reported in
the first volume of this series [3, 4].

II. PHOSPHORUS IN LIVING SYSTEMS

A. Uniqueness of Phosphorus in Life Processes

Many elements such as phosphorus, sulfur, nitrogen, and carbon
are involved in both biochemical and geochemical reactions. Generally,
in life systems, phosphorus and sulfur perform group and energy transformation functions in contrast with nitrogen. Similarly, carbon is
associated with living matter, whereas silicon is found in inorganic
substances. There are reasons for these characteristics [5], but
they are seldom expressed in chemistry, geology, and biochemistry
lectures or texts.

The atoms of living tissue are those whose nature allows formation of covalent multiple bonds whereas atoms that are reluctant or
unable to form covalent bonds are generally excluded from physiological functions. Atoms associated with life are mostly small and tend
to form flexible bonds that show high-energy characteristics, form a
variety of linkages with other atoms, and have an intrinsic instability that facilitates atom exchange. Living organisms are predominantly hydrogen, oxygen, nitrogen and carbon. These are the smallest
elements of the periodic system that achieve stable electronic con-
figuration, by addition of one, two, three, and four electrons respectively. They also form relatively stable bonds and the latter
three elements participate in multiple bonding. Although silicon is
about 135 times more abundant than carbon and also adds four electrons,
it is larger than carbon and does not form multiple bonds. Furthermore, its oxide, SiO_2, can polymerize to an insoluble substance,
quartz, and is thereby removed from continuing reactions. The C-C
bond is stable in water whereas the Si-Si bond is not.

It view of the relative paucity of phosphorus and sulfur, how
does one explain why these function as agents of group and energy
transfer in preference to oxygen and nitrogen? Both phosphorus and
sulfur are unique in so far as they are the major agents of transfer
of energy and because they are third-period elements. Phosphorus
has an advantage over nitrogen, oxygen, and sulfur in that it forms

the more open and weaker bonds (Tables 1 and 2). One must remember
that the available energy in a reaction derives from resonance stabilization, ionization, electrostatic forces and consequences of the
reaction and not just the bond energy. In contrast with nitrogen,
both phosphorus and sulfur may expand covalent linkages beyond four
through their $3d$ orbitals. They are unique also among third-period
elements in that they multiple bond, a characteristic which seems to
require small atoms able to approach others closely.

TABLE 1

Comparison of Covalent Bond Radii (Å)

	N	O	P	S
Single bonds	0.74	0.73	1.08	1.03
Double bonds	0.62	0.62	1.00	0.94

TABLE 2

Comparison of Bond Energies (kcal/mole)

C-H	93.8	Si-H	70.4
N-H	93.4	P-H	76.4
O-H	110.6	S-H	81.1

B. Importance of Phosphorus in Plant Nutrition
and Physiology

Deficiencies in any of the major nutritive elements normally
supplied to plants by the soil are not difficult to locate in any
given region. Phosphorus, however, is exceptional in that it is
nearly universally deficient. Indeed, areas of deficient soil supply
are expanding because of depletion of reserves. Some native plants
seem to have adapted to low rates of supply, i.e., they do not respond to phosphate fertilization. Crop changes, however, often ex-
pose these deficiencies [6].

Phosphorus normally constitutes less than 1% of the dry weight
of plants. It is present in all cells as part of their nucleic acid
and lipid material, and in some carbohydrate and related components.
In addition to genetic nucleic acid, phosphorus has a novel function

of special importance in the processes of energy storage and transfer. Photosynthetic phosphorylation produces energy-rich compounds,
a major one being adenosine triphosphate (ATP, see Fig. 1) from
which many other energy-rich compounds may be derived. The free energies available vary from a few calories per mole to upwards of
10-12 kcal/mole for materials like phosphoenolpyruvate and creatine
phosphates. Biochemists often classify those energy-releasing compounds as energy-rich, which are capable of generating > 5000 cal/
mole, and the energy-low, which generate < 5000 cal/mole.

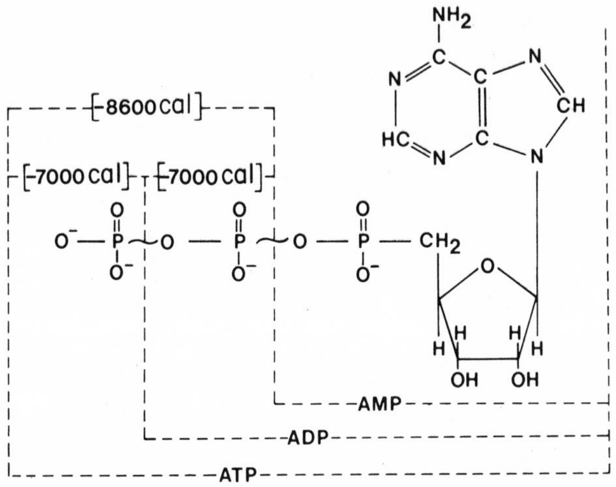

Fig. 1. Energy release from hydrolysis of ATP to adenosine
diphosphate (ADP), ADP to adenosine monophosphate (AMP), and ATP to
AMP + pyrophosphate (calories per mole).

There are, of course, other possibilities for energy-rich compounds, but the phosphorus compounds are most important because they
have kinetic stability in water, the biological medium, and possess
thermodynamic lability. To illustrate, acetic anhydride has a
half-life in water of a few minutes, acetylphosphate has about the
same energy potential but is water stable for several hours, and
ATP has "infinite" water stability [7]. Consequently, ATP is able
to exist until the proper enzyme demand occurs while nonphosphorylated
energy-rich compounds degrade too quickly to be useful.

III. ORGANIC PHOSPHORUS IN THE SOIL SYSTEM

A. Components and Quantities

The constitution and amounts of the different phosphorus compounds associated with the organic matter fraction in soils have been
discussed recently [3, 4, 8]. One of the major problems encountered
in organic phosphorus studies has been the development of reliable
methods for its determination since it is usually determined by difference between a total phosphorus value and one for total inorganic
phosphorus. There are errors in both extraction and ignition methods
caused by mineralization of organic phosphorus during extraction in
the first instance, and caused by an increase in the acid-extractable
"total" phosphorus in the second. The first type of error results
in low values, whereas the second gives values that are high. McKercher and Anderson [9] found that if they corrected for the inorganic
phosphorus released during ignition by using soil parent material
(C horizon) samples, the two methods (extraction and ignition) were
in good agreement.

In a method employing ultrasonic dispersion and an aqueous alkaline acetylacetone solvent [10], the organic phosphorus removed from
three of the soils exceeded that measured by the Mehta acid-alkaline
extraction method and were more in agreement with those obtained
with an ignition method. A method utilizing an acid pretreatment
(1 M HCl) followed by a 3- to 5-minute ultrasonic dispersion in an
alkaline solution (0.5 M NaOH) has recently been said to be generally
superior to the commonly used extraction procedures in terms of efficiency and speed [11]. Normal extraction procedures require long
shaking periods to allow the extractant to penetrate into the clay
minerals and solubilize the associated organic matter, whereas ultrasonic dispersion provides almost immediate access to these areas.
Consequently, the complete rapid extraction of organic phosphorus
from a soil is dependent on effective physical and chemical treatments.

The literature on total amounts of organic phosphorus in soils
is extensive and only some of the more recent published data are pre-

sented illustratively in Table 3. Readers should recognize that different methods have been used to obtain total organic phosphorus.
The methods are considered the most efficient for the soils within
the local areas but organic phosphorus values will vary somewhat depending on the procedure.

Reviews [3, 4, 8] on the individual organic phosphorus compounds
identified to date indicate that approximately 1% of the organic
phosphorus in soils is found in the phospholipid fraction, from 5 to
10% in the nucleic acid fraction, and up to 60% in the inositol phosphate fraction. In many instances, however, the amounts reported,
particularly the inositol phosphate fractions, are much lower (see
Table 3 for estimates of inositol phosphates in soils from different
areas). In addition to these three main groups of organic phosphates
there is some evidence that phosphoproteins, sugar phosphates (glucose 1-phosphate, glucose 6-phosphate), and glycerol phosphates are
present in soil systems but quantitative estimates have not been made.

TABLE 3

Some Values for Inositol Hexa- and Pentaphosphates
and for Total Organic Phosphorus

Location and reference	Inositol P		Organic P	
	µg P/g soil	Percent of org. P	µg P/g soil	Percent of total P
Denmark [12]	163	46	354	61
New Zealand [13, 14]	22-340	5-26	120-1360	30-77
Australia [22]	1-356	0.5-38	40-900	--
Scotland [15, 47]	56-460	24-58	200-920	22-74
England [23]	54-451	9-24	420-1750	--
Nigeria [23]	25-145	16-25	160-1160	--
Canada [16, 47]	10-150	10-30	80-710	9-54
United States [17]	30-80	10-25	4-85	3-52

1. Inositol Phosphates

By means of chromatographic techniques it has been demonstrated
that pentaphosphates (IP_5) and hexaphosphates (IP_6) of inositol are
the predominant forms in most soils [3, 8]. Several stereoisomeric
forms of the inositol phosphates are apparently found only in soils

[8, 18, 19]. Five of the possible nine stereoisomers (myo, scyllo, neo, and racemic DL-chiro forms) have been isolated from soil systems. Although a major part of the inositol hexaphosphate is found in the myoinositol form, the lower phosphate esters of myoinositol and of the other isomers have been detected [3, 8, 20, 21].

The distribution of inositol phosphates in soils can vary widely [22, 23], even in soils derived from similar parent materials and under similar environmental conditions. For example, in 47 Australian soils [22] the inositol phosphates (IP_5 + IP_6) comprised from 0.4 to 38% of the total organic phosphorus and the mean value for all soils was 16%. In a smaller sampling of English and Nigerian soils [23] the inositol phosphates (IP_1 to IP_6) accounted for 11-30% of the organic phosphorus. Myoinositol hexaphosphate was the most abundant form. The lower esters accounted for less than 3% of the organic phosphorus with the lowest amounts in the soils from Nigeria. Only the myoisomer was detected in the lower ester forms, although other isomers may have been present in quantities too low to detect. Of interest was the low proportion of the scylloisomeric form relative to the myo form in the Nigerian soils. Ratios of myo + DL to scyllo were between 6.4 and 10.0 in contrast to ratios of 5 or less in soils from many other countries [8].

Myoinositol monophosphate was the main identifiable organic phosphorus compound in a study of the organic phosphorus components in $CaCl_2$ extracts of soils [20]. The authors suggested that the inositol monophosphate may have been a hydrolysis product of a higher polyester form of inositol, or of phosphoinositide (Fig. 2), a constituent of animal, plant, and microbial cells. Alkaline hydrolysis of phosphoinositide yields myoinositol 1-phosphate whereas alkaline or enzymatic hydrolysis of the hexaphosphate yields myoinositol 2-phosphate as the main monoester.

The proportion of higher inositol phosphates (IP_5 and IP_6) to lower esters varies with the degree of soil development [21]. Higher amounts of the penta and hexa forms were present in the more

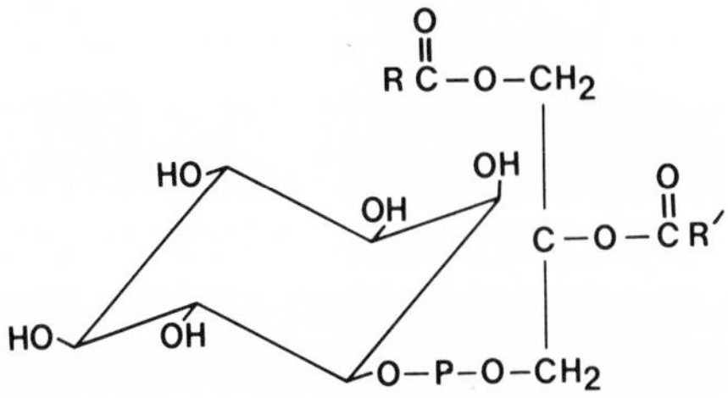

Fig. 2.   The general structure of a phosphoinositide.

weathered samples increasing from western Canada to eastern Canada.
Martin [24] used an isotope dilution method to correct for lower recoveries of myoinositol penta- and hexaphosphates from resin columns.
This approach made it possible to account for 86-100% of the extracted
organic phosphorus with 10-12% present as the lower inositol phosphates, and 28-62% as inositol hexa- and pentaphosphates.

   Although it was suggested earlier that myoinositol is the only
phosphorylated inositol occurring in biological systems apart from
soils, recent reports [25, 26] indicate the myo- and DL-chiroinositol are constituents of the needles of *Pinus ponderosa* (pine) and
that myo-, D-chiro-, and mucoinositol phosphates are present in the
leaves of *Prosopis juliflora* var. *velutine* (velvet mesquite). The
soils underlying the *P. ponderosa* contained the myo- and DL-chiroinositol phosphates whereas under the *Prosopis juliflora* only the
D-chiro and myo forms were identified. The authors suggest the
possibility of an epimerization reaction involving a cyclic ketone
intermediate as a pathway between the muco- and D-chiro- and between
the myo- and D-chiroinositol moieties.

2. Nucleic Acids

   The nucleic acids arise in soil from decomposing microbial,
plant, and animal remains in greater amounts than most other phosphate esters [3]. The presence of the nucleic acid bases (adenine,
guanine, cytosine, thymine, traces of uracil) in a bound form in
humic acid fractions, and the proportions in which they occur are
indicative of DNA-derived polynucleotides of microbial origin.

These bases, however, could account for only up to 2.4% of the soil organic phosphate if a 1:1 ratio of base:phosphorus was assumed. In his earlier writings, Anderson indicated that there was little possibility of isolating nucleic acids from soils in forms pure enough for quantitative measurement by phosphorus determination alone. In 1970, however, Anderson [27] isolated two pyrimidine nucleoside diphosphates, thymidine 3',5'-diphosphate and deoxyuridine 3',5'-diphosphate, from soils, and confirmed the existence of characteristic structural units of DNA in the soil system. Although the present available information is indicative of a low amount of nucleic acid material in soil, as is to be expected from extraction of soil biomass, the continued application of modern techniques to the problem of extraction, separation and identification of this fraction of soil organic phosphorus should provide more reliable estimates of its significance in the future.

3. Phospholipids

Phospholipids may enter soils in plant debris, in animal wastes, or by microbial synthesis and also like nucleic acids, they can be adsorbed by soil colloids. Phospholipid phosphorus, as presently determined, comprises less than 1% of the total organic phosphorus in soil [3, 28, 29]. The reported values ranged from 3 to 7 ppm for five British soils, 0.6 to 14.5 ppm (mean = 3.4 ppm) for 20 Saskatchewan surface soils, and 0.09 to 13.0 ppm for a group of Alberta Chernozemic soils. The subsurface horizons of the Saskatchewan soils contained less than 1 ppm phosphorus in the phospholipid form as measured, whereas one surface humus horizon contained up to 31 ppm phosphorus. The extracted material contained a fraction from which glycerophosphate, choline and ethanolamine were released on hydrolysis.

Phosphatidylcholine appears to be the predominant soil phospholipid comprising about 40% of the phospholipid phosphorus. Phosphatidylethanolamine accounts for about 30% of this form of phosphorus. The concentrations of lipid phosphorus were highly correlated with total phosphorus and soil organic carbon in a study in

Saskatchewan [28]. The authors suggest an accumulation of phospholipid material in soils from bacterial and fungal biomass, although
both of the isolated components are also present in plant tissue.
They also point out that an examination of the associated fatty acid
may be useful in establishing the origin of the material since bacterial fatty acids tend to be saturated, and are either branched or
cyclic types [30]. Plant components tend to be unsaturated and are
substituted normally at the 2-position on the choline moiety. The
importance of this group of phosphorus compounds in supplying phosphorus to plants cannot be overlooked since their synthesis and degradation may be fairly rapid in the soil system.

4. Other Phosphate Esters

Since little is known of the binding or stabilization of phosphate esters in soil, estimates for the three classes of compounds
just discussed may be low. However, there is considerable evidence
that much of the soil organic phosphorus is present in as yet unidentified forms [3]. Relatively small amounts of acid-labile esters
are present in many soils. Dilute alkali-labile components are also
present and are indicative of phosphoprotein. Separation of uniden-
tifiable components has also been reported. In one instance [31],
hydrolysis failed to yield any identifiable compounds (inositols,
carbohydrates, amino acids, or nucleotides), whereas in the other instance [8] many sugars found in the soil polysaccharide fraction were
recovered after hydrolysis. Total analyses showed 25% carbon, 0.75%
nitrogen and 1.4% phosphorus. Anderson [32] has recently detected
an ester with a C:P ratio of about 7 which on enzyme hydrolysis re-
leases a polyol containing a COOH group. Its identity was not established.

Gel filtration techniques are being used [23, 33-37] to obtain
molecular weight distributions of the soil organic phosphorus, and
hopefully, to obtain improved fractionations for identification pur-
poses. These have shown that a significant part of the soil organic
phosphorus is of high molecular weight. The question of whether or
not these macromolecules are naturally occurring or are artifacts of

the extraction system is difficult to resolve. The bulk of the inositol polyphosphates are recovered in a molecular weight range of 11,000 to 50,000. Inositols are also found in even higher molecular weight fractions [36]. Analysis of a fraction excluded from a G-200 column showed that it contained higher amounts of iron and aluminum and lower amounts of sodium, potassium and inositol than the fraction excluded from a G-150 column. Omotoso and Wild [23, 38] recovered 83% of soil organic phosphorus in a fulvic acid fraction following precipitation of the humic material. Separation by gel filtration (Sephadex) followed by constituent analysis indicated that 26% of the organic phosphorus was present as the higher ester forms of inositol (IP_4, IP_5, IP_6), 4.2% as the lower esters (IP_1, IP_2, IP_3), and 16.6% as sugar phosphates. Approximately 9.2% was hydrolysed and the remaining material was not identified. From these results the authors suggested that organic phosphorus was present in an organic complex separated from the bulk of the soil organic matter. The latter is presumed to be of a much higher molecular weight. This supposition that the organic phosphorus is in a complex separate from the soil organic matter is in agreement with other results [21, 39] in which the bulk of the organic phosphorus has been recovered in hot acid extracts of certain soils.

B. Amount of Phosphorus in Relation to Other Constituents

The ratios of organic carbon, nitrogen, organic phosphorus and sulfur in soils can vary widely, and the amounts of these constituents may or may not be interrelated. For example, average C:N:S:organic P values of 120:10:1.2:2.7 for New Zealand soils [40] were similar in magnitude to corresponding values of 140:10:1.4:2.4 for Scottish soils [41]. Organic phosphorus, however, was closely related to the carbon, nitrogen and sulfur levels only in the New Zealand soils.

Prior to 1953 reported ratios were in the order 110:9:1 for carbon, nitrogen and organic phosphorus. More recently N:P ratios varying from as low as 3 to more than 70 have been reported. In

Finnish soils [42], organic carbon and organic nitrogen were related
to organic phosphorus in the samples even though the ratios were not
constant. The carbon to organic phosphorus contents were similar in
cultivated and virgin mineral soils ranging from 61 to 276 in the
former and 67 to 311 in the latter. These ratios were much higher,
from 141 to 526, in cultivated humus soils. The C:organic P and
N:organic P ratios were low in Costa Rican soils relative to those
obtained for two Brazilian soils [43], and this was attributed to
low levels of organic phosphorus in the Brazilian soils due to their
advanced stage of weathering. For Nigerian soils, however, Enwezor
[44] found that C:organic P ratios ranged from 34 to 678, and that
these two parameters were correlated. A significant negative correlation between organic phosphorus (as percentage of total) and soil
pH was indicative of a more stable form of organic phosphorus at
higher pH. Other studies [45] have shown that part of the variation
in ratios of carbon and nitrogen to organic phosphorus is also attrib-
utable to pH variations; other soil properties (percent base saturation, total phosphorus, free iron, carbon, and nitrogen) did not cor-
relate significantly with pH. In contrast, a study with cultivated
samples from a number of locations [46] revealed that organic phosphorus was positively correlated with organic carbon and nitrogen;
these ratios were not related to the pH of the sample.

Williams and Anderson [22] found a wide range in the N:organic
P ratios of some Australian soils; these were lowest in the Kraznozems
(7.9), and increased through Alpine Humus (9.1), Black Earth (9.5),
Podzolic (12.8), alkaline soils (15.5), and acid sands (37.3). The
amounts of inositol phosphate in the samples were not consistently
related to soil pH nor to any other tested soil property. Top-
dressing leguminous pastures with superphosphate for a number of
years increased nitrogen, organic phosphorus, and inositol phosphorus
in the soils. The increases in inositol phosphorus were associated
with the increases in total organic phosphorus, but the percentage
of organic phosphorus in the inositol form in the fertilized soils
was appreciably lower than that in the unimproved soils. Obviously,

in this situation organic phosphorus compounds other than inositols
are synthesized and accumulate through plant or microbial action.
Comparisons of nitrogen, organic phosphorus and inositol phosphate
in cultivated and uncultivated wheat soils indicated a greater loss
of nitrogen (50%) than of organic phosphorus (37%) during cultivation. This lower relative mineralization of soil organic phosphorus
resulted in lower N:organic P ratios in the cultivated samples. A
higher proportion of the total organic phosphorus as the inositol
fraction of the cultivated soils (19%) compared with the uncultivated
ones (15%) suggests that certain fractions of the soil organic phosphorus are mineralized more rapidly than is the inositol fraction.

The association of inositol phosphates with other soil chemical
properties is not well defined from the studies completed to date.
McKercher and Anderson [47] found that inositol phosphorus in a
group of Canadian soils was correlated with total phosphorus, total
organic phosphorus and phosphorus retention capacity but not with
nitrogen and carbon. In contrast, the inositol phosphates measured,
in a number of Scottish and Canadian soils [19], and in Australian
soils [22], were not consistently related to other determined soil
properties. The soils with the highest pH values were found to have
higher proportions of scylloinositol hexaphosphate relative to myo,
suggesting that alkaline conditions may favor the organisms that
synthesize the scyllo isomer.

C. Some Reactions of Organic Phosphorus in Soil

1. Microbiological Activities

Although the contribution of the microbial population to turnover of the phosphorus fraction of the soil organic matter is not
clearly understood, there is little doubt that the microbial population both mineralizes and immobilizes phosphorus in the system,
thereby affecting its availability for plant nutrition. A major
part of the soil organic phosphorus undoubtedly originates through
microbial metabolism although its chemical nature is uncertain [4].
After reviewing literature on soil microorganisms and their ability

to mineralize soil organic phosphorus, Cosgrove [4] concluded that
soils contained a wide range of microorganisms capable of dephos-
phorylating all known organic phosphorus compounds of plant origin.

Published estimates [48, 49] indicate that approximately 20%
of the 5 x 10^{10} tons of organic matter produced annually in photo-
synthesis becomes microbial cell substance. The soil micropopulation
is estimated at 4-20 tons of fresh cell material per hectare which
corresponds to 5-10% of the total nitrogen in a field soil with 2-4%
organic matter. If one assumes an average nitrogen content of 0.25%
in the soil, then the microbial cell nitrogen would be 0.025%, and
using a N:organic P ratio of 10:1 for the soil microbial population,
then approximately 0.0025% or 25 ppm organic phosphorus could be
associated with the soil microorganisms. This is approximately
5-10% of the total organic phosphorus found in many soils. Such calculations probably give modest values since the assumed N:P ratio
of 10:1 is likely the widest that one might encounter. The leaf
throughfall and rhizosphere are considered to have a rich microflora
respective to general soil levels [50].

At the present time, estimates indicate that nucleic acid and
phospholipid phosphorus constitute from 5 to 10% of the total soil
organic phosphorus. Nucleic acids (DNA, RNA) are rapidly degraded
in soil, with release of inorganic phosphate and purine and pyrimidine bases, by nuclease-producing microorganisms [51]. Nucleic
acids adsorbed on montmorillonite are degraded presumably by microbial nucleases and not free soil nucleases, because complexes are
degraded in a manner that brings about a uniform structural collapse
of the clay mineral. According to Anderson [3], the polynucleotides
persisting in soil are derived mainly from bacterial DNA, although
the amount in the soil is probably greater than what can be accounted
for within bacterial cells. Using analytical methods presently
available, DNA has not been a useful measure of ocean biomass, whereas ATP assays provide satisfactory estimates [52]. An ATP assay
method [53] for estimating bacterial populations in soil has given
ATP concentrations of 8 x 10^{-3} to 1.3 x 10^{-1} µg ATP per gram of soil

in a wide range of soils. These values suggest that ATP has accumulated in the soils since they exceed ATP values calculated from viable cell counts using an average ATP content of 10^{-10} µg per cell.
Although the technique did not provide an accurate index of the bacterial population, it was capable of detecting ATP in a variety of
soil types.

The question of the origin of phospholipids in soils is still
unanswered because phosphatidylcholine and phosphatidylethanolamine,
the two major phospholipid compounds so far identified, are present
in plant and animal tissues as well as in microbial cells [3, 4, 28,
30]. On the basis of activity against a 0.1% lecithin concentration,
it has been shown [54] that actinomycetes are the major organisms
responsible for decomposition of phospholipids in soil organic
matter; less than 15% of the bacteria and fungi and from 65 to 80%
of the actinomycetes showed phospholipase activity.

Although inositol phosphates are the major soil organic phosphorus components known, their origin as already mentioned has not
been elucidated. Cosgrove [4] suggests that myoinositol phosphates
may be in part of direct plant origin, whereas scyllo, DL-chiro, and
neo are probably of microbiological origin since soils from different
countries contain the same isomers of inositol in similar proportions.
This similarity might be shown in a mixed population of soil organisms
and any such test would seem worthwhile.

Hydrolysis of myoinositol hexaphosphate (sodium salt) was inhibited in soil and sand-soil mixtures, but in coarse sand inoculated
with a dilute soil suspension, approximately 80% of the substrate
phosphorus was released with a marked increase in bacterial numbers
[55]. The fact that isolated organisms grew relatively slowly when
myoinositol hexaphosphate was used as the sole source of carbon and
phosphorus, but relatively quickly when myoinositol was used as the
carbon source suggests that these inositol phosphates are not readily
available for microbial metabolism. When the less soluble salts of
myoinositol hexaphosphate (Ca, Mg, Fe, Al) were used as substrates,
soil microorganisms were unable to release significant amounts of

phosphorus at either pH 5.0 or 6.8. Only the sodium salt was hydrolyzed to an appreciable extent at pH 6.8. In soil, however, the inositols may be present as salts of organic bases and could be more
easily metabolized.

In a recent series of papers [56-61], the phytase enzymes of
two organisms (*Neurospora crassa* and *Pseudomonas* spp.) were shown to
produce D-myoinositol 1,2,4,5,6-pentaphosphate as the major breakdown
product of myo-IP_6, whereas with bran phytase, the major product was
L-myoinositol 1,2,3,5,6-pentaphosphate. Theodorou [62] found that a
mycorrhizal fungus, *Rhizopogon luteolus*, possessed two pathways for
hydrolysis of myoinositol hexaphosphate, the major pathway was similar to that described above for the *N. crassa* and *Pseudomonas* spp.
whereas the minor product was similar to that produced by the bran
phytase. Earlier, Greaves et al. [63] had reported that hydrolysis
of myoinositol hexaphosphate by *Aerobacter aerogenes* produced a
pentaphosphate identical with that produced by the bran phytase.
The enzyme was inactive against scylloinositol hexaphosphate.

Cosgrove and his co-workers [58-61] utilized the *Pseudomonas*
isolate with its high phytase activity to study the hydrolysis of
myo-, scyllo-, and DL-chiroinositol hexaphosphates. The inositol
phosphate intermediates were isolated, by ion-exchange chromatography,
and identified; the following hydrolysis pathways were proposed:

1. Myoinositol hexaphosphate ⟶ D-myoinositol 1,2,4,5,6-
pentaphosphate ⟶ D-myoinositol 1,2,5,6-tetraphosphate
⟶ D-myoinositol 1,2,5- and/or 1,2,6-triphosphate
⟶ D-myoinositol 1,2-diphosphate ⟶ D-myoinositol
monophosphate.

2. Scylloinositol hexaphosphate ⟶ 1,2,3,4,5-pentaphosphate
⟶ either or both enantiomorphs of DL-1,2,3,4-tetraphos-
phate ⟶ 1,2,3-triphosphate ⟶ predominantly or solely
through one enantiomorph of DL-1,2-diphosphate.

3. D-chiroinositol hexaphosphate pathway is less certain, but
is believed to proceed through the 1,2,3,5,6- and 1,2,3,4,6-
pentaphosphate ⟶ 1,2,3,5-tetraphosphate ⟶ 1,2,6-tri-
phosphate ⟶ 1,6-diphosphate.

4. Neoinositol hexaphosphate pathway not established, although
the enzyme was active against this compound.

The partially purified phytase from *Pseudomonas* (acid phosphomonoesterase) had a pH optimum of 5.5 at 40°C, and could hydrolyze
only *p*-nitrophenyl phosphate and inositol hexaphosphates. Rates of
hydrolysis of the hexaphosphate forms were in the order of myo =
neo >> D-chiro ≈ L-chiro > scyllo. Cosgrove concludes from these
studies that at least two phytase enzymes exist in biological systems,
one primarily in plants and the other apparently restricted to microorganisms. Following the initial attack on the substrate molecule
both of the enzymes continue the dephosphorylation by attacking a
phosphate group adjacent to the free hydroxyl provided that it is
not sterically attached as an axial group. A model suggesting a
pathway for the *Pseudomonas* phytase degradation of the inositol hexaphosphates was also proposed [61].

2. Chemical and Physical Reactions

It is unclear whether or not organic phosphorus compounds participate in reactions similar to those of inorganic phosphorus. Research on inorganic phosphorus is more abundant and one is tempted
to draw comparisons of the behavior of organic phosphorus with that
of inorganic phosphorus. Steric configurations and molecular weights
of even the simplest of the known soil organic phosphorus compounds
such as glycerol and glucose 1-phosphate are much larger than most
of the inorganic forms except as in the source minerals. Further,
it has been established that even though modest amounts of organic
phosphates may be present in the soil solution [20], they appear for
the most part, to exist as insoluble complexes with other organic
materials [38, 60, 64, 65], as relatively insoluble ferric and calcium salts or as absorbates with amorphous and crystalline clays
[51, 66]. Some, of course, are part of the soil biological tissue
[4, 28]. Thus at least part of the organic phosphorus is no more
readily available for soil reactions than is the inorganic fraction,
although there is indirect evidence of a role of organic phosphorus
in plant nutrition [67].

Organic phosphorus may be extremely important to soil fertility, in an indirect fashion, by participating in fixation reactions and satisfying part of the soil's retention capacity [6, 68]. If organic phosphorus can compete effectively with inorganic in this manner, it is conceivable that as a result some of the inorganic might be more readily available. Displacement studies [69] have shown the removal of inorganic phosphorus by organic phosphorus compounds. Recently, it has been shown [70] that inositol hexaphosphate competes with inorganic phosphorus for the same sorption sites and that high levels of organic phosphorus greatly reduce sorption of inorganic phosphorus. Accumulation of components of organic phosphorus [47] or of the total organic phosphorus [71] have been observed below the surface horizon indicating certain of these compounds have unusual mobility. These mobile components are probably reasonably stable forms, otherwise they would not survive in sufficient quantity to allow detection. The work of McKercher and Anderson [47] and Martin [71] has indicated that inositol phosphates are involved.

3. Rhizosphere

Rhizosphere studies inspect the associations between root, soil and soil solution, and microorganisms and are of particular biochemical interest with respect to organic phosphorus. It is generally considered that plants are able to absorb $H_2PO_4^-$ and HPO_4^{2-} although arguments have been presented to suggest that plants do not feed upon HPO_4^{2-} [72]. There is good evidence that some plants may be nurtured by soil organic phosphorus compounds. Enzymes in soil and on roots and excreted by many soil organisms are able to facilitate the hydrolysis of organic phosphates to inorganic phosphate [4]. If these reactions occur in intimate association with the plant roots, there is little probability that the mineralized phosphate will become fixed and unavailable before plant feeding occurs.

The availability to plants of soluble organic phosphate compounds in soils has been of interest to soil scientists for considerable time. Early reports indicated that plants absorbed inorganic but not organic phosphate from aqueous soil extracts [73, 74]. Wild

and Oke [20] describe an early study in which, under aseptic conditions, glycerol phosphate, sugar phosphates, inositol hexaphosphate
and nucleic acids were able to supply phosphorus to a growing crop.
The availability of inositol hexaphosphate to plants under aseptic
conditions was confirmed by others (see Wild and Oke). In 1966, Wild
and Oke [20] found that the $CaCl_2$ extracts of soils contained three organic phosphorus fractions, two of these contained mostly myoinositol
monophosphate while the third fraction contained unidentified organic phosphorus material. Of the first two fractions, one was resistant to hydrolysis and had a low availability to plants grown under
aseptic conditions, whereas phosphorus in the other fraction, containing the myoinositol monophosphate component, was readily utilized
by the plants. The phosphorus (unidentified) in the third fraction
was also available to the plant.

It has never been fully resolved, however, whether organic
phosphorus must be mineralized prior to plant uptake. Work by Flaig
et al. [75] suggests this may be so. They introduced ^{32}P-labeled
phytate to the soil and found the label in the plants after a brief
time period; the ^{32}P was associated with organic compounds other
than those added to the soil. Theodorou [76] found phytase activity
in the mycorrhizal fungi of *Pinus radiata*, which was active toward
calcium and sodium phytates but not ferric phytate. Although this
established a potential source of plant phosphate, it was shown that
the inositol was not utilized as a carbon source; this suggests that
the phytate molecule per se did not enter the plant.

In a discussion of soil enzymes, Skujins [77] notes that plant
roots and residues are among the sources of soil enzymes, and that
enzyme activity in the rhizosphere is different than in other parts
of the soil system because of differences in microbial population
at these sites. Greater numbers of organisms capable of hydrolyzing
organic phosphorus have been found in rhizosphere than in nonrhizo-
sphere soils [78]. Undoubtedly, many of these organisms, capable of
producing extracellular phosphatase enzymes, will be involved in
phosphate utilization by the plant. It is next to impossible to

entirely separate roots and their microflora, but Barber and Loughman [79] were able to conduct experiments which demonstrated that at low phosphorus levels, microorganisms accumulated the phosphorus from organic sources in competition with the plant roots. Fardeau et al. [80] found increased uptake of phosphorus by rye grass from phytin ($NaIP_6$) added to soil. From the discussion following the presentation of his paper it was apparent that uptake of phosphorus from phytin was dependent on mineralization of the phosphorus before uptake, and that uptake varied with the cation present in the phytic acid salt and on the soil itself. For example, uptake from sodium phytate ranged from 38% in an acid sand to only 10% in a calcareous soil. Corresponding values were 16 and 5% for magnesium phytate, 7 and 1% for calcium phytate, and negligible amounts were available from iron and aluminum phytate. It would seem, therefore, that utilization of organic phosphorus in the rhizosphere is dependent on the solubility of the compound, and on its susceptibility to hydrolysis prior to utilization by the plant. In contrast to the above hypothesis, Friend and Birch [81] found that the water-soluble organic phosphorus in East African soils was not related to phosphate response, and they believed that the phosphorus in the organic complex of the soil rather than the water-soluble organic phosphorus was the main source for the plant.

In studies of the effect of cropping on soil organic phosphorus [82, 83] soils contained lower amounts of extractable organic phosphorus after four crops. This plant-induced decrease in soil organic phosphorus was thought to be due to enhanced phosphatase activity in the soil around the root or to the direct absorption of soil organic phosphorus by the roots. Unfortunately, experimental tests of the phosphatase hypothesis were not successful probably due to the fact that the rate of mineralization of soil inositol phosphates was controlled by their solubility and not the level of phytase activity [84]. Incubation of soils with concentrated washings from pea roots and from sand cultures in which peas had grown produced no significant change in the phosphorus extracted with weak acid [85].

Phosphatase activity in fluids removed from around roots in liquid
medium was not affected by microorganisms [86], and the phosphatase
activity in fluids removed from around roots in liquid medium was
not affected by microorganisms in the rhizoplane.

D. Progress and Prospects for Identification and Characterization of Soil Organic Phosphorus

A budget categorizing the total soil phosphorus cannot be for-
mulated at present due to incomplete knowledge of all the components
of the phosphorus pool, whether organic or inorganic. In addition,
there is some uncertainty associated with the estimation of the total
quantity in the pools. The Na_2CO_3 fusion method [87] is generally
accepted as the most efficient for conversion of all the soil phosphate to a soluble orthophosphate form. Other methods of extraction,
however, may function satisfactorily in some instances [88]. In
addition the choice of reducing agent in the colorimetric procedure
may profoundly affect the final values [89]. Differences in total
phosphorus of as much as 200 ppm may be encountered depending on the
procedures used on any given soil.

Differences occurring between methods for total phosphorus, if
small relative to the total, are not serious if comparisons of totals
or large fractions thereof are being considered. For organic phosphorus work, however, even small differences can be serious since
organic phosphorus estimations are normally obtained by calculating
the difference between total and inorganic phosphorus. Even if the
errors as indicated are kept small they are quite important in estimating those organic phosphorus components in the budget which are
present in low quantities. For example, phospholipids which are
rarely present in excess of a few ppm [3, 29, 30] may be much more
important nutritionally relative to other components than would
appear from a budget. Consequently, an accurate estimate of their
concentration in soils is important.

Another analytical problem was encountered by Irving and Cosgrove [90], in which myoinositol hexaphosphate interfered with the

accuracy of orthophosphate determinations. It is difficult to estimate the magnitude of problems of this kind when the nature of the
organic compounds in solution are not fully known as is the case
with soil organic phosphorus. A satisfactory amount of analytical
control can usually be kept where the problems are known.

Variable amounts of the soil organic phosphorus have been isolated and examined and several recent reports have enlarged on the
chemical characteristics of already known components. It has been
shown [62, 91] that the pentaphosphates are likely to exist in certain stereoisomeric forms. The chiroinositols, which have been
described mainly as racemates, are now believed to occur as the D-
chiroenantiomer [26, 92]. The use of nuclear magnetic resonance (NMR)
in these and other studies has shown that NMR is a useful tool in
the study of inositol stereoisomers [25, 26, 93]. The Australians
have used a series of chromatographic and electrophoretic techniques
for the isolation and identification of inositol hexaphosphates and
their intermediates in the soil system [57-61]. This interesting
research has culminated in a substantially complete picture of the
dephosphorylation pathways of the inositol hexaphosphates by plant
and microbial enzymes.

Techniques of separation and characterization that have been
discussed in the foregoing portion of this chapter will undoubtedly
remain popular. For rapid extraction of relatively large amounts
of organic phosphorus material, the HCl pretreatment followed by a
3- to 5-minute ultrasonic vibration in 0.5 N NaOH offers a quick,
efficient method [11]. Recently, an extraction procedure that prom-
ises greater efficiency and a higher purity for inositol phosphates
has been developed in Professor Tinsley's laboratory [94]. His
basic routine consists of a boiling extraction of inorganic phosphates
employing an $HCl-HF-TiCl_4$ solution. The organic phosphates precipitated during the first extraction by the Ti are then redissolved in
an HCl, cupferron solution for recovery by Ba precipitation and
chromatographic fractionations by established procedures. Improved
resolution on ion exchange and gel filtration columns, and use of

electrophoretic separations has enabled researchers to identify more
accurately many of the phosphorus components of the soil organic
matter. The flexibility and wide application of the various chromatographic systems have been of particular value since most of them
provide high recoveries of unaltered materials.

Isotope dilution analysis can correct for low recoveries during
extraction, fractionation, and purification of organic phosphorus
material. Martin [24] used this method with success to determine
the efficiency of his ion-exchange fractionations. It has the advantage of allowing one to measure a compound through the tracer
atom and does not require the purification procedures that handicap
many techniques. The use of isotopes also offers many possibilities
to assess mineralization and synthesis of the various organic phosphorus components in soils.

One promising recent technique is that of mass spectrometry
[95, 96] and although this may be considered a destructive procedure,
as materials are for the most part altered or lost in the analytical
processes, resolutions of molecular weight to 1 part in 100,000 are
possible, and the samples need a minimum of preparation and handling.
The constituents of small amounts of material can be identified
and quantitative estimates may also be made. The high cost of
these spectrometers, particularly if coupled to other analytical
instruments and equipped with data processing, will undoubtedly limit
their use. Another problem with this technique is provision of
standards, a necessity for confirmation of compound identity.

IV.   ROLE OF SOIL ORGANIC PHOSPHORUS
IN THE PHOSPHORUS CYCLE

Nutrient cycles consist of the biological cycle, which is within
the plant community, and the geological cycle (which includes the
cycling of nutrients from the sea and atmosphere into and out of

the biosphere). We must conclude that because the chemical nature
and formation of the soil organic phosphorus fraction is not well
understood, the contribution of this fraction to plants and to
other forms of soil phosphorus, and thus to the phosphorus cycle,
is not well known. In a study of soil organic matter accumulation,
Walker and Adams [40] state that of the four structural elements
(C, N, S, P) in soil organic matter, only phosphorus (under virgin
conditions) must be supplied by the parent materials. This would
also be true for sulfur if none was returned from the atmosphere.
Phosphorus transformations during pedogenesis convert apatite
phosphorus to organic phosphorus and secondary forms of inorganic
phosphorus [97-99]. These secondary forms of phosphorus (organic
and inorganic) accumulate in the finer textured fractions of the
soil, whereas the primary phosphorus (apatite) tends to remain in
the sand fractions [100, 101]. The data for mineralization of soil
organic phosphorus in incubation experiments [102, 103] indicate
that many soils are able to release sufficient phosphorus from the
organic form to adequately supply the phosphorus needs of a crop.
The source of this mineralized phosphorus has, of course, not been
established.

Studies of the phosphorus cycle in native grassland systems
[6, 99], in which the native species failed to respond to applications of phosphorus, have shown that the organic phosphorus in a
$NaHCO_3$ extract fluctuated throughout the season. The $NaHCO_3$ soluble
organic phosphorus was related to phosphatase activity of the soil
and to the soil microbial population during the growing season (Figs.
3 and 4). Estimates of the organic phosphorus released annually
in the top 10 cm of soil exceeded the plant phosphorus requirement
indicating that organic phosphorus may play a major role in the
phosphorus cycle at this location.

According to Cosgrove [4], phosphate-containing organic matter
is almost certainly accumulated in soil as the result of microbial
activity. Organic phosphorus in plant and animal remains probably
decomposes rapidly enough to prevent a build-up of organic phosphorus

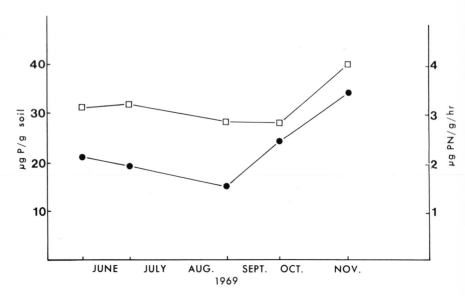

Fig. 3. Relationship between $NaHCO_3$ extractable organic phosphorus [(●) µg P/g soil] and phosphatase activity [measured by p-nitrophenylphosphate assay; (□) µg PN/g soil/hr] with season. (From [6] by permission of the authors.)

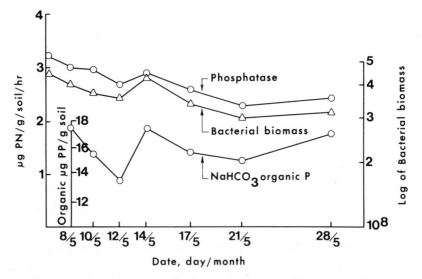

Fig. 4. Relationship of phosphatase activity (measured by p-nitrophenylphosphate assay, PN), bacterial biomass, and $NaHCO_3$ extractable organic phosphorus. (From [104] by permission of the author.)

from these materials. In soils low in phosphorus, applications of
phosphate increased both the organic matter and the organic phosphorus contents [4, 40, 105] through additions of plant remains,
roots and animal excretions. Plant growth in some of the soils, following conversion of the inorganic phosphorus to an organic form, was
dependent upon mineralization of the organic phosphorus. If mineralization was not sufficiently rapid, plant material low in phosphorus
was returned to the soil resulting in high C:P and C:N ratios.

Martin and Molloy [106] estimated that the annual amounts of
humic acid-associated organic phosphorus and inositol polyphosphate
phosphorus contributed to the topsoil from sheep faeces, residual
herbage and roots would not exceed 3% or the amount already present
in the soil. The use of manure and fertilizers in long-term field
experiments in Russia [107] increased organic phosphorus levels in
the upper soil horizons. A 20-year Canadian study of the effect of
organic amendments to a sand and to a clay soil [108] showed that
all amendments increased the phosphatase enzyme activity in the two
soils, but only deciduous tree leaves, alfalfa and manure had a
positive effect on organic phosphorus accumulation. These studies
give no evidence to support or deny the assumption that the accumulation of these organic constituents is caused by microbial rather
than by plant residual effects.

In a recent paper [109] marked seasonal fluctuations in the soil
organic phosphorus were observed in phosphorus-fertilized soils on
which alfalfa was growing. These changes were attributed to bonding
of the phosphate to humic substances in the presence of calcium ions.
The importance of this in terms of the cycling of phosphorus is not
readily apparent, but this phenomenon could provide an adequate supply of phosphorus to plants without the need of enzyme activity.
Seasonal fluctuations in levels of organic phosphorus have also been
reported from Russia [110, 111]. In these instances it would appear
microbial activities are involved but the difficulties in deciding
the true function of microbial activity on the supply of nutrient
phosphorus have prevented any clear assessment of these findings [112].

The scope of this chapter mainly concerns the cycling of phosphorus within the soil system. Nevertheless, because of the great
interest in phosphorus in the environment at large as evidenced by
numerous recently published articles on organic phosphorus in lakes
and rivers and their sediments, a short discussion seems merited.

A major problem concerns the changes in level of nutrients that
occur both annually and seasonally in lake and stream waters. The
location of urban population centers greatly influences all nutrient
levels in the water. Hammer [113] has reviewed these and other
aspects of drainage systems in the temperate climate zone of North
America and includes records of soluble phosphorus levels in one
such river system.

Identifiable organic phosphorus compounds represent but a very
small proportion of the total organic matter in lakes [114]; the
phosphorus contents of these compounds ranges from approximately
2% in vitamin B_{12} to 28% in phytic acid. Soluble phosphorus in
lakes in the summer is primarily organic and these substances play
an important role in the phosphorus chemistry of the water system,
although little is known of their chemical nature in either lake or
sea water. Studies with algal cultures indicated that a large part
of such organic phosphorus occurs in a large molecular weight fraction, possibly nucleic acid material.

The organic phosphorus content of lake sediments, similar to
that of soils, constitutes from 10 to 70% of the total [115, 116].
Fractionation of organic phosphorus in a number of sediments from
Wisconsin lakes by ion exchange chromatography following extraction
with acid and alkali [117] revealed that 48 to 80% of the NaOH
extracted organic phosphorus was in the fraction containing high
molecular weight humic-fulvic complexes. The fraction with exchange
properties similar to those of monophosphate esters contained 14 to
35% of the NaOH-extracted organic phosphorus, whereas the third
fraction (polyphosphate esters) represented less than 10% of the
extracted organic phosphorus. The inositol penta- and hexaphosphates
comprised less than 10% of the total organic phosphorus. The total

and high molecular weight fractions of organic phosphorus in sediments were associated with the organic carbon, total nitrogen and
oxalate-extractable aluminum.

The ATP content of nine lake sediments ranged from 0.34 to 9.5
μg ATP/g sediment [118, 119]. The significance of these values is
not obvious, but the ATP assay may serve as an index of microbial
biomass in aquatic environments. Interestingly, these values are
from 3 to 70 times higher than the highest reported earlier for
the solution phase of terrestrial soils. The concentrations of
free phosphatase enzymes in lake water is also indicative of phytoplankton and bacterial populations [120].

V. CONCLUSIONS

Our knowledge of soil organic phosphorus continues to expand
albeit slowly. The application of techniques from other chemical
and biochemical disciplines to this area of work has permitted progress in the understanding of some of the many aspects of organic
phosphorus transformations in the soil system. Some of the more
important of these in the last few years include improved methods
of extraction, separation, and identification studies of the origin
of soil phosphates with particular reference to soil microorganisms
and their associated phosphatase enzymes, and proposed dephosphorylation pathways for specific organic phosphorus compounds (particularly inositols) and mode of action of these enzymes.

The importance of phosphorus in our environment, and our lack
of knowledge of its role in both biological and geological cycles,
reemphasizes the need for a greater understanding of this important
nutrient. There is much yet to be discovered about its organic
forms in soil and water systems. It is hoped that the approach
and experience of the soil scientist will prove valuable for the
study of phosphorus in other areas of the environment, particularly
in water and sediments of lakes and streams.

REFERENCES

1. C. A. Black and C. A. I. Goring, *Agronomy 4*, 123 (1953).
2. B. Ulrich and J. H. Benzler, *Z. Pflanzenernähr. Düng. Bodenk.*, *70*, 220 (1955).
3. G. Anderson, in *Soil Biochemistry* (A. D. McLaren and G. H. Peterson, Eds.), Vol. 1, p. 67, Dekker, New York, 1967.
4. D. J. Cosgrove, in *Soil Biochemistry* (A. D. McLaren and G. H. Peterson, Eds.), Vol. 1, p. 216, Dekker, New York, 1967.
5. G. Wald, in *Horizons in Biochemistry* (M. Kasha and B. Pullman, Eds.) p. 126, Academic, New York, 1962.
6. B. J. Halm, J. W. B. Stewart, and R. L. Halstead, in *Symposium on the Use of Isotopes and Radiation in Research on Soil-Relationships Including Applications in Forestry*, p. 571, IAEA, SM-151/7, Vienna, 1972.
7. T. P. Bennett and E. Frieden, *Modern Topics in Biochemistry*, p. 66, Macmillan, New York, 1967.
8. R. B. McKercher, *Trans. 9th Int. Congr. Soil Sci.*, Adelaide, *3*, 547 (1968).
9. R. B. McKercher and G. Anderson, *Soil Sci.*, *105*, 198 (1968).
10. R. L. Halstead, G. Anderson and N. M. Scott, *Nature (London)*, *211*, 1430 (1966).
11. J. H. Steward and J. M. Oades, *J. Soil Sci.*, *23*, 38 (1972).
12. E. J. N. Pedersen, *Plant Soil*, *4*, 252 (1953).
13. J. K. Martin, *N. Z. J. Agr. Res.*, *7*, 750 (1964).
14. J. K. Martin and A. J. Wicken, *N. Z. J. Agr. Res.*, *9*, 529 (1966).
15. G. Anderson, *Trans. 8th Int. Congr. Soil Sci.*, Bucharest, *4*, 563 (1964).
16. R. L. Thomas and D. L. Lynch, *Can. J. Soil Sci.*, *40*, 113 (1960).
17. A. G. Caldwell and C. A. Black, *Soil Sci. Soc. Amer. Proc.*, *22*, 296 (1958).
18. D. J. Cosgrove, *Rev. Pure Appl. Chem.*, *16*, 209 (1966).
19. R. B. McKercher and G. Anderson, *J. Soil Sci.*, *19*, 302 (1968).
20. A. Wild and O. L. Oke, *J. Soil Sci.*, *17*, 356 (1966).
21. R. L. Halstead and G. Anderson, *Can. J. Soil Sci.*, *50*, 111 (1970).
22. C. H. Williams and G. Anderson, *Austral. J. Soil Res.*, *6*, 121 (1968).
23. T. I. Omotoso and A. Wild, *J. Soil Sci.*, *21*, 216 (1970).
24. J. K. Martin, *N.Z. J. Agri. Res.*, *13*, 930 (1970).
25. M. F. L'Annunziata and W. H. Fuller, *Soil Sci. Soc. Amer. Proc.*, *35*, 587 (1971).
26. M. F. L'Annunziata, W. H. Fuller, and D. S. Brantley, *Soil Sci. Soc. Amer. Proc.*, *36*, 183 (1972).
27. G. Anderson, *J. Soil Sci.*, *21*, 96 (1970).
28. C. G. Kowalenko and R. B. McKercher, *Soil Biol. Biochem.*, *3*, 243 (1971).

29. J. F. Dormaar, *Soil Sci.*, *110*, 136 (1970).
30. C. G. Kowalenko and R. B. McKercher, *Can. J. Soil Sci.*, *51*, 19 (1971).
31. D. J. Cosgrove, *Austral. J. Soil Res.*, *1*, 203 (1963).
32. G. Anderson, private communication, 1972.
33. J. H. Steward and M. E. Tate, *J. Chromatogr.*, *60*, 75 (1971).
34. R. L. Thomas and B. T. Bowman, *Soil Sci. Soc. Amer. Proc.*, *30*, 799 (1966).
35. J. R. Moyer and R. L. Thomas, *Soil Sci. Soc. Amer. Proc.*, *34*, 80 (1970).
36. R. L. Veinot and R. L. Thomas, *Soil Sci. Soc. Amer. Proc.*, *36*, 71 (1972).
37. M. Levesque, *Can. J. Soil Sci.*, *49*, 365 (1969).
38. T. I. Omotoso and A. Wild, *J. Soil Sci.*, *21*, 224 (1970).
39. J. F. Dormaar, *Plant Soil*, *28*, 268 (1968).
40. T. W. Walker and A. F. R. Adams, *Soil Sci.*, *85*, 307 (1958).
41. C. H. Williams, E. G. Williams, and N. M. Scott, *J. Soil Sci.*, *11*, 334 (1960).
42. A. Kaila, *Soil Sci.*, *95*, 38 (1963).
43. E. Bornemisza, *Soils Fert.*, *33*, 7 (1970), Abst. 45.
44. W. O. Enwezor, *Soil Sci.*, *103*, 62 (1967).
45. M. K. John, P. N. Sprout, and C. C. Kelley, *Can. J. Soil Sci.*, *45*, 87 (1965).
46. R. L. Halstead, *Can. J. Soil Sci.*, *43*, 97 (1963).
47. R. B. McKercher and G. Anderson, *J. Soil Sci.*, *19*, 47 (1968).
48. D. M. Webley and D. Jones, in *Soil Biochemistry* (A. D. McLaren and J. Skujins, Eds.), Vol. 2, p. 446, Dekker, New York, 1971.
49. H. L. Jensen, *Sci. Hort.*, *16*, 15 (1962-1963).
50. F. E. Clark and E. A. Paul, *Adv. Agron.*, *22*, 375 (1970).
51. M. P. Greaves and M. J. Wilson, *Soil Biol. Biochem.*, *2*, 257 (1970).
52. O. Holm-Hansen, *Limnol. Oceanogr.*, *14*, 740 (1969).
53. N. H. MacLeod, E. W. Chappelle, and A. M. Crawford, *Nature (London)*, *223*, 267 (1969).
54. Ko Wen Hsuing and F. K. Hora, *Soil Sci.*, *110*, 355 (1970).
55. M. P. Greaves and D. M. Webley, *Soil Biol. Biochem.*, *1*, 37 (1969).
56. L. F. Johnson and M. E. Tate, *Ann. N.Y. Acad. Sci.*, *165*, 526 (1969).
57. D. J. Cosgrove, *Ann. N.Y. Acad. Sci.*, *165*, 677 (1969).
58. D. J. Cosgrove, G. C. Irving, and S. M. Bromfield, *Austral. J. Biol. Sci.*, *23*, 339 (1970).
59. D. J. Cosgrove, *Austral. J. Biol. Sci.*, *23*, 1207 (1970).
60. G. C. Irving and D. J. Cosgrove, *Austral. J. Biol. Sci.*, *24*, 547 (1971).
61. G. C. Irving and D. J. Cosgrove, *Austral. J. Biol. Sci.*, *24*, 559 (1971).
62. C. Theodorou, *Soil Biol. Biochem.*, *3*, 89 (1971).
63. M. P. Greaves, G. Anderson, and D. M. Webley, *Biochim. Biophys. Acta*, *132*, 412 (1967).

64. G. Anderson and R. J. Hance, *Plant Soil*, *19*, 296 (1963).
65. N. Medveczky and H. Rosenberg, *Biochim. Biophys. Acta*, *192*, 369 (1969).
66. G. Anderson and E. Z. Arlidge, *J. Soil Sci.*, *13*, 218 (1962).
67. G. S. Sekhon and C. A. Black, *Plant Soil*, *29*, 299 (1968).
68. E. G. Williams, *Agrochimica*, *3*, 279 (1959).
69. B. T. Bowman, R. L. Thomas, and D. E. Elrick, *Soil Sci. Soc. Amer. Proc.*, *31*, 477 (1967).
70. G. Anderson and E. G. Williams, private communication, 1972.
71. J. K. Martin, *N.Z. J. Agri. Res.*, *13*, 522 (1970).
72. D. G. Edwards, *Trans. 9th Int. Soc. Soil Sci.*, Adelaide, *2*, 183 (1968).
73. W. H. Pierre and F. W. Parker, *Soil Sci.*, *24*, 119 (1927).
74. H. T. Rogers, R. W. Pearson, and W. H. Pierre, *Soil Sci. Soc. Amer. Proc.*, *5*, 285 (1940).
75. W. Flaig, G. Schmid, E. Wagner and H. Keppel, *Landw. Forsch. Sonderh.*, *14*, 48 (1960).
76. C. Theodorou, *Trans. 9th Int. Soc. Soil Sci.*, Adelaide, *3*, 483 (1968).
77. J. J. Skujins, in *Soil Biochemistry* (A. D. McLaren and G. H. Peterson, Eds.), Vol. 1, p. 371, Dekker, New York, 1967.
78. M. P. Greaves and D. M. Webley, *J. Appl. Bacteriol.*, *28*, 454 (1965).
79. D. A. Barber and B. C. Loughman, *J. Exp. Bot.*, *18*, 170 (1967).
80. J. C. Fardeau, D. Delille, and C. Abramovici, *Proc. of Symp. on Isotopes and Radiation in Soil Organic Matter Studies*, IAEA, p. 555 (1968).
81. M. T. Friend and H. F. Birch, *J. Agri. Sci.*, *54*, 341 (1960).
82. G. S. Sekhon and C. A. Black, *Plant Soil*, *31*, 321 (1969).
83. E. J. Thompson and C. A. Black, *Plant Soil*, *32*, 335 (1970).
84. R. H. Jackman and C. A. Black, *Soil Sci.*, *73*, 167 (1952).
85. A. D. Rovira, *Plant Soil*, *7*, 209 (1956).
86. E. H. Ridge and A. D. Rovira, *New Phytol.*, *70*, 1017 (1971).
87. J. W. Muir, *The Analyst*, *77*, 313 (1952).
88. J. K. Syers, J. D. H. Williams, and T. W. Walker, *N.Z. J. Agri. Res.*, *11*, 757 (1968).
89. G. E. G. Mattingly, *J. Agri. Sci. Camb.*, *74*, 79 (1970).
90. G. C. Irving and D. J. Cosgrove, *Anal. Biochem.*, *36*, 381 (1970).
91. M. E. Tate, *Anal. Biochem.*, *23*, 141 (1968).
92. D. J. Cosgrove, *Soil Biol. Biochem.*, *1*, 325 (1969).
93. M. F. L'Annunziata and W. H. Fuller, *Soil Sci. Soc. Amer. Proc.*, *35*, 655 (1971).
94. J. Tinsley, private communication, 1972.
95. J. Seibl, *Experientia*, *25*, 1009 (1969).
96. J. E. Van Lear and F. W. McLafferty, *Ann. Rev. Biochem.*, *38*, 289 (1969).
97. J. K. Syers, R. Shah, and T. W. Walker, *Soil Sci.*, *108*, 283 (1969).
98. J. K. Syers and T. W. Walker, *J. Soil Sci.*, *20*, 57 (1969).
99. J. K. Syers and T. W. Walker, *J. Soil Sci.*, *20*, 317 (1969).
100. R. L. Halstead, *Soil Sci. Soc. Amer. Proc.*, *31*, 414 (1967).

101. E. G. Williams and W. M. H. Saunders, *J. Soil Sci.*, *7*, 90 (1956).
102. C. A. Bower, *Iowa Agri. Expt. Sta. Res. Bull.*, 362 (1949).
103. R. L. Halstead, J. M. Lapensee, and K. C. Ivarson, *Can. J. Soil Sci.*, *43*, 97 (1963).
104. B. J. Halm, Ph.D. Thesis, University of Saskatchewan, Saskatoon, 1972.
105. T. W. Walker and A. F. R. Adams, *Soil Sci.*, *87*, 1 (1959).
106. J. K. Martin and L. F. Molloy, *N.Z. J. Agri. Res.*, *14*, 329 (1971).
107. Yu. K. Kudzin and V. A. Kubenko, Transl. from *Agrokhimiya*, *9*, 3-10 (1970).
108. R. L. Halstead and F. J. Sowden, *Can. J. Soil Sci.*, *48*, 341 (1968).
109. J. F. Dormaar, *Can. J. Soil Sci.*, *52*, 107 (1972).
110. N. M. Grindel' and N. G. Zyrin, *Sov. Soil Sci.*, *12*, 1391 (1965).
111. A. A. Yaskin, *Dokl. Soil Sci.*, *13*, 1823 (1968).
112. J. R. Ramirez Martinez, *Folia Microbiol.*, *13*, 161 (1968).
113. U. T. Hammer, *Hydrobiologia*, *37*, 473 (1971).
114. S. D. Faust and J. Hunter, *Organic Compounds in Aquatic Environments*, Dekker, New York, 1971.
115. C. R. Frink, *Soil Sci. Soc. Amer. Proc.*, *33*, 369 (1969).
116. L. E. Sommers, R. F. Harris, J. D. H. Williams, D. E. Armstrong, and J. K. Syers, *Limnol. Oceanogr.*, *15*, 301 (1970).
117. L. E. Sommers, R. F. Harris, J. D. H. Williams, D. E. Armstrong, and J. K. Syers, *Soil Sci. Soc. Amer. Proc.*, *36*, 51 (1972).
118. C. C. Lee, R. F. Harris, J. D. H. Williams, D. E. Armstrong, and J. K. Syers, *Soil Sci. Soc. Amer. Proc.*, *35*, 82 (1971).
119. C. C. Lee, R. F. Harris, J. D. H. Williams, J. K. Syers, and D. E. Armstrong, *Soil Sci. Soc. Amer. Proc.*, *36*, 86 (1971).
120. W. Reichardt, J. Overbeck, and L. Steubing, *Nature (London)*, *216*, 1345 (1967).

CHAPTER 3

HYDROXAMIC ACIDS IN SOIL SYSTEMS

J. S. Waid

Department of Botany
University of Canterbury
Christchurch, New Zealand

I.   INTRODUCTION

A variety of plants and microorganisms form hydroxamic acids
and, although many of these substances are biologically active as
antibiotics, growth factors, and chelating agents, little consider-
ation has been given to their possible role in soil systems. It is
the purpose of this review to draw attention to hydroxamic acids as
substances of biochemical and biological interest to soil scientists
as well as to put forward some speculations about their possible
participation in certain soil processes.

II. CHEMISTRY OF HYDROXAMIC ACIDS

The chemistry and reactions of hydroxamic acids have been described by various authors [1-4], so it is only necessary to describe
briefly the basic structure and reactions of hydroxamic acids that
are relevant to this account. Hydroxamic acids are organic compounds that contain the reactive group

$$-\overset{\overset{\displaystyle O}{\|}}{C}-\overset{\overset{\displaystyle H}{|}}{N}-OH$$

They exist either in a keto form (hydroxamic) (1) or in an enol
form (hydroximic) (2), and such keto-enol tautomerism provides
possible sites for chelation. Hydroxamic acids form highly colored
complexes with a great variety of metal ions, and much experimental
work has been done with hydroxamic acids to detect, separate and
determine a large number of metallic ions [5-7]. It seems that an
acidic medium, in which the keto form predominates, is required
for most metal-hydroxamate complexes to precipitate or form colors
[8, 9]. One of the best-known characteristic reactions of molecules containing the hydroxamate group is the formation of red or
violet coordination compounds with ferric ions. These have been
the basis for the quantitative determination of acyl compounds,
which are first converted to the hydroxamic acid and then to the

$$R-\overset{\overset{\displaystyle O}{\|}}{C}-\overset{\overset{\displaystyle H}{|}}{N}-OH$$

(1)

$$
\begin{array}{c}
\overset{\displaystyle O\,H}{\underset{\displaystyle |}{}} \\
R\!-\!C\!=\!\!=\!N\!-\!OH
\end{array}
$$

(2)

ferric hydroxamate, the color of which is measured photometrically
[10]. It is probable that the structure of the majority of ferric
hydroxamates [2] is

Because ferric iron can be firmly bound in such complexes,
they may be important in the iron nutrition of many microorganisms,
and possibly plants as well.

Hydroxamates are of biological interest on two counts. They
are among the few organic compounds of biological origin that contain N-O bonds [11], other examples being β-nitropropionic acid
[12] and chloramphenicol [13], and because many of the hydroxamic
acids participate as growth factors, antibiotics, antibiotic anta-
gonists and iron-transporting compounds. Further work may reveal
that they play an important role in the economy of microorganisms
and plants.

III. HYDROXAMIC ACIDS FORMED BY ORGANISMS

Hydroxamic acids of natural origin contain one, two, or three
hydroxamic acid linkages. In the following accounts of the better-
known naturally occurring hydroxamates they will be referred to by
their trivial names but sufficient citations are given to permit

the reader to find out more about their chemistry. During the last
10 years various authors have reviewed general and more specific
aspects of the naturally occurring hydroxamic acids and their derivatives [14-22].

A. The Monohydroxamates

1. The Aspergillic Acids

The first naturally occurring cyclic hydroxamic acid to be
described was aspergillic acid (3), a pyrazine derivative which was
isolated from a culture of *Aspergillus flavus* [23, 24]. Acids related to aspergillic acid are hydroxy-, neohydroxy-, meta- and
neoaspergillic acids [25, 26] and they are all formed by various
members of the fungal genus *Aspergillus*. All aspergillic acids are
cyclodipeptide antibiotics [27] and inhibitory to gram-negative
bacteria, but because they are also toxic to animals they have no
clinical application [23, 28].

(3)

The N-hydroxyamide structure of aspergillic acid forms a stable
complex with iron but when it is chelated with iron its antibiotic
activity is suppressed [29, 30]. Its inhibitory action is also
lost when it is reduced by the loss of the oxygen atom on the hydroxyl group of the hydroxamic acid moiety to form deoxyaspergillic
acid [31, 32]. This suggests that the mode of action of these
antibiotics is to interfere with the utilization of iron (or the
functioning of iron-containing molecules) by susceptible organisms.

Aspects of the biosynthesis of these compounds have been
studied and it would seem that the hydroxamate moiety is formed by
oxidation of a peptide bond [33].

2. *cis*-Fusarinine

cis-Fusarinine [21], 5-N-(*cis*-5-hydroxy-3-methylpent-2-enoyl)-
5-N-hydroxyornithine (4), is an ornithine monohydroxamate formed
by the imperfect fungus *Fusarium roseum* when grown in media containing low concentrations of iron [34]. It can also be formed
into a linear dihydroxamate (fusarinine A) and a linear trihydroxamate (fusarinine B), in which two and three *cis*-fusarnine units,
respectively, are joined by ester linkages [35]. *cis*-Fusarinine
is also found joined by ester linkages in the cyclic trihydroxamate

(4)

fusigen, which is formed by *Fusarium cubense* [35-37]. Accordingly
cis-fusarinine might well be a precursor of fusigen and also of
those cyclic trihydroxamates in which 5-N-hydroxyornithine residues
are joined by peptide linkages [35], such as ferrirhodin and ferrichrome [38]. This would imply that the cyclic hydroxamates are
not formed by the incorporation of amino acids into peptides, which
then acquire hydroxyamino groups by N-hydroxylation [34].

    cis-Fusarinine does not chelate iron as strongly as the tri-
hydroxamates, such as ferrichrome, but the purple-iron complexes of
this monohydroxamate show a greater tenacity for iron than those of
other monohydroxamates, and are sufficient to maintain iron in solution at pH 11. The additional chelating power of this substance

is probably due to the presence of unsubstituted amino and carboxyl groups. *cis*-Fusarinine can form a chelate complex with copper unlike other hydroxamates which form precipitates with copper [34].

cis-Fusarinine shows neither growth factor nor antibiotic activity toward fungi or bacteria [34].

3. Hadacidin

Hadacidin, N-formylhydroxyaminoacetic acid (5), is formed by *Penicillium frequentens* from which it was first isolated [39] and identified [40]. Its formation seems to depend on the presence of amino acids in the medium and with *P. auranto-violaceum* yields can be as high as 10 mg/ml [41]. A similar compound has been isolated from cultures of *Aspergillus flavus* [42].

Hadacidin possesses antibiotic-like activity and inhibits the formation of adenylic and deoxyadenylic acids. The molecule is an analogue of aspartic acid and competitively inhibits the synthesis of adenylsuccinate from inosinic and aspartic acids [43, 44]. It inhibits tumor growth [40] and the formation of chloroplasts by *Euglena* [45] and has a marked retarding effect on plant growth [46].

$$H-\overset{\overset{\displaystyle O}{\|}}{C}-\overset{\overset{\displaystyle OH}{|}}{N}-CH_2-COOH$$

(5)

4. Benzoxazin Hydroxamic Acids

DIMBOA, 2,4-dihydroxy-7-methoxy-1,4-benzoxazine-3-one (6), has been extracted from corn and graminaceous seedlings. It is a cyclic monohydroxamate and contains a benzoxazine ring system [1]. In the plant it is linked to a sugar moiety by a glycosidic bond, which is broken by enzyme action during extraction [47-50]. There is evidence that DIMBOA is formed by the N-hydroxylation of a carbon-nitrogen bond [48]. A similar compound, 2,4-dihydroxy-1,4-benzoxazin-3-one, has been isolated from rye seedlings in which it

too is present in the glucoside form but on extraction decomposes
enzymatically to form 2-benzoxazoline [47, 51-53]. The rye hydroxamate inhibits the growth of *Fusarium nivale* and various bacteria
[54].

(6)

Evidence of the presence of a third cyclic hydroxamate, 2,4-
dihydroxy-6,7-dimethoxy-1,4-benzoxazine-3-one, has been obtained
in other studies on corn tissue [55, 56]. It was shown that
DIMBOA and this hydroxamate can form chelates with iron and the
possible participation of these chelates in the absorption and
transport of iron in higher plants was suggested [57]. The occurrence of such cyclic hydroxamic acids in graminaceous plants has
aroused interest because there appears to be a correlation between
their presence and the plant's resistance to several fungal and
bacterial diseases [54, 58-62], as well as to insect attack [60,
61, 63-66]. For example, Couture et al. [62] found that genotypes
of corn deficient in cyclic hydroxamates were significantly more
susceptible to *Helminthosporium turcicum*, a fungal leaf blight,
than were genotypes possessing cyclic hydroxamates. By bioassay
it was shown that DIMBOA can inhibit spore germination of this
fungus at concentrations of 1 ppm and almost completely at 8 ppm.

The resistance of corn to the 2-chloro-S-triazine herbicides,
atrazine and simazine, has been attributed to detoxication by a
non-enzymatic hydroxylation of these two herbicides to hydroxya-
trazine and hydroxysimazine, respectively [67-72]. This detoxication reaction was catalyzed by DIMBOA and other benzoxazinone

cyclic hydroxamates from corn and the resistance of certain plants
to simazine appeared to be related to the concentration of benzoxazine derivatives in their tissues [67-71, 73]. Other work has
indicated that there is no direct correlation between the concentration of hydroxamate and resistance to the triazine among
selected genotypes of corn and that, although this is an important
mechanism, it is not essential for resistance to the triazine
herbicides [74-77]. Another approach to this problem has demonstrated that the primary factor for resistance to atrazine by the
corn plant is the activity of an enzyme glutathione S-transferase
[78-82]. Studies on the conversion of simazine to hydroxysimazine
in soil indicate it is probably a nonbiological process [83, 84],
although it is conceivable that cyclic hydroxamates derived from
plant residues might be involved.

5. Actinonin

Actinonin (7) is an antibiotic isolated from a *Streptomyces*
sp. and active against gram-positive and gram-negative bacteria [85].

(7)

B. The Dihydroxamates

1. Mycobactins

Mycobactin P and mycobactin T (8) are iron-free cyclic dihy-
droxamates that are synthesized by the acid-fast bacilli *Mycobacterium phlei* and *M. tuberculosis*, respectively, and which act as
growth factors for *M. paratuberculosis (M. johnei)*, a pathogen with
fastidious nutrient requirements [86-93]. Mycobactins are formed

by at least eight other species of *Mycobacterium*, each forming a
different type of mycobactin, and it has been suggested that iden-
tifying mycobacteria by the mycobactins they form might be a useful
taxonomic tool [20]. The most significant chemical characteristic
of the mycobactins is that they form very stable chelates with
ferric iron; they also form complexes with aluminium and are lipophilic. It seems that ferric-iron is bound at a chelation center
formed by two hydroxamic acid residues and a third consisting of
a phenolic hydroxyl situated in an appropriate position relative
to the nitrogen atom of an oxazoline ring [20]. The hydroxamic
residues are formed by 2-amino-6-hydroxyaminohexanoic acid which
on hydrolysis gives N^6-hydroxylysine but there is no evidence that
the hydroxylysine is a precursor of mycobactin [94]. Like many
other hydroxamates the production of mycobactin is promoted by iron
deficiency in the growth medium [20, 95].

Mycobactins act as growth factors for the acid-fast bacilli.
Because their chemical properties are so similar to those of certain siderochromes they have been classified as sideramines [20],
but they contain only two hydroxamic acid residues so they are
considered separately here.

(8)

2. Mycelianamide

Certain strains of *Penicillium griseofulvum* can form an antibiotic, active against gram-positive bacteria, called "mycelia-
namide" [96-98], which gives a red ferric test. It is of interest
because it contains two N-hydroxyamide residues in a cyclic molecule (9) and like many other hydroxamates of biological origin it
is a derivative of mevalonic acid [99-101]. There is evidence that
the hydroxamate moieties of the molecule are formed by oxidation
of a peptide bond [100].

(9)

3. Pulcherriminic Acid

The red pigment, pulcherrimin, is produced by strains of
Candida pulcherrima [102] when they are grown in media containing
copious iron. The pigment was also formed by strains of *Bacillus
cereus* and *B. subtilis* that were isolated from soil and dung [103]
as well as by a strain of *Micrococcus violagabriellae* [104, 105].
Pulcherrimin is a diketopiperazine-iron polymer formed from pulcherriminic acid (10). This acid resembles aspergillic acid (3),
but has two hydroxamate moieties in the molecule instead of one
[106-108]. Its biological function is not known.

An iron-free form of pulcherriminic acid is synthesized by
Bacillus cereus growing in an iron-free medium. Addition of

chloramphenicol to the growth medium does not affect the formation
of this acid suggesting that its biosynthesis is not related to
protein synthesis [103].

(10)

4. Schizokinen

When grown in aerobic cultures containing low concentrations of
iron, *Bacillus megaterium* excretes a dihydroxamate [109, 110],
called schizokinen [111], which plays a role in either solubilizing
iron or in iron transport [112-115]. Schizokinen is so called because its excretion is essential to maintain the rate of cell division of *B. megaterium* in the exponential phase of growth [111].
Recently a structure for schizokinen has been proposed [116], namely
a symmetrical diamide conjugate of 2 mole of 1-amino-3-(N-hydroxy-
N-acetyl)aminopropane with 1 mole of citric acid (11). There is
some evidence that ferric iron is chelated by linkage to the two
hydroxamic acid groups, but it is not certain how the citric acid
participates in the formation of the ferric complex [116].

5. Aerobactin

Cultures of a strain of *Aerobacter aerogenes* when grown in
an iron-deficient medium were found to excrete a dihydroxamate
consisting of a conjugate of 2 mole of 6-(N-acetyl-N-hydroxyamino)-2-aminohexanoic acid with 1 mole of citric acid [117]. The

relationship of the iron content of the medium to the formation of
the hydroxamic acid seems to be the same for the strain of *A. aerogenes* as for many other organisms that form hydroxamates. When
iron was added to the growth medium the formation of aerobactin
was repressed.

Aerobactin resembles schizokinen in containing citric acid
[116] and also the mycobactins in containing two residues of N^6-
hydroxylysine linked through a hydroxy acid [117].

(11)

6. Arthrobactin (Terregens Factor)

Terregens factor has recently been isolated and characterized
from the culture medium in which *Arthrobacter pascens* had been
grown. The iron-free compound is a dihydroxamic acid containing
2 mole of 5-(N-acetyl-N-hydroxyamino)-1-aminopentoic acid linked
symmetrically to 1 mole of citric acid by peptide bonds. The name
"arthrobactin" has been proposed for this iron-free compound [233].

This compound, like aerobactin, resembles schizokinen (11) in
its basic structure. Terregens factor has for some time been believed to be a trihydroxamate [18], as various siderochromes are
known to replace it as a growth factor for strains of *Arthrobacter*
(see Section IV, A).

7. Rhodotorulic and Dimeric Acids

Rhodotorulic acid, the diketopiperazine of N-acetyl-N-hydroxy-
ornithine (12) has been isolated from iron-deficient cultures of

the red yeast *Rhodotorula pilmanae* [118] as well as from strains
of other *Rhodotorula* spp. and other yeast genera *(Leucosporium,*
Rhodosporidium, Sporidiobolus and *Sporobolomyces)* [119]. This secondary hydroxamic acid has the capacity to strongly bind ferric
iron and to act as a growth factor for *Arthrobacter* species [118].
Its production is repressed by the presence of iron in the medium.

Dimeric acid has a structure closely related to that of rhodotorulic acid and is produced by the fungus *Fusarium dimerum* [120].

(**12**)

8. Ferribactin

The dihydroxamate ferribactin is an iron-complexing polypeptide,
which is excreted by *Pseudomonas fluorescens* when grown in cultures
containing low concentrations of iron [121].

C. The Trihydroxamates (Siderochromes)

Natural products containing ferric trihydroxamates have been
called "siderochromes" because of the red-brown, remarkably strong
chelation complexes they form with ferric iron. It has been proposed [122] that the term "siderochrome" be used for natural ferric
trihydroxamates complexes, which contain a ferric-ion coordinated
with six oxygen atoms of three hydroxamate residues and thus
forming three five-membered chelate rings, e.g., ferroxamine E (13).
A great deal of structural diversity is found among siderochromes,
but a common feature is that the hydroxylamino group is formed
from an amino acid, often ornithine, in which an amino group has

(**13**)

been replaced by a hydroxylamino group. The siderochromes have
characteristic broad absorption bands at 425-440 nm that do not
shift or diminish to any great extent with alteration of pH from
7 to 2 [123, 124]. The siderochromes have molecular weights ranging
from 500-1200 and their molecular structure is such that the three
hydroxamic acid groups can engage all six coordination positions
of a ferric iron ion. The ferric iron can be removed by fairly
severe alkaline treatment, with an excess of a chelating agent,
such as 8-hydroxyquinoline (oxine), or by reduction and trapping
with cyanide. The colorless or near colorless iron-free forms of
these compounds are called "desferrisiderochromes" and each has a
very high affinity for trivalent iron [125-127, 14].

One system of classification of the siderochromes is based on
their biological activity; *sideramines* act as growth-promoting substances for microorganisms, e.g., ferrichrome, and *sideromycins* as
antibiotics, e.g., albomycin and ferrimycin [14, 15, 125]. Recently
Neilands [17] has pointed out that this division is not clear cut
because members of both groups of compounds can act as growth factors

or antibiotics, and some compounds that act as antibiotics for some organisms will function as growth factors for others. He prefers to classify the siderochromes on the basis of their chemical structure, which for most of them is quite well established [128] and has enabled a few siderochromes to be synthesized in the chemical laboratory [129, 130]. Neilands recommends the term "ferrioxamine" for those trihydroxamates with repeating units of 1-amino-ω-hydroxy-aminoalkane (from which the hydroxamic acid bond is formed and where the alkane can be butane or pentane) and succinic or acetic acid.

The term "ferrichrome" is applied to cyclic hexapeptides with hydroxamic acid linkages provided by three residues of acyl-N^5-hydroxyornithine. The three remaining peptide residues in the ferrichrome are glycine or serine, or a combination of these two amino acids. The acyl moiety varies from acetic acid to higher unsaturated acids, such as *trans*-β-methylglutaconic acid or the corresponding cis and trans alcohol analogs of this acid. Emery [34] has pointed out that it can hardly be coincidental that all acyl groups of naturally occurring hydroxamates are mevalonic acid derivatives. Mevalonic acid, $CH_3COH(CH_2COOH)CH_2CH_2OH$, is formed by a head-to-head condensation between acetyl coenzyme A and acetoacetyl-CoA and is a precursor for the isoprenoids which include terpenes, carotenoids, steroids, and rubber [131, 132]. Emery [38] has shown that in the case of the production of ferrichrome in *Ustilago sphaerogena*, N^5-hydroxyornithine is formed from L-ornithine followed by acylation to acyl-N^5-hydroxyornithine. In studies of the biosynthesis of ferrichromes by *Fusarium cubense* Anke and Diekmann [133] found that leucine and mevalonate were precursors of acyl components of fusigen, mevalonate being considered the more direct precursor. Table 1 lists and indicates the biological activity of many of the naturally occurring siderochromes that have been recorded.

All the naturally occurring trihydroxamates that have been isolated and purified have been obtained from aseptic cultures of

TABLE 1

Naturally Occurring Siderochromes and Their Biological Activities[a]

Ferrichromes	Activity[b]	Reference	Ferrioxamines	Activity	Reference
Ferrichrome	g.f.,a.a.	[19, 135]	Ferrioxamine A$_1$	g.f.	[126, 127, 160]
Ferrichrome A	inactive	[136-138]	Ferrioxamine A$_2$	g.f.	[126, 127, 160]
Ferrichrome C	--	[139]	Ferrioxamine B	g.f.,a.a.	[127, 163, 164]
Ferrichrysin	g.f.,a.a.	[122, 140]	Ferrioxamine C	g.f.	[127]
Ferrichrocin	g.f.,a.a.	[122, 140]	Ferrioxamine D	g.f.	[127, 165]
Ferrirubrin	a.a	[122, 138, 141]	Ferrioxamine D$_2$	g.f.	[127, 160]
Ferrirhodin	a.a.	[122, 138]	Ferrioxamine E[d]	g.f.,a.a.	[127, 166, 167]
Albomycin	a.	[16, 142, 143]	Ferrioxamine F	g.f.	[127]
Grisein[c]	a.	[144-146]	Ferrioxamine G	g.f.	[168]
Coprogen	g.f.	[147-149]	Ferrimycin A$_1$	a.	[125, 127]
Compound X Fe[e]	g.f.	[150, 151]	Ferrimycin A$_2$	a.	[125, 127]
Succinamycin	a.	[152]	Ferrimycin B	a.	[125, 127]
Danomycin[e]	a.	[153]	A 22765[e]	a.	[169, 170]
L.A. 5352[e]	a.	[156]			
L.A. 5937[e]	a.	[156]			
Fusarinine B	g.f.	[35]			
Fusigen	g.f.	[133, 157, 158]			
RO 5-2667[e]	a.	[159]			
Ro 7-7730[e]	a.	[159]			
Ro 7-7731[e]	a.	[159]			
A 1787[e]	a.	[161]			
SC-A pigment	--	[162]			
SC-D pigment	--	[162]			

[a]Data from [15-18, 128, 134].

[b]g.f., growth factor; a., antibiotic; a.a., antibiotic antagonist.

[c]Probably equivalent to albomycin [17].

[d]Equivalent to nocardamin [171].

[e]Structure or classification uncertain.

bacteria, actinomycetes, and fungi that have been grown in aerobic conditions, often with very low concentrations of iron supplied in the medium. Many organisms that form siderochromes belong to genera and species that are found in the soil environment. The microorganisms include the genera listed in Table 2.

TABLE 2

Genera of Microorganisms Known to Form Siderochromes[a]

Bacteria	Actinomycetes	Fungi
Acalaginęs	*Actinomyces*	*Aspergillus*
Arthrobacter	*Chainia*	*Chaetomium*
Chromobacterium [172]	*Micromonospora*	*Cryptococcus* [139]
Sarcina	*Nocardia*	*Fusarium* [157]
	Streptomyces	*Gibberella* [157]
	Streptosporangium	*Glomerella*
		Neurospora
		Paecilomyces
		Penicillium
		Pythium
		Rhizopus
		Saccharomyces
		Spicaria
		Sphacelotheca
		Ustilago

[a]Data from [15-18, 134].

Members of most of the genera listed are known to form ferrichromes but until recently ferrioxamines had only been isolated from cultures of *Streptomyces* spp. and some other strains of actinomycetes. However, Müller and Zähner [172] have obtained ferrioxamine B and ferrioxamine E from cultures of two bacteria, namely *Arthrobacter simplex* and *Chromobacterium violaceum*, respectively, and a further search will no doubt reveal more bacterial strains with ferrioxamine-producing potential.

Some organisms can form more than one siderochrome, for example, single strains of streptomycetes can form a mixture of ferrioxamines [17] and, as shown in Table 3, some siderochromes are formed by several quite unrelated species of microorganisms.

TABLE 3

Source and Biological Activities
of Selected Naturally Occurring Siderochromes

Name	Source	Biological activity
Ferrichromes		
Coprogen [147-149]	*Sarcina lutea* *Alcaligenes bookeri* *Streptomyces* sp. *Aspergillus carbonarius* *Neurospora crassa* *Penicillium camemberti* *P. chrysogenum* *P. citrinum* *P. notatum* *P. urticae* *Ustilago zeae*	Growth factor for *Arthrobacter* J.G. 9 *Pilobolus kleinii;* weakly reverses inhibition of albomycin-type antibiotics
Ferrichrome [19, 135, 136]	*Aspergillus niger* *Penicillium resticulosum* *Ustilago maydis* *U. sphaerogena*	Growth factor for *Arthrobacter terregens* *Arthrobacter* J.G. 9 *Microbacterium lacticum* *Micrococcus glutamicus* *Pilobolus kleinii;* completely reverses inhibition of albomycin-type antibiotics
Albomycin [16, 142, 143]	*Actinomyces subtropicus*	Closely related perhaps identical antibiotics; Active against gram-positive and gram-negative bacteria
Grisein [144-146]	*Streptomyces griseus*	
Ferrioxamines		
Ferrioxamine B [125, 126, 163, 164, 175]	*Arthrobacter simplex* *Nocardia asteroides* *Streptomyces pilosus* *Streptomyces* spp. *Micromonospora fusca*	Growth factor for *Microbacterium lactium;* reverses inhibition by ferrimycin antibiotics
Ferrimycin A_1 [125, 127]	*Streptomyces griseoflavus* *S. galilaeus* *S. lavendulae*	A potent antibiotic against gram-positive bacteria; antagonized by ferrioxamines

[a]Data from [15, 17, 19, 130, 134].

Although authentic cyclic trihydroxamates have only been isolated, purified, and identified from microorganisms Zähner et al.
[137] and E. R. Page [173, 174] have shown by bioassay the presence
of siderochrome-like substances in vegetable tissue (but it is not
clear that the plant tissues were aseptic) and in culture fluids in
which the green unicellular alga *Chlamydomonas eugametos* [137] had
been grown. It would seem, therefore, that knowledge of the potential of microorganisms and plants to form siderochromes is far from
complete.

IV. POSSIBLE ROLES OF HYDROXAMIC ACIDS IN SOILS

A. Growth Factors

Many of the naturally formed di- and trihydroxamates function
as potent and specific growth factors (Table 4) and some are required in very small amounts to give a growth-promoting effect.
For example, less than 10^{-9} M or 0.1 ng ferrichrome per millimeter
will give a response by *Arthrobacter* J.G. 9 and the length of the
lag period of growth of *Bacillus megaterium* is reduced by the presence of schizokinen [177]. The potency of some of the hydroxamic
acids suggests that they may play a role as coenzymes in cellular
metabolism but a recent review by Emery [178] leads to the conclusion that the apparent growth factor activity of these substances
is related to their ability to chelate iron. This will be discussed
in some detail in Section IV, B.

Arthrobactin, the terregens factor [233], is a potent growth
factor for the two bacteria *Arthrobacter flavescens* and *A. terregens*
and for several other exacting strains of organisms which require
soil extract but for which no vitamin or yeast extract is able to
promote growth. This factor was first isolated from culture fluids
in which *A. pascens* had grown. This factor is required by *A. terregens* in amounts as small as 1 ng/ml of purified factor from
culture filtrates of *A. pascens* [154, 155, 179, 180]. Various

TABLE 4

Some Naturally Occurring Hydroxamic Acids with Growth Factor Activity

Dihydroxamates	Trihydroxamates[a]
Schizokinen	Ferrioxamines
Mycobactins	Coprogen
Rhodotorulic acid	Ferrichrome
Terregens factor (arthrobactin)	

[a]For a more complete list see Table 1.

siderochromes can replace this dihydroxamate [181, 182]; e.g., 0.15 ng ferrichrome per milliliter will support half-maximal growth of this bacterium although catalase production is limited [181]. Lochhead [183] showed that about one-fifth of the bacteria he isolated from soil and the root region formed substances with activity resembling that of the terregens factor [183]. It was also shown that many organisms present in the soil (about 5×10^5 per gram) require the terregens factor. This factor can be detected and isolated from water extracts of soil [184]. By bioassay with *A. terregens* Lochhead estimated the terregens factor content of normal soil and barley rhizosphere to be about 150 ng/g [194]. However, using *Arthrobacter* JG 9, another bioassay organism for this growth factor, Page [174] detected siderochromes in soil but failed to detect them in root exudates.

It is possible that soil and dung are major sources of siderochromes. Unfortunately, most surveys of siderochrome-forming organisms were made before it was realized that they are formed most abundantly in media deficient in iron. Coprogen is a growth factor for the coprophilic phycomycete *Pilobolus kleinii* and in one survey nine out of 68 microorganisms tested produced undefined substances with coprogen-like activity toward *P. kleinii* [147]. Burnham and Neilands [176] found that 35 out of a total of 47 microorganisms formed ferrichrome-like substances when assayed with *Arthrobacter* JG 9. Such observations and work on the terregens factor suggest that soil organisms may be active in hydroxamate synthesis.

B. Iron Chelation and Transport

Many kinds of hydroxamates formed by aerobic organisms appear to be involved in iron transport or transfer. The naturally formed hydroxamates have remarkably strong and specific affinities for ferric iron (Table 5). They are also sufficiently strong chelates to maintain ferric iron in solution at pH's as alkaline as 11.0 whereas ferric hydroxide is extremely insoluble at this pH. In the case of the siderochromes the complex stability constant with ferric iron is many times (10^4-10^7) more powerful than that between EDTA and ferric iron. However, only weak complexes are formed between the siderochromes and ferrous iron and other ions of biological interest; e.g., the log K's for complexes between desferriferrioxamine B and Fe^{2+}, Ca^{2+}, Co^{2+}, Cu^{2+}, and Zn^{2+} are 7.2, 2.6, 10.3, 13.5, and 7.9, respectively [123]. The removal of ferric iron from siderochromes requires fairly strong alkaline treatment, reduction, or the use of an agent as powerful as oxine (8-hydroxyquinoline).

TABLE 5

Stability Constants of the Fe^{3+} Complexes of Various
Hydroxamic Acids and Other Chelating Substances
Determined at 20°C [a]

Chelating agent	Log_{10} stability constant (log K)
Acetohydroxamate	$28.3^{[c]}$
Desferriferrichrome	29.1
Desferriferrichrysin	30.0
Desferriferrioxamine B	30.5
Desferriferrioxamine D_1	30.8
Desferriferrioxamine E	32.4
DIMBOA[b]	$21.3^{[c]}$
Citric acid	11.9
Oxalic acid	10.0
EDTA (ethylenediamine tetracetate)	25.1
Tetracycline	$25.0^{[c]}$
8-Hydroxyquinoline (oxine)	$36.0^{[c]}$

[a] Data from [123, 186, 187].

[b] Determined at 25°C.

[c] 3:1 Complex of ligand and iron.

The mycobactins are also selective for ferric iron and the stabilities of their complexes with ferric iron are far higher than with
any other metallic ion at physiological pH values. The stability
constants of the mycobactin-ferric complexes have not been determined
(they are water insoluble) but two lines of indirect evidence indi-
date that mycobactin P has a greater affinity for ferric-iron than
desferriferrioxamine B [20].

Many of the naturally formed hydroxamates are synthesized and
excreted by microorganisms growing under iron-deficient conditions
or in media without added iron. The presence of iron, however, sup-
presses hydroxamate synthesis. For example, the trihydroxamate
ferrichrome A is formed by the fungus *Ustilago sphaerogena* in the
absence of iron in amounts as large as 1 g/liter, but the presence
of as little as 1 mg Fe per liter prevents ferrichrome synthesis [19].
Fusarium roseum synthesizes the dihydroxamate fusarine in iron-
deficient media and Emery [34] obtained yields of 2 g/liter of mycelium (dry weight) and 800 mg/liter of extracellular hydroxyornithine,
but concentrations of iron as low as 4×10^{-7} M halved the amount
of hydroxamate formed [34]. Mycobactin formation by *Mycobacterium
phlei* was found to be inversely related to iron supply [188] and
similar results have been recorded for rhodotorulic acid [189, 190],
schizokinen [191], aerobactin [192], and ferribactin [121].

Siderochrome-like substances have been detected by a bioassay
method (*Arthrobacter* J.G. 9) in aqueous extracts of leaves of several
plants. It has been suggested [173] that such substances are formed
in a desferri form, but when the supply of iron is adequate their
formation could be suppressed by negative feedback. This hypothesis
was supported by evidence that chlorotic watercress suffering from
iron deficiency appeared to contain more siderochrome than normal
green watercress [173].

There is evidence that hydroxamates may play a role in the
economy or metabolism of iron in various microorganisms and perhaps
in plants as well. The three main ways these chelating substances
could function might be (1) to scavenge for iron, (2) to transport

iron across the cytoplasmic membrane, and (3) to donate iron to specific enzymes or other receptors.

Because hydroxamic acids have such a high affinity for ferric iron it has been suggested that they may be formed and act as scavenging molecules in environments where the insoluble ferric ion predominates, the acquisition of iron by the living cell presents difficulties, but this is not the case in reduced environments where the soluble ferrous form abounds. The formation and excretion of powerful iron-binding agents under conditions of iron deprivation have an obvious advantage and may be a way to guard against iron deficiency provided the complexed iron can be taken up by iron-deficient cells. The hypothesis that hydroxamates can act as iron-scavenging molecules in well-aerated environments has support from observations made on various aerobic organisms. Ferrichromes will substitute for one another as growth factors for the coprophilous fungus *Pilobolus kleinii* [19] and the soil bacterium *Arthrobacter terregens* [193] and in every case they appear to act as useable sources of iron in otherwise iron-free media. The requirements of *Arthrobacter* JG 9 for ferrichrome does not seem to be strictly for a specific growth factor because its iron requirements seemed to be catered for by a variety of iron-complexing hydroxamic acids including aspergillic acid, terregens factor, coprogen, nocardamin, mycobactin, and grisein, as well as haemin [176]. Likewise terregens factor, the natural growth-factor requirement for *Arthrobacter terregens*, can be replaced by a limited selection of iron-chelating substances. These are 8-hydroxyquinoline, salicylaldehyde, and acetylacetone. The properties that seem to confer biological activity upon these bidentate chelators are their ability to form stable chelate complexes with ferric iron and also their lipophilic nature [193].

When dilute solutions (1 mM per 10 g soil) of such monohydroxamates as acetohydroxamate, caprohydroxamate and benzohydroxamate are added to soil, pink-colored solutions can be obtained either by centrifuging soil samples or by leaching soil columns and

collecting the eluates [194, 195]. The intensity of the color and
the amount of ferric iron brought into solution is proportional to
the amount of hydroxamate added to the soil, and spectrophotometric
evidence supports the view that ferric hydroxamates are formed [204].
Thus, besides scavenging for small amounts of iron present in solution hydroxamates seem capable of complexing solid phase ferric
iron. By mobilizing iron it is possible that the water-soluble
hydroxamates formed by soil microorganisms [174, 183, 185] may play
a role in their iron nutrition and also in the downward movement of
iron in soils. When hydroxamates are added to acidic soils it is
found that the amount of phosphate in solution is increased. This
increase may be brought about by displacement of the phosphate anion
from soil cationic sites, such as hydrous iron [196] by the competing
hydroxamate anion. During such competition, ferric iron may be released [194, 197] and, like phosphate, presumably becomes available
for plant or microbial use. Attempts to demonstrate the same phenomenon in a highly calcareous soil fail, probably because phosphate is
associated mainly with calcium in such soils and hydroxamates form
far less stable complexes with calcium than they do with ferric
iron [195].

     The part hydroxamic acids may play in the transport of iron
across cellular membranes has been reviewed by Emery [22], who
points out that the transport of lipophobic cationic iron across a
lipophilic cell membrane presents a formidable problem. Neilands
[19] has proposed that ferrichrome could act as an iron-transporting
agent if it were excreted from cells to firmly chelate extracellular
iron and the complex then entered the cell to give up the iron with
the release of the ligand for further use. Work by Emery [198]
with the fungus *Ustilago sphaerogena* showed that under iron-deficient
conditions ^{59}Fe- and ^{14}C-ferrichrome were taken up rapidly by the
cells and that the ^{59}Fe was retained by the cells, whereas the
^{14}C-ferrichrome ligand, desferriferrichrome, was released. Other
evidence showed that ferrichrome can be concentrated in cells by an
active transport mechanism specific for ferrichrome and not for its

ligand, desferriferrichrome, or for any other ferrihydroxamate however closely related in structure, e.g., ferrichrome A. Transport
of the iron chelate, ferrichrome, across the cell membrane into the
cell and egress of the ligand desferriferrichrome probably depends
on the flexibility of the structure of the cyclic peptide and the
extensive conformational changes imposed upon it by the chelation
process [22, 198]. Investigations of other iron-transporting hydroxamates do not seem to be as advanced as with Emery's work on
U. sphaerogena.

Interest in the ability of hydroxamates to chelate and transport iron has not been confined to studies on microorganisms but has
included animals [18] and plants. Page [174] has suggested that
siderochromes possess properties that would explain how iron may be
absorbed and translocated by plants, and Price [199] has discussed
the chemistry of such chelates and their possible role when iron is
deficient for plants. Tipton and Buell [57] have determined the
stability constants of ferric iron complexes of two glucosides of
the benzoxazine hydroxamic acids of maize (see Section III, A, 4).
Although the stability constants for DIMBOA (log K = 21.3) and the
other hydroxamic acid (log K = 19.4) were several orders of magnitude less than those of trihydroxamic acids (log K about 30, see
Table 5) they were much higher than that of citric acid (log K =
11.9), which is reported to function in iron absorption and transport in higher plants [209]. Tipton and Buell concluded that at
the concentrations (10^{-5}-10^{-3} M) at which these compounds occur in
young maize plants a high proportion of the ferric iron present
must be bound as complexes of the hydroxamic acids, and may therefore play a role in the iron metabolism of plants [57].

A limited amount of experimental work has shown that plants
can use iron chelated by hydroxamates. According to Neilands [19],
I. Orlando showed that ferrichrome and ferrichrome A were effective
in supplying iron to tomato plants in water culture and the latter
was superior to EDTA in alkaline media. Stutz [201] used [59]Fe-
ferrioxamine B and was able to demonstrate that the chelated-iron

was absorbed and translocated more rapidly than ferric chloride to shoots of tomato plants growing in water culture. The siderochrome antibiotic albomycin was found by Lisá and Prát [202] to support increased growth of the alga *Scenedesmus obliquus* when it was supplied as an ingredient of a culture solution with a low inorganic iron content.

It has been assumed [19, 22] that siderochromes can transport iron into the cell and that there the iron is reduced by an enzyme system to the ferrous state and transferred to porphyrin, with the formation of heme. It is possible that siderochromes act as growth factors by functioning as coenzymes in the synthesis of microbial heme although experimental evidence is lacking to support this hypothesis. It may be that siderochromes are useful sources of reducible iron and not true cofactors.

C. Antibiotics

Many of the naturally occurring hydroxamic acids, e.g., hadacidin, have antibiotic activity (Table 6) or can interfere with metabolism. The ways in which they act upon the cells they antagonize have not been fully elucidated. The trihydroxamate antibiotics are of interest because their antibiotic activity can be antagonized by

TABLE 6

Some Naturally Occurring Hydroxamic Acids
with Antibiotic Activity

Monohydroxamates	Dihydroxamates	Trihydroxamates[a]
Aspergillic acids	Mycelianamide	Ferrimycins
Actinonin	---	Albomycin

[a]For a more complete list, see Table 1.

other siderochromes; for example, albomycin and ferrimycin are both antagonized by ferrioxamine B [15]. This relationship appears to be specific because the growth factor trihydroxamates do not antagonize other types of antibiotics, such as penicillin. Presumably, the

common feature of these substances is their ability to chelate iron
but, so far, the mechanism of interference has not been worked out
[17, 22].

There appear to be no reports of hydroxamate antibiotics being
present and active in natural habitats.

D. Nitrification

There is evidence that hydroxamates are possible intermediates
in nitrification of ammonium ion by heterotrophic microorganisms.
The most detailed work is that of Verstraete and Alexander [203,
204], who isolated an *Arthrobacter*, from municipal sewage, that could
oxidize ammonium heterotrophically to nitrite and nitrate. One of
the key intermediates is an unidentified hydroxamate formed presumably
by assimilation of ammonium with the formation of an amide that is
then oxidized to the unknown hydroxamate. Hydroxylamine was formed
when cell-free extracts were fed with acetohydroxamic acid. The
hydroxylamine was oxidized by extracellular enzymes with the production of nitrite and nitrate. Acetohydroxamate was also oxidized
slowly in another pathway with the formation of nitrosoethanol.

A strain of the fungus *Aspergillus flavus* that forms nitrate
when supplied with ammonium as its sole nitrogen source also forms
hadacidin [42]. The growing mycelium of *A. flavus*, but not cell-
free extracts can convert malonyl monohydroxamate to nitrate yet
does not oxidize succinyl or propinyl monohydroxamate [205]. Bacteria, actinomycetes, and fungi were isolated from soil that oxidized
hadacidin to nitrate by elective techniques and two strains of fungi
and two of bacteria were also isolated that could oxidize benzohydroxamate to nitrate [206].

E. Urease Inhibition

Several monohydroxamic acids (including hydroxyurea) and a
dihydroxamic acid, all unknown in biological systems, have been
found to be highly specific and potent inhibitors of urease prepared

and purified from sword bean, jack bean, and the bacterium *Proteus vulgaris* [207-214]. Kobashi et al. [207] found that the inhibition of urease by acetohydroxamic acid (AHA) was reversible but Fishbein et al. [215] claimed that the inhibition was irreversible, complete, and probably noncompetitive. Blakeley et al. [214] have reexamined the inhibition of jack bean urease by AHA and chloroacetohydroxamic acid and found it to be strong but completely reversible, in agreement with the work of Kobashi et al. [207].

Many substances are known which will inhibit urease but most are toxic to cells of animals, plants or microorganisms. Some of the monohydroxamic acids, however, notably AHA, have a very low toxicity to bacteria and animals together with a capacity to inhibit urease specifically [207, 210, 215]. In the case of AHA this quality is combined with no evidence of inhibition at concentrations of 1 x 10^{-3} M to a variety of plant and animal enzymes other than urease [207]. AHA has certain features that make it a potential agent to control the rate of hydrolysis of urea to ammonium carbonate in those situations in which it is desired to prevent the formation of toxic concentrations of ammonia. Its potential usefulness has attracted the attention of pharmacologists endeavoring to control the effects of urease-forming bacteria in the intestine [212, 215-217] and of animal nutritionists concerned with the use of urea as a dietary replacement for protein [218, 219]. Both intestinal and rumen bacteria are believed to contribute to the formation of concentrations of ammonia in the blood too high for the liver to convert to urea (ammonaemia and hepatic coma) and AHA has been used with some success in experimental investigations of its potential as a urease inhibitor.

In most soils urea is hydrolysed rapidly by urease to ammonium carbonate and the resulting accumulation of ammonium and rise in pH can lead to loss of nitrogen as volatile ammonia and the formation of phytotoxic concentrations of ammonia or nitrite [220, 221]. Because of the growing importance of urea as a fertilizer [222] several attempts have been made to improve its efficiency as a nitrogen source.

One line of approach has been to find compounds that will slow down
the rate of urea hydrolysis, and thereby prevent any accumulation
of ammonium carbonate [223].

The effectiveness of hydroxamic acids as urease inhibitors in
soils has been investigated by Pugh and Waid who evaluated the effects
of several carboxylic hydroxamic acids on the disappearance of urea
[195, 224] and ammonia losses from a selection of soils treated with
urea [195, 224-226]. They found that AHA and then benzohydroxamic
acid were the two most effective compounds tested. The hydroxamates
delayed the onset of ammonia loss for several days following the
addition of urea to the soils and they also reduced the maximum rate
of ammonia loss. Bremner and Douglas [227-229] used a rapid method
to evaluate more than 100 different compounds as inhibitors of urease
activity in soils and confirmed the findings of Pugh and Waid that
AHA inhibits urease in soil. However, Bremner and Douglas have also
demonstrated that compared to dihydric phenols, quinones, and various
other organic and inorganic substances [229] AHA was far less effective as an inhibitor. Both groups of workers [195, 225, 229] found
that the effectiveness of AHA decreased markedly with increase in
time of incubation of soil with AHA before the addition of urea.
They concluded that this compound is decomposed rapidly [224] in
soils and has no effect on urea hydrolysis by soil urease when it is
added to soil several days before addition of urea.

Pugh and Waid [226] showed that if sulfanilamide and AHA were
incorporated together the delay before ammonia was volatilized was
prolonged although sulfanilamide alone caused only a short delay
to the onset of ammonia loss. This effect was attributed to toxicity
of sulfanilamide towards urease-forming soil organisms.

Further work may elucidate why AHA and other hydroxamates that
are potent specific inhibitors of urease *in vitro* are relatively
ineffective in soils when compared to other less specific inhibitors
of urease. Possible explanations are unfavorable pH; adsorption
onto soil surfaces; inactivation of inhibitors by formation of
ferric chelates; biological decomposition of hydroxamates; failure

of hydroxamates to permeate cells and inhibit intracellular urease;
and proliferation and formation of urease by soil microorganisms.
Armed with such knowledge it may be possible to contribute to a
general strategy to control transformations brought about by organisms
in soil to the advantage of man and without detriment to the environment.

F. Substrates for Growth

Although cyclic peptides are known to be resistant to degradation by common plant and proteolytic enzymes [230], Warren and
Neilands [231] isolated from soil a *Pseudomonas* that in the presence
of ferrichrome A, formed an inducible peptidase [232] to degrade
the hydroxamate and use it as the sole source of carbon and nitrogen
[231].

REFERENCES

1. H. L. Yale, *Chem. Rev.*, *33*, 209 (1943).
2. R. T. Coutts, *Can. J. Pharm. Sci.*, *2*, 1 (1967).
3. R. T. Coutts, *Can. J. Pharm. Sci.*, *2*, 27 (1967).
4. J. B. Bapat, D. St. C. Black, and R. F. C. Brown, *Advan.
    Heterocyclic Chem.*, *10*, 199 (1969).
5. V. C. Bass and J. H. Yoe, *Talanta*, *13*, 735 (1966).
6. W. W. Brandt, *Rec. Chem. Prog.*, *21*, 159 (1960).
7. F. Feigl, *Spot Tests in Organic Analysis*, Elsevier, London,
    1960.
8. R. L. Dutta, *J. Ind. Chem. Soc.*, *36*, 285 (1959).
9. F. Mathis, *Bull. Soc. Chim. France*, D9-22 (1953).
10. F. Lipmann and L. C. Tuttle, *J. Biol. Chem.*, *159*, 21 (1945).
11. J. W. Cramer, J. A. Miller, and E. C. Miller, *J. Biol. Chem.*,
    235, 885 (1960).
12. P. D. Shaw, *Biochemistry*, *6*, 2253 (1967).
13. R. McGrath, L. C. Vining, F. Sala, D. W. S. Westlake,
    Can. J. Biochem., *46*, 587 (1968).
14. V. Prelog, *Pure Appl. Chem.*, *6*, 327 (1963).
15. W. Keller-Schierlein, V. Prelog, and H. Zähner, *Fortschr.
    Chem. Org. Naturstoffe*, *22*, 279 (1964).
16. O. Mikeš and J. Turková, *Chem. Listy*, *58*, 65 (1964).
17. J. B. Neilands, *Structure and Bonding*, Vol. I, p. 59, Springer,
    Berlin, 1966.
18. J. B. Neilands, *Science*, *156*, 1443 (1967).
19. J. B. Neilands, *Bacteriol. Rev.*, *21*, 101 (1957).

20. G. A. Snow, *Bacteriol. Rev.*, *34*, 99 (1970).
21. H. Maehr, *Pure Appl. Chem.*, *28*, 603 (1971).
22. T. Emery, *Advan. Enzymology*, *35*, 135 (1971).
23. E. C. White and J. H. Hill, *J. Bacteriol.*, *45*, 433 (1943).
24. J. D. Dutcher and O. Wintersteiner, *J. Biol. Chem.*, *155*, 359 (1944).
25. B. J. Wilson, *Bacteriol. Rev.*, *30*, 478 (1966).
26. J. C. MacDonald, R. G. Micetich, and R. H. Haskins, *Can. J. Microbiol.*, *10*, 90 (1964).
27. I. D. Spenser in *Comprehensive Biochemistry* (M. Florkin and E. H. Stotz, Eds.), Vol. 20, p. 231, Elsevier, Amsterdam, 1968.
28. G. T. Newbold, W. Sharp, and F. S. Spring, *J. Chem. Soc.*, 2679 (1951).
29. S. A. Waksman, *Microbial Antagonisms and Antibiotic Substances*, p. 244, Commonwealth Fund, New York, 1947.
30. W. A. Sexton, *Chemical Constitution and Biological Activity*, p. 277, Spon, London, 1963.
31. J. D. Dutcher, *J. Biol. Chem.*, *171*, 321 (1947).
32. J. D. Dutcher, *J. Biol. Chem.*, *171*, 341 (1947).
33. J. C. MacDonald, *J. Biol. Chem.*, *236*, 512 (1961).
34. T. Emery, *Biochemistry*, *4*, 1410 (1965).
35. J. M. Sayer and T. F. Emery, *Biochemistry*, *7*, 184 (1968).
36. H. Diekmann, *Arch. Mikrobiol.*, *58*, 1 (1967).
37. H. Diekmann, and H. Zähner, *Eur. J. Biochem.*, *3*, 213 (1967).
38. T. Emery, *Biochemistry*, *5*, 3694 (1966).
39. C. O. Gitterman, E. L. Dulaney, E. A. Kaczka, D. Hendlin, and H. B. Woodruff, *Proc. Soc. Exp. Biol. and Med.*, *109*, 852 (1962).
40. E. A. Kaczka, C. O. Gitterman, E. L. Dulaney, and K. Folkers, *Biochemistry*, *1*, 340 (1962).
41. R. Stevens and T. Emery, *Biochemistry*, *5*, 74 (1966).
42. K. Doxtader and M. Alexander, *J. Bacteriol.*, *91*, 1186 (1966).
43. H. T. Schigeura and C. N. Gordon, *J. Biol. Chem.*, *237*, 1932 (1962).
44. H. T. Schigeura and C. N. Gordon, *J. Biol. Chem.*, *237*, 1937 (1962).
45. J. L. Mego, *Biochem. Biophys. Acta*, *79*, 221 (1964).
46. E. L. Dulaney and R. A. Gray, *Mycologia*, *54*, 476 (1962).
47. E. Honkanen and A. I. Virtanen, *Acta Chem. Scand.*, *14*, 1214 (1960).
48. J. E. Reimann and R. U. Bjerrum, *Tetrahedron Lett.*, *4*, 211 (1964).
49. O. Wahlroos and A. I. Virtanen, *J. Pharm. Sci.*, *53*, 844 (1964).
50. J. B. Bredenberg, E. Honkanen, and A. I. Virtanen, *Acta Chem. Scand.*, *16*, 135 (1962).
51. O. Wahlroos and A. I. Virtanen, *Acta Chem. Scand.*, *13*, 1906 (1959).
52. P. K. Hietala and A. I. Virtanen, *Acta Chem. Scand.*, *14*, 502 (1960).
53. A. I. Virtanen and P. K. Hietala, *Acta Chem. Scand.*, *14*, 499 (1960).

54. A. I. Virtanen and P. K. Hietala, *Acta Chem. Scand.*, *9*,
     1543 (1955).
55. C. L. Tipton, J. A. Klun, R. R. Husted, and M. Pierson,
     Biochemistry, *6*, 2866 (1967).
56. J. A. Klun, C. L. Tipton, J. F. Robinson, D. L. Ostrem, and
     M. Beroza, *J. Agric. Food. Chem.*, *18*, 663 (1970).
57. C. L. Tipton and E. L. Buell, *Phytochemistry*, *9*, 1215 (1970).
58. M. A. Elnaghy and P. Linko, *Physiologia Plant.*, *15*, 764 (1962).
59. J. N. Be Miller and A. J. Pappelis, *Phytopathology*, *55*,
     1237 (1965).
60. P. Anglade and P. M. Molot, *Annls Epiphyt.*, *18*, 279 (1967).
61. P. M. Molot and P. Anglade, *Annls Epiphyt.*, *19*, 75 (1968).
62. R. M. Couture, D. G. Routley and G. M. Dunn, *Physiol. Plant
     Pathol.*, *1*, 515 (1971).
63. S. D. Beck and E. E. Smissan, *Ann. Entomol. Soc. Amer.*, *54*,
     53 (1961).
64. J. A. Klun and J. F. Robinson, *J. Econ. Entomol.*, *62*, 214
     (1969).
65. J. A. Klun and T. A. Brindley, *J. Econ. Entomol.*, *59*, 711 (1966).
66. J. A. Klun, C. L. Tipton, and T. A. Brindley, *J. Econ.
     Entomol.*, *60*, 1529 (1967).
67. P. Castelfranco and M. S. Brown, *Weeds*, *10*, 131 (1962).
68. P. Castelfranco, C. L. Foy, and D. B. Deutsch, *Weeds*, *9*,
     580 (1961).
69. R. H. Hamilton and D. E. Morland, *Science*, *135*, 373 (1962).
70. W. Roth, *Compt. Rend.*, *245*, 942 (1957).
71. W. Roth and E. Knüsli, *Experientia*, *17*, 312 (1961).
72. R. H. Hamilton, R. Bandurski and E. H. Reusch, *Cereal
     Chem.*, *39*, 107 (1962).
73. A. Gysin and E. Knüsli, *Adv. Pest Control Res.*, *3*, 289 (1960).
74. R. H. Hamilton, *J. Agri. Food Chem.*, *12*, 14 (1964).
75. R. H. Hamilton, *Weeds*, *12*, 27 (1964).
76. R. D. Palmer and C. O. Crogan, *Weeds*, *13*, 219 (1965).
77. H. H. Funderburk and D. E. Davis, *Weeds*, *11*, 101 (1963).
78. D. S. Frear and H. R. Swanson, *Phytochemistry*, *9*, 2123 (1970).
79. G. L. Lamoureux, R. H. Shimabukuro, H. R. Swanson, and D. S.
     Frear, *J. Agr. Food Chem.*, *18*, 81 (1970).
80. R. H. Shimabukuro and H. R. Swanson, *J. Agri. Food Chem.*, *17*,
     199 (1969).
81. R. H. Shimabukuro, H. R. Swanson, and W. C. Walsh, *Plant
     Physiol.*, *46*, 103 (1970).
82. R. H. Shimabukuro, D. S. Frear, H. R. Swanson, and W. C.
     Walsh, *Plant Physiol.*, *47*, 10 (1971).
83. C. I. Harris, *Weed Res.*, *5*, 275 (1965).
84. C. I. Harris and T. J. Sheets, *Weeds*, *13*, 215 (1965).
85. W. D. Ollis, A. J. East, J. J. Gordon, and I. O. Sutherland,
     in *Chemistry of Microbial Products*, p. 204, Institute of
     Applied Microbiology, University of Tokyo, 1964.
86. J. Francis, J. Madinaveitia, H. Macturk, and G. A. Snow,
     Nature (London), *163*, 365 (1949).

87. J. Francis, H. Macturk, J. Madinaveitia, and G. A. Snow, *Biochem. J.*, *55*, 596 (1953).
88. G. A. Snow, *J. Chem. Soc.*, 2588 (1954).
89. G. A. Snow, *J. Chem. Soc.*, 4080 (1954).
90. G. A. Snow, *Biochem. J.*, *81*, 4 P (1961).
91. G. A. Snow, *Biochem. J.*, *94*, 160 (1965).
92. G. A. Snow, *Biochem. J.*, *97*, 166 (1965).
93. G. A. Snow, *Biochem. J.*, *115*, 199 (1969).
94. J. E. Tateson, *Biochem. J.*, *118*, 747 (1970).
95. J. H. Hanks, *Bacteriol. Rev.*, *30*, 114 (1966).
96. W. R. Anslow and H. Raistrick, *Biochem. J.*, *25*, 39 (1931).
97. A. E. Oxford and H. Raistrick, *Biochem. J.*, *42*, 323 (1948).
98. W. A. Sexton, *Chemical Constitution and Biological Activity*, pp. 201, 277, Spon, London, 1963.
99. A. J. Birch, R. A. Massey-Westropp, and R. W. Richards, *J. Chem. Soc.*, 3717 (1956).
100. A. J. Birch and H. Smith, in *Ciba Foundation Symposium on Amino Acids, Peptides and Antimetabolic Activity* (G. E. W. Wolstenholme, Ed.), p. 247, Churchill, London, 1958.
101. R. B. Bates, J. H. Schauble, and M. Soucek, *Tetrahedron Let.*, 1683 (1963).
102. A. J. Kluyver, J. P. van der Walt, and A. J. van Triet, *Proc. Nat. Acad. Sci. (U.S.)*, *39*, 583 (1953).
103. D. G. Kupfer, R. L. Uffen, and E. Canale-Parola, *Archiv. Mikrobiol.*, *56*, 9 (1967).
104. J. N. Campbell, J. L. Nichols and S. A. Berry, *Can. J. Microbiol.*, *10*, 659 (1964).
105. J. C. MacDonald, *Can. J. Microbiol.*, *12*, 55 (1966).
106. A. H. Cook and C. A. Slater, *J. Chem. Soc.*, 4133 (1956).
107. J. C. MacDonald, *Can. J. Chem.*, *41*, 165 (1963).
108. A. Ohta, *Chem. Pharm. Bull. (Tokyo)*, *12*, 125 (1964).
109. J. A. Garibaldi and J. B. Neilands, *Nature (London)*, *177*, 526 (1956).
110. B. R. Byers, M. V. Powell, and C. E. Lankford, *J. Bacteriol.*, *93*, 286 (1967).
111. C. E. Lankford, J. R. Walker, J. B. Reeves, N. H. Nabbut, B. R. Byers, and R. J. Jones, *J. Bacteriol.*, *91*, 1070 (1966).
112. J. L. Arceneaux and C. E. Lankford, *Biochem. Biophys. Res. Commun.*, *24*, 370 (1966).
113. C. E. Lankford, T. Y. Kustoff, and T. P. Sergeant, *J. Bacteriol.*, *74*, 737 (1957).
114. W. B. Davis, M. J. McCauley, and B. R. Byers, *J. Bacteriol.*, *105*, 589 (1971).
115. W. B. Davis and B. R. Byers, *J. Bacteriol.*, *107*, 491 (1971).
116. K. B. Mullis, J. R. Pollack, and J. B. Neilands, *Biochemistry*, *10*, 4894 (1971).
117. F. Gibson and D. I. Magrath, *Biochem. Biophys. Acta*, *192*, 175 (1969).
118. C. L. Atkin and J. B. Neilands, *Biochemistry*, *7*, 3734 (1968).
119. C. L. Atkin, J. B. Neilands, and H. J. Phaff, *J. Bacteriol.*, *103*, 722 (1970).

120. H. Diekmann, *Arch. Mikrobiol.*, *73*, 65 (1970).
121. B. Maurer, A. Müller, W. Keller-Schierlein and H. Zähner, *Arch. Mikrobiol.*, *60*, 326 (1968).
122. H. Zähner, W. Keller-Schierlein, R. Hütter, K. Hess-Leisinger, and A. Deer, *Arch. Mikrobiol.*, *45*, 119 (1963).
123. G. Anderegg, F. l'Epplattenier, and G. Schwarzenbach, *Helv. Chim. Acta*, *46*, 1409 (1963).
124. R. A. J. Warren and J. B. Neilands, *J. Gen. Microbiol.*, *35*, 459 (1964).
125. H. Bickel, E. Gäumann, W. Keller-Schierlein, V. Prelog, E. Vischer, A. Wettstein, and H. Zähner, *Experientia*, *16*, 129 (1960).
126. H. Bickel, E. Gäumann, N. Nussberger, P. Reusser, E. Vischer, W. Voser, A. Wettstein, and H. Zähner, *Helv. Chim. Acta*, *43*, 2105 (1960).
127. H. Bickel, G. E. Hall, W. Keller-Schierlein, V. Prelog, and E. Vischer, *Helv. Chim. Acta*, *43*, 2129 (1960).
128. H. Zähner, E. Bachmann, R. Hutter, and J. Nuesch, *Pathol. Microbiol.*, *25*, 708 (1962).
129. S. Rogers and J. B. Neilands, *Biochemistry*, *2*, 6 (1963).
130. S. Rogers and J. B. Neilands, *Biochemistry*, *3*, 1850 (1964).
131. J. Bonner, in *Plant Biochemistry* (J. Bonner and J. E. Varner, Eds.), p. 665, Academic, New York, 1965.
132. J. H. Richards and J. B. Hendrickson, *Biosynthesis of Steroids, Terpenes and Acetogenins*, P. 205, Benjamin, New York, 1964.
133. H. Anke and H. Diekmann, *FEBS Lett.*, *17*, 115 (1971).
134. D. Perlman, *Advan. Appl. Microbiol.*, *7*, 103 (1965).
135. J. B. Neilands, *J. Amer. Chem. Soc.*, *74*, 4846 (1952).
136. J. A. Garibaldi and J. B. Neilands, *J. Amer. Chem. Soc.*, *77*, 2429 (1955).
137. H. Zähner, R. Hutter, and E. Bachmann, *Arch. Mikrobiol.*, *36*, 325 (1960).
138. W. Keller-Schierlein, *Helv. Chim. Acta*, *46*, 1920 (1963).
139. C. L. Atkin, J. B. Neilands, and H. J. Phaff, *J. Bacteriol.*, *103*, 722 (1970).
140. W. Keller-Schierlein and A. Deer, *Helv. Chim. Acta*, *46*, 1907 (1963).
141. H. Diekmann, *Arch. Mikrobiol*, *74*, 301 (1971).
142. G. F. Gause, *Brit. Med. J.*, 1177 (1955).
143. J. Turková, O. Mikeš, J. Schramel, O. Kessl, and F. Sörm, *Coll. Czech. Chem. Commun.*, *30*, 118 (1965).
144. D. M. Reynolds, A. Schatz, and S. A. Waksman, *Proc. Soc. Exp. Biol. Med.*, *64*, 50 (1947).
145. D. M. Reynolds and S. A. Waksman, *J. Bacteriol.*, *55*, 739 (1948).
146. F. A. Kuehl, M. N. Bishop, L. Chaiet, and K. Folkers, *J. Amer. Chem. Soc.*, *73*, 1770 (1951).
147. C. W. Hesseltine, C. Pidacks, A. R. Whitehill, N. Bohonos, B. L. Hutchings, and J. H. Williams, *J. Amer. Chem. Soc.*, *74*, 1362 (1952).
148. C. Pidacks, A. R. Whitehill, L. M. Pruess, C. W. Hesseltine, B. L. Hutchings, N. Bohonos, and J. H. Williams, *J. Amer. Chem. Soc.*, *75*, 6064 (1953).

149. W. Keller-Schierlein and H. Diekmann, *Helv. Chim. Acta, 53,* 2025 (1970).
150. G. Padmanaban and P. S. Sarma, *Arch. Biochem. Biophys., 108,* 362 (1965).
151. G. Padmanaban and P. S. Sarma, *Arch. Biochem. Biophys., 111,* 147 (1965).
152. T. H. Haskell, R. H. Bunge, J. C. French, and Q. R. Bartz, *J. Antibiotics, 16,* 67 (1963).
153. H. Tsukiura, M. Okanishi, T. Ohmori, H. Koshiyama, T. Miyaki, H. Kitazima, and H. Kawaguchi, *J. Antibiotics, 17,* 39 (1964).
154. A. G. Lochhead, M. O. Burton, and R. H. Thexton, *Nature (London), 170,* 282 (1952).
155. A. G. Lochhead and M. O. Burton, *Can. J. Bot., 31,* 7 (1953).
156. P. Sensi and M. T. Timbal, *Antibiotics and Chemotherapy, 9,* 160 (1958).
157. H. Diekmann, *Arch. Mikrobiol., 58,* 1 (1967).
158. H. Diekmann and H. Zähner, *European J. Biochem., 3,* 213 (1967).
159. H. Maehr and J. Berger, *Biotech. and Bioeng., 11,* 1111 (1969).
160. W. Keller-Schierlein, P. Mertens, V. Prelog, and A. Walser, *Helv. Chim. Acta, 48,* 710 (1965).
161. H. Thrum, *Naturwissenschaften, 44,* 561 (1957).
162. S. Sato, M. Tadenuma, and T. Hasuo, *Agr. Biol. Chem., 35,* 950 (1971).
163. H. Bickel, G. E. Hall, W. Keller-Schierlein, V. Prelog, E. Vischer, and A. Wettstein, *Helv. Chim. Acta, 43,* 2129 (1960).
164. H. Bickel, H. Keberle, and E. Vischer, *Helv. Chim. Acta, 46,* 1385 (1963).
165. W. Keller-Schierlein and V. Prelog, *Helv. Chim. Acta, 44,* 709 (1961).
166. A. Stoll, A. Brack, and J. Renz, *Schweiz. Z. Path. Bacteriol., 14,* 225 (1951).
167. W. Keller-Schierlein and V. Prelog, *Helv. Chim. Acta, 44,* 1981 (1961).
168. W. Keller-Schierlein and V. Prelog, *Helv. Chim. Acta, 45,* 590 (1961).
169. F. Knüsel, B. Schiess, and W. Zimmerman, *Arch. Mikrobiol, 68,* 99 (1969).
170. W. Zimmermann and F. Knüsel, *Arch. Mikrobiol., 68,* 107 (1969).
171. I. R. Bick, G. J. Jann, and D. J. Cram, *Antibiotics and Chemotherapy, 2,* 255 (1952).
172. A. Müller and H. Zähner, *Arch. Mikrobiol, 62,* 257 (1968).
173. E. R. Page, *Biochem. J., 100,* 34 P (1966).
174. E. R. Page, *16th Annual Report, National Vegetable Research Station,* 1965, 30 (1966).
175. H. Zähner, E. Bachmann, R. Hutter, and J. Nuesch, *Pathol. Microbiol., 25,* 708 (1962).
176. B. F. Burnham and J. B. Neilands, *J. Biol. Chem., 236,* 554 (1961).
177. B. R. Byers, M. V. Powell, and C. E. Lankford, *J. Bacteriol., 93,* 286 (1967).

178. T. Emery, *Advan. Enzymol.*, *35*, 135 (1971).
179. M. O. Burton and A. G. Lochhead, *Can. J. Botany*, *31*, 145 (1953).
180. A. G. Lochhead, *Bacteriol. Rev.* *22*, 145 (1958).
181. B. F. Burnham, *J. Gen. Microbiol.*, *32*, 117 (1963).
182. M. O. Burton, *Can. J. Microbiol.*, *3*, 107 (1957).
183. A. G. Lochhead, *Soil Sci.*, *84*, 395 (1957).
184. M. O. Burton, F. J. Sowden, and A. G. Lochhead, *Can. J. Bio-chem. Physiol.*, *32*, 400 (1954).
185. A. G. Lochhead and M. O. Burton, *Soil Sci.*, *82*, 237 (1956).
186. C. L. Tipton and E. L. Buell, *Phytochemistry*, *9*, 1215 (1970).
187. A. Albert, *Selective Toxicity*, 3rd ed., pp. 38, 230, Methuen, London, 1965.
188. A. D. Antoine and N. E. Morrison, *J. Bacteriol.*, *95*, 245 (1968).
189. C. L. Atkin and J. B. Neilands, *Biochemistry*, *7*, 3734 (1968).
190. C. L. Atkin, J. B. Neilands, and H. J. Phaff, *J. Bacteriol.*, *103*, 722 (1970).
191. W. B. Davis, M. J. McCauley, and B. R. Byers, *J. Bacteriol.*, *105*, 589 (1971).
192. F. Gibson and D. I. Magrath, *Biochim. Biophys. Acta*, *192*, 175 (1969).
193. N. E. Morrison, A. D. Antoine, and E. E. Dewbrey, *J. Bact.*, *89*, 1630 (1965).
194. J. S. Waid, in *The Soil Ecosystem* (J. G. Sheals, Ed.), p. 199, Systematics Association, Publication 8, 1969.
195. K. B. Pugh, *Hydroxamate Inhibition of Urease in Soils*, Ph.D. Thesis, Reading University, 1970.
196. K. S. LaFleur and G. R. Craddock, *Soil Sci. Soc. Amer. Proc.*, *31*, 324, 1967.
197. E. W. Russell, *Soil Conditions and Plant Growth*, 9th Ed., Longmans, Green, London, 1961.
198. T. F. Emery, *Biochemistry*, *10*, 1483 (1971).
199. C. E. Price, *Ann. Rev. Plant Physiol.*, *19*, 239 (1968).
200. J. C. Brown and L. C. Tiffin, *Plant Physiol.*, *40*, 395 (1965).
201. E. Stutz, *Experientia*, *20*, 430 (1964).
202. L. Lisá and S. Prát, *Biologia Plantarum*, *8*, 476 (1966).
203. W. Verstraete and M. Alexander, *J. Bacteriol.*, *110*, 955 (1972).
204. W. Verstraete and M. Alexander, *J. Bacteriol.*, *110*, 962 (1972).
205. K. G. Doxtader and M. Alexander, *Can. J. Microbiol.*, *12*, 807 (1966).
206. K. G. Doxtader and M. Alexander, *Soil Sci. Soc. Amer. Proc.*, *30*, 351 (1966).
207. K. Kobashi, J. Hase, and K. Uehara, *Biochim. Biophys. Acta*, *65*, 380 (1962).
208. K. Kobashi, J. Hase, and T. Komai, *Biochem. Biophys. Res. Commun.*, *23*, 24 (1966).
209. G. R. Gale, *Biochem. Pharmacol.*, *14*, 693 (1965).
210. W. N. Fishbein and P. P. Carbone, *Clin. Res.*, *12*, 453 (1964).
211. W. N. Fishbein and P. P. Carbone, *J. Biol. Chem.*, *240*, 2407 (1965).
212. T. Aoyagi and W. H. J. Summerskill, *Lancet*, 296 (1966).
213. J. Hase and K. Kobashi, *J. Biochem. (Tokyo)*, *62*, 293 (1967).

214. R. L. Blakeley, J. A. Hinds, H. E. Kunze, E. C. Webb, and
     B. Zerner, *Biochemistry*, *8*, 1991 (1969).
215. W. N. Fishbein, P. P. Carbone, and H. D. Hochstein, *Nature
     (London)*, *208*, 46 (1965).
216. W. N. Fishbein, *Biochemical Medicine*, *1*, 111 (1967).
217. W. H. J. Summerskill, F. Thorsell, J. H. Feinberg, and
     J. S. Aldrete, *Gastroenterology*, *54*, 20 (1967).
218. K. Bainter, *Allattenyesztes*, *13*, 373 (1964); *Chem. Absts.*, *63*,
     3531 (1965).
219. G. A. Jones, *Can. J. Microbiol.*, *14*, 409 (1968).
220. M. N. Court, R. C. Stephen, and J. S. Waid, *Nature*, *194*,
     1262 (1962).
221. M. N. Court, R. C. Stephen, and J. S. Waid, *J. Soil Sci.*, *15*,
     42 (1964).
222. J. K. R. Gasser, *Soils Fert.*, *27*, 175 (1964).
223. J. F. Parr, *Soils Fert.*, *30*, 207 (1967).
224. J. S. Waid and K. B. Pugh, *Chem. Ind.*, 71 (1967).
225. K. B. Pugh and J. S. Waid, *Soil Biol. Biochem.*, *1*, 195 (1969).
226. K. B. Pugh and J. S. Waid, *Soil Biol. Biochem.*, *1*, 207 (1969).
227. J. M. Bremner and L. A. Douglas, *Soil Sci. Soc. Amer. Proc.*,
     35, 575 (1971).
228. L. A. Douglas and J. M. Bremner, *Soil Biol. Biochem.*, *3*,
     297 (1971).
229. L. A. Douglas and J. M. Bremner, *Soil Biol. Biochem.*, *3*,
     309 (1971).
230. M. Bodansky and D. Perlman, *Nature*, *204*, 840 (1964).
231. R. A. J. Warren and J. B. Neilands, *J. Biol. Chem.*, *240*,
     2055 (1965).
232. M. Villavicencio and J. B. Neilands, *Biochemistry*, *4*, 1092
     (1965).
233. W. D. Linke, A. Crueger, and H. Dielzman, *Arch. Microbiol.*,
     85, 44 (1972).

ADDENDUM

J.B. Nielands has published an account of microbial iron transport compounds (siderochromes) in which he describes what is known
about their structure, formation, mechanisms of uptake, and function
in the iron nutrition of aerobic microorganisms [J.B. Nielands, in
Inorganic Biochemistry (G.L. Eichhorn, Ed.), Volume I, p. 167,
Elsevier, Amsterdam, 1973].

CHAPTER 4

FACTORS AFFECTING PESTICIDE LOSS FROM SOIL

R. G. Burns
Biological Laboratory
University of Kent
Canterbury, Kent, England

I. INTRODUCTION

It is the object of this chapter to examine, in some detail, the reactions of pesticides in the soil environment. This will not include a detailed description of the biochemistry of pesticide degradation, which has been dealt with adequately in previous volumes of this series [1, 2].

Pesticides may enter the soil either directly, by surface application, injection, and incorporation, or indirectly, by plant foliage run-off and inaccurate spraying techniques. Even compounds absorbed by the plant through the leaves may remain unchanged and become part of the soil organic matter with the death and subsequent decay of that plant.

Once in the soil, pesticides may be destroyed, inactivated, or removed in five basic ways: microbial decay, nonbiological decomposition, volatilization, water movement, and plant uptake. The vast proportion of pesticides are subject to elimination by a combination of these mechanisms. It should be remembered that the removal of a pesticide from the soil is not synonymous with whole environment decontamination and may, in fact, represent the transfer of the chemical from one environmental situation (soil) to another (air, water).

Volatilization is frequently the major way in which initial loss of a pesticide occurs. With subsequent penetration into soil and adsorption onto soil components, volatilization is rapidly reduced. Volatilization is itself influenced by a variety of factors, including soil moisture, soil type, above- and below-ground temperatures, wind velocity, and the vapor pressure and water solubility of the chemical involved.

Pesticide loss by water movement is predominantly in a downward direction. Leaching is dependent on the physical and chemical nature of both the soil and the agrochemical and, of course, on the quantity of water entering the soil system. Leaching may give rise to horizons of very high pesticide concentrations.

Uptake by plants (and microorganisms) may account for much of the disappearance of pesticides. This loss may be of a temporary nature, if the plant is returned to the soil upon its death, or of a more permanent nature if a major metabolic change in the chemical takes place within the plant or the crop is harvested. The process

of biological uptake of pesticides by microorganisms is, in some
instances, analogous to the immobilization of elements involved
in the nitrogen, sulfur, and carbon cycles.

Organic pesticides represent substrates that can be utilized
for growth and energy. In consequence a high proportion of pesticides are degraded by microorganisms in the soil. The rate and
final outcome of this breakdown is determined by a number of environmental factors, most of which are either directly or indirectly
related to soil adsorption.

Nonbiological breakdown of pesticides is associated with the
soil mineral and organic components and the soil water and may also
include photodecomposition at the soil surface. The products of
nonbiological degradation are frequently identical to those resulting
from biological reactions.

Although, in the interests of clarity, we must review separately
the factors influencing pesticide loss, it should be remembered that
the soil is a heterogenous environment in which the multitude of
interactions make it extremely difficult to understand what contribution each component makes toward the microbiology and biochemistry
of the whole soil.

The factors affecting pesticide loss from soil have been summarized by Lambert et al. [3] and are divided into five categories.

1. *Type of soil:* Makeup (clay, silt, sand, organic matter),
structure (bulk density, surface area, heterogeneity), and prior
treatment (chemical, agricultural practice)
2. *Type of chemical:* Physical properties and solubility,
vapor pressure, and stability
3. *Climatic conditions:* Rainfall, pressure, temperature, and
sunlight
4. *Biological population:* Type, nutrient requirements, adapta-
tions, and life cycles
5. *Method of application:* Granular, wettable powder, or solvent

In this review the major soil physical and chemical factors are
discussed together with the effect of climatic variation. Other
important influences determining pesticide loss are outlined.

II. SOIL CHEMICAL AND PHYSICAL FACTORS

A. Clay

The soil clay fraction is composed of inorganic fragments less than 2 μm in size. The fundamental structural units of clay minerals are tetrahedral silicon oxide and octahedral aluminum oxide or hydroxide sheets [4, 5]. These components may be associated either 1:1 (kaolinite) or 2:1 (montmorillonite, vermiculite, illite, and chlorite). Frequently, isomorphous substitutions occur, whereby the silicon in tetrahedrons is replaced by aluminum and the aluminum in octahedrons by magnesium or iron. When this happens some of the valences of the oxygen atoms are left unsatisfied and the clay unit takes on a net negative charge. The phenomenon is particularly characteristic of 2:1 layer silicates. The need to neutralize these charges is met by the adsorption of sodium, calcium, potassium, and hydrogen. These may, in turn, be exchanged for other cations and their propensity to do so is measured as the clay's cation-exchange capacity.

As a result of these structural and physical properties, kaolinitic clays have nonexpanding lattices, an external adsorption area, and low exchange capacities. Montmorillonite and vermiculite clays, however, have expanding lattices, both internal and external adsorption areas, and high exchange capacities. Illites and chlorites which are 2:1 clays with nonexpanding or only partially expanding lattices, show intermediate adsorption capacities (Table 1). It is because the chemical reactivity of these inorganic particles is directly related to their surface area that soil clays, especially those of the expanding-lattice type, assume a high degree of importance in soil-pesticide interactions.

Although positive charges, which occur at exposed edges of clay particles, may play a part in the adsorption of organic anions, it is generally true that cationic pesticides exhibit more or less strong adsorption, whereas neutral and anionic pesticides are weakly

TABLE 1

Physical Properties of Soil Constituents[a]

Soil constituent	Surface area (m^2/g)	Cation-exchange capacity $(mEq/100\ g)$
Kaolinite	7-30	3-15
Chlorite	25-40	10-40
Illite	65-100	10-40
Montmorillonite	600-800	80-150
Vermiculite	600-800	100-150
Organic Matter	500-800	200-400

[a]From Bailey and White [182].

adsorbed. Mechanisms of adsorption, which include ion exchange, protonation, hemisalt formation, hydrogen bonding, ion-dipole or coordination, van der Waals forces, and π-bonding have been described recently by White and Mortland [6] and will not be detailed here.

Sometimes pesticide adsorption within clay lattices is irreversible except by destruction of the clay structure. When this type of association occurs, usually with highly cationic compounds, the tenacity of adsorption is such as to render the pesticide biologically inactive. Other pesticides are either weakly adsorbed into interlamellar spaces or not adsorbed at all. External adsorption onto montmorillonite and kaolinite surfaces is usually a reversible reaction.

In many instances the clay type affects both quantitative adsorption and the pesticide's subsequent resistance to desorption. Coats et al. [7], using the strongly cationic herbicide diquat, observed that 2.0-2.5 mg were adsorbed per gram of kaolinite and 80-100 mg per gram of the expanding-lattice clay bentonite. Desorption of diquat from kaolinite induced phytotoxicity in wheat, whereas only very small quantities of bentonite-adsorbed herbicide were released. Using paraquat-saturated Ca-montmorillonite, Weber et al. [8] estimated this quantity to be between 5% and 10%. The relationship

between clay type and strength of retention of bipyridylium herbicides
has also been demonstrated by Weber and Scott [9] and Weed and Weber
[10]. Similarly, expanding lattice clays may reduce 2,4-D phytotoxicity, whereas kaolinite has no effect [11]. Talbert and Fletchall
[12] showed that atrazine and simazine were adsorbed to a greater
degree by montmorillonite than by illite and that no adsorption
occurred on kaolinite. Considerable quantities of amiben, however,
may be adsorbed by illite [13]. In contrast, the adsorption of trifluralin [14] and aldrin [15] appear unrelated to clay expansion.
CIPC phytotoxicity is also unaffected by clay additions, whether
these are kaolinite or montmorillonite [11] and amitrole is reversibly adsorbed even by montmorillonite. Grover [17] reported that
there was no adsorption of picloram on montmorillonite, kaolinite,
or cation-exchange resins.

Clay adsorption, especially by montmorillonite, has been shown
to retard leaching of parathion [18], diphenamid [19], thiocarbamates
[20], monuron [21], and many others. Slow desorption of phorate,
demeton, and dimethoate from clay soils allows some leaching, whereas dicamba is adsorbed weakly or not at all and may leach rapidly
[22]. As might be expected, volatilization rates are reduced by
clay adsorption and have been illustrated for a wide range of pesticides.

Upon adsorption biological and nonbiological decomposition
rates are frequently and drastically changed and both retardation and
acceleration effects are observed [23]. In the first instance, let
us assume the clay surface to have an infinite number of adsorption
sites. As a result, the comparatively finite number of substrate
(pesticide) and enzyme molecules may be adsorbed distant from each
other and interacton is delayed until sorption flux brings the
reactants together. In addition, the adsorption of pesticides into
interlamellar spaces may protect them from enzyme attack. Conversely,
adsorption may concentrate enzyme and substrate at one site, cata-
lyze nonbiological reactions, or immobilize the pesticide in an area
where the proliferation of sorbed microbes can occur. All three of

these mechanisms could lead to an increase in the rate of pesticide decay. A review by Marshall [24] concerning sorptive interactions and microbial activity appears in Volume 2 of this series.

Rosenfield and Van Valkenburg [25], describing the enhanced decomposition of the organophosphorus insecticide Ronnel adsorbed onto bentonite, suggested that it was a nonbiological reaction catalyzed by aluminum, whereas the breakdown of several organophosphates, adsorbed onto montmorillonite, may be catalyzed by copper [26]. Other reports of the stimulation of nonbiological degradation on clay adsorption, often related to pH effects, are not uncommon and concern the hydrolysis of atrazine [27, 28], triazines in general [29], dichlorobenil and acrylonitrile [30], and DDT [31]. As shown with malathion, adsorption-stimulated breakdown [32] may be occurring only on external surfaces and not within crystal lattices [33]. Harris [34] reported that clay surface adsorption protected triazines from breakdown. Photodecomposition of paraquat and diquat by ultraviolet light is reduced by interlamellar adsorption [35]. Similarly, the resistance of DDT to ultraviolet radiation is increased when it is adsorbed onto clay as compared with silt-clay or gravelly-loam [36].

Weber and Coble [37] found that the addition of montmorillonite clay to liquid microbial cultures actively degrading diquat severely retarded breakdown rates. Kaolinite additions had no apparent effect on the rate of microbial decay. Desorption of paraquat from organic matter followed by adsorption onto inorganic matter successfully retarded microbial breakdown [38]. Nevertheless, as described earlier, microbial decay of some pesticides may be stimulated by adsorption. Groves and Chough [39] found that the microbial degradation of DCNA was associated with fine clay particles and were able to isolate from the colloidal fraction a *Bacillus* sp. which decomposed DCNA rapidly.

B. Silt and Sand

Sand particles, which are described as coarse, medium, fine, and very fine, range in size from 1 to 0.05 mm. The soil silt

fraction contains particles smaller than 0.05 mm, and yet larger than
0.002 mm. This latter dimension is the uppermost limit of the clay-
size fraction.

It is as a direct consequence of the particle size of these
inorganic fractions that the activity of pesticides in soils with a
high proportion of silt and sand is somewhat different to that seen
in fine textured soils. Particle size determines the surface area
available for both biological and nonbiological reactions and, in
this respect, sand and silt have surface areas <0.4% and <0.9%, respectively, when compared with expanding-lattice clays.

The adsorptive capacity of a soil is inversely related to the
size of its inorganic components, whereas its porosity is directly
related to this parameter. In consequence, retention of pesticides
in sands and silts is of a more tenuous nature than that observed in
clays. Nevertheless, Harris [40] described the inactivation of
diazinon and to some extent parathion by dry silt and sand fractions,
and a positive correlation between silt and ametryne adsorption has
been reported by Liv et al. [41]. An oat bioassay conducted by Day
et al. [42] indicated silt and sand adsorption of simazine.

Because of low pesticide adsorption rates in sand and, to a
lesser degree in silt soils, the plant's availability is enhanced.
Parochetti and Warren [43] found that both IPC and CIPC were ten
times more toxic to buckwheat grown in quartz sand than in silt-loam
soil. The generally higher levels of phytotoxicity recorded in
coarse as opposed to fine soils are discussed by Sheets et al. [44]
and involve variations in both organic and inorganic matter content.

Increases in soil porosity play an important role in the movement of pesticides in soil. Coarse textured soils, with the resultant
larger pore spaces, show an increase in both water movement and
gaseous diffusion. Lindstrom et al. [45] found that the diffusion
coefficients for 2,4-D in nine saturated soils, ranging from sandy
loam (7.2% clay) to clay (63.7%), were inversely related to soil
texture, whereas Hanson and Nex [46] indicated that soil porosity was
the most important factor in diffusion of the fumigant ethylene dibromide.

Textural differences, including those caused by silt and sand, may be responsible for the increases in leaching rates observed in coarse soils [22, 47-50], and even the retention of the strongly adsorbed herbicide diquat by sandy loam is <0.5% of that recorded for bentonite clay [7]. Sherburne et al. [51] studied the effect of soil type and precipitation on the movement of radioactive monuron and found that leaching was greater in sandy loam soil than in clay-loam soil. The leaching of pesticides in sand has also been investigated by Rodgers [52]. In contrast, only 39% of phosphamidon leached through silt columns was recovered, the remainder being adsorbed [53].

Microbial degradation, which is frequently retarded by adsorption, might be expected to show an increase in coarse textured soils. This is generally not the case and it should be remembered that sandy soils (and to a lesser extent silty soils) accumulate far less amorphous organic matter than do heavier soils [54]. As a result coarse textured soils frequently support a comparatively small indigenous microbial population. Residues of simazine were found to be greater in sandy soils than in clay or peat [55, 56] and coarse textured soils exhibited a greater carryover of propazine, atrazine, TCBC, and linuron [57] than did fine textured soils.

Nonbiological degradation in sand is also somewhat retarded as illustrated by Guenzi and Beard [58] who showed temperature degradation of DDT to DDE to be considerably less in loamy sand than in a silty-clay loam.

C. Organic Matter

Soil organic matter consists of an amorphous colloidal fraction, humus, and a macro- or microscopically recognizable component made up of plant and animal material at various stages of decay. A high proportion of agricultural soils contain between 2% and 10% organic matter, although this level may range from less than 1% in sands to greater than 50% in muck and peat soils.

In most agricultural soils the nonhumic fraction represents

only a small proportion of the total organic carbon. Nevertheless,
in organic soils, such as peat and muck, pesticide-macroorganic matter
interactions are of considerable importance. Plant material may become contaminated with pesticides, by spraying, root uptake, and
atmospheric fallout [59-61]. Subsequently, the death of the plant
introduces pesticide-organic matter complexes to the soil. Odum [62]
and Walker and Crawford [63] have found DDT associated with plant
detritus in river estuaries. Soil fauna, such as insects, earth-
worms, and slugs may ingest these pesticide-organic matter complexes
[64-66], accumulate residues and produce environmental problems if
subsequently involved in food chains [67-71]. Microorganisms themselves may accumulate pesticides by cellular incorporation during
contaminated organic matter breakdown [72-74] or by adsorption [75].
Chlorinated hydrocarbons were found associated with fungal and ac-
tinomycete mycelia and plant materials at levels far in excess of
those found in the soil from which they were extracted [74, 76].

In mineral soils most of the organic matter is colloidal in
form and intimately associated with the inorganic fraction to form
the organomineral complex [77-80]. These complexes, usually of a
clay-humus nature, are the site of high biological [81] and nonbiological activity. It is not surprising that both organic matter and
clays have been correlated with pesticide adsorption and associated
phenomena (volatility, leachability, degradation) when one considers
their relationship to each other. It is fair to say that clay minerals exert at least an indirect effect on pesticide decay arising
from their influence on both soil aggregation and the properties of
the organic matter associated with them [63, 82, 83]. However, organic matter has been adjudged by many as the most important, or
only, parameter correlating pesticide adsorption with persistence
in soil [83-87]. It is apparent that clay free of organic matter is
an uncommon occurrence in many soils [54, 88] and whereas the study
of pesticide-clay reactions may tell us a great deal about adsorption
phenomena its relevance to soil organomineral-pesticide interactions
needs careful interpretation.

Doherty and Warren [89] investigated the retention of prometryne, simazine, linuron, and pyrazon by fibrous peat, sphagnum moss, muck, and bentonite and found that, in general, fibrous peat and muck soil were much more adsorptive than bentonite and sphagnum. Shin et al. [75] and Doherty and Warren [89] reported that DDT adsorption by organic matter increased with increasing humification and that with dichlorobenil was inversely related to the hydrophilic properties of the reactants [90]. Peterson et al. [91] have suggested that the adsorption of DDT by soil organic matter is the principal means of detoxication. Wade [92] found that adsorption of the fumigant ethylene dibromide was proportional to the soil organic carbon content. The persistence of organochlorine insecticides in muck soils with 40% organic matter was far in excess of that observed in silt loam with 3.8% organic matter [93]. Adsorption effects have been positively correlated with soil organic matter levels for many other pesticides including lindane [94], diuron and ametryne [95], and the triazines [13]. Anionic chlorinated aliphatic acids, such as TCA and dalapon, show only a limited adsorptive response to organic matter [96, 97], although Upchurch and Mason [98] have reported that dalapon is strongly adsorbed by soil organic matter. In many instances quantitative adsorption by soil organic matter is in excess of that exhibited by clay minerals [12].

The removal of organic matter by hydrogen peroxide treatment may [15, 99] or may not [100] reduce soil adsorptive capacity. This variability depends, to a large extent, on the type of pesticide involved and the ability of the hydrogen peroxide to separate the components of the organomineral complex.

The adsorptive capacity of extracted soil humic material is probably in excess of its contribution to whole soil adsorption. This results, at least in part, in the release of adsorption sites previously occupied in either organomineral complexing or the adsorption of metabolites.

Soil humic material has been considered as made up of four major fractions, each one classified according to the procedure used in its extraction [101]. These components are bitumen, humic acid, fulvic acid, and humin. Some workers recognize a fifth component, hymatomelanic acid.

The composition of humic acids has been extensively studied in recent years [102-105], and the porosity and large internal surface area of these fractions [63, 102, 106] is reflected in their high adsorptive capacity as compared to other organic compounds (Table 2). Macnamara and Toth [99] extracted a humic acid fraction from peat and showed it to have a far greater adsorptive capacity for linuron and malathion than did kaolinite, illite, or montmorillonite clay systems. Humic acid adsorption of triazines [107-110] and of paraquat [111] has also been demonstrated. Wershaw et al. [112] found that humic acid strongly adsorbed 2,4,5-T from solution.

TABLE 2

Adsorption of Atrazine by Organic Materials[a]

Adsorbent	Pesticide adsorbed (μg/g)
Starch	15
Amylopectin	17
Chitin	23
Cellulose	30
Lignin	359
Humic acid (from peat)	418
Humic acid (from leonardite)	478

[a]From Dunigan and McIntosh [109].

High adsorption rates of diuron [114] and paraquat [111] onto lignin are described, whereas there is little adsorption of triazines onto soil polysaccharides and fulvic acid fractions [110] or of diuron and paraquat onto cellulose [111, 114]. Fulvic acid can combine with lyophobic organic compounds mediating the mobilization or immobilization of pollutants [113]. The adsorption of nonpolar pesticides, such as the chlorinated hydrocarbons, may be by hydrophobic bonding to lipids, which form between 1.2% and 6.3% of the humus fraction [115]. The mechanisms of pesticide adsorption onto organic matter,

with special emphasis on the triazines, have been discussed recently
by Hayes [116] and others [150, 182].

The adsorption of pesticides onto organic matter is also reflected
in their phytotoxicity and it is well documented that as soil organic
matter increases correspondingly higher doses of some pesticides are
required to produce a like response [98]. Grover [117] found that
peat moss amendments to soil reduced simazine phytotoxicity, and a
wide range of herbicides studied by Upchurch and Mason [98] were adsorbed onto organic matter and, as a result, their toxicity reduced.
Lichtenstein et al. [118] were able to reduce the uptake of aldrin,
dieldrin, heptachlor, and heptachlor epoxide by peas by adding carbon
to loam or quartz sand containing these insecticides. The presence
of carbon also reduced insecticidal toxicity to *Drosophila melonogaster*.
Tomkins et al. [119] reported that the phytotoxicity of atrazine was
considerably reduced when lignin was added to sand cultures. This
reduction of pesticide availability, resulting from organic matter
adsorption, has been recorded by many other workers [11, 22, 42, 86,
119-124] and may in some instances be in excess of that shown by
clays. For example, Scott and Weber [11] reported that the addition
of organic soil to a growth medium containing CIPC reduced phytotoxicity, whereas additions of montmorillonite and kaolinite did not.
Similarly, Thompson [125] showed that the incorporation of peaty
muck into soil reduced the phytotoxicity of prometryne more than
additions of Na-montmorillonite.

With an increase in organic matter a reduction of leaching
caused by adsorption effects has been shown for diphenamid [19],
the chlorinated hydrocarbons [122, 126, 127], phorate [128], carba-
mates [129], picloram [130], and di- and triallate [131]. The depth
of leaching of five thiocarbamates was seen to decrease with increasing
organic matter and in a peat soil (35% organic matter) no leaching
was detected [20]. Others, such as amiben [132] and the benzoic
acid herbicides [22], are only adsorbed to a small degree and may,
as a result, show extreme mobility in soil. With some pesticides
organic matter adsorption, although quantitatively in excess of clay

adsorption, appears more tenuous and desorption followed by trans-
ference to clay adsorption sites may serve to stabilize the compound.
This kind of situation has been suggested for the bipyridylium
herbicides [38, 111].

Getzin and Chapman [128] showed that volatilization losses of
phorate adsorbed onto muck were considerably less than those observed
from silt-loam and sand soils. Among other factors, an increase in
soil organic matter caused a decrease in lindane and DDT volatilization at 30°C [58]. These same insecticides may complex with organic
colloids to decrease volatility even at 186°C [133].

Adsorption of dichlorobenil onto organic matter protects it
from hydrolysis [134], whereas soil adsorption, as described previously
may be partially responsible for the catalytic nonbiological breakdown of Ciodrin [136], atrazine and other triazines [27, 34, 136],
malathion [32], and others [146]. Acid-extracted humic material may
cause some degradation of atrazine [137]. Pesticide persistence
may also be prolonged by internal complexing with organic matter
during humic acid synthesis [118, 138], probably in much the same
way as has been recently proposed for the persistence of the soil
enzyme urease [139, 140]. For example, propanil undergoes rapid
microbiological degradation to dichloroaniline, which may then form
extremely resistant complexes with humic acids [141].

Microbial degradation of linuron in nonsterile soils may be
stimulated by organic matter amendments [142], and the stability of
linuron and atrazine [142a], diuron and s-triazines [143] decreases
with an increase in microbial energy sources. Paraquat adsorbed
onto organic matter that has been separated from soil is highly
susceptible to microbial decay [38].

From the foregoing discussion it would appear that there are a
number of ways in which organic matter may determine pesticide persistence [144a]. In the first instance, a certain minimum level of
organic matter (probably >1%) is essential to ensure that an active
autochthonous microbial population will confront the amended pesticide [142]. The species diversity arising in these situations may
increase the possibility of enzyme systems able to attack organic

pesticide molecules [64, 105]. On the other hand, the high adsorptive
capacity of organic matter (Table 1) may retard pesticide loss in much
the same way as does the clay fraction. This kind of dual relationship has been shown for a range of thiocarbamates by Koren et al.
[129]. These workers suggested that inactivation may be caused by
strong adsorption in soils with high adsorptive capacities, by volatilization in low adsorptive soils, and by microbial activity in soils
with moderate adsorptive capacities. The organic matter level at
which inhibition of pesticide loss overtakes the stimulation effect
will vary from soil to soil and be influenced by the many factors
affecting adsorption. Clearly, one would expect to see a gradation
between acceleration and retardation effects.

D. Reaction

Soil pH may affect pesticide loss by its influence upon adsorption and its relationship to microbial and nonmicrobial activities.

In mineral soils the adsorption of molecules often increases
with decreasing pH [12, 108, 147, 148]. Frissel and Bolt [148]
found that the adsorption of triazines began to increase rapidly
at about 3-4 pH units above the dissociation constant (pK_a) of the
herbicide and that it continued to increase below the pK_a down to
around a pH of 1. In contrast, Weber and co-workers [149, 150] have
observed these adsorptive reactions to be at their maximum at a pH
in the vicinity of the acidic dissociation constant of the pesticide
and subsequently to decrease as the reaction becomes more acid.

It was suggested that, below the optimum pH, decreases in adsorption may be caused by hydrogen ion competition with triazine
molecules for adsorption sites [149]. Frissel and Bolt [148] postulated that as the pH is lowered hydrogen ions associate with the
weakly basic triazine molecules (protonation), imparting cationic
characteristics and resulting in greater adsorption from coulombic
binding. In agreement, Harris and Warren [151] indicated that the
greater adsorption of atrazine at pH 4.1 compared with pH 8.2 was
the result of an increased electropositivity of the herbicide molecules

upon association with protons at the clay surface. Frissel [152] proposed that the adsorption of trietrazine on Na-montmorillonite at alkaline pH was solely the result of van der Waals forces, whereas at neutral to acid pH adsorption was caused by both van der Waals and coulombic forces. He further stated that in neutral and alkaline situations triazines were adsorbed as neutral molecules and that in acid conditions as positively charged particles.

Many soil adsorptive reactions involving pesticides appear independent of pH. For instance, the adsorption of substituted ureas by montmorillonite [153] was seen to be insensitive to pH changes. This effect has also been shown for chloroxuron in soils [154] and by Leopold et al. [97] for 2,4-D adsorbed onto activated carbon.

Bailey et al. [155] have proposed that adsorption of acidic pesticides is dependent upon suspension pH and begins at approximately 1-1.5 pH units above the dissociation constant of the acid. In contrast, the adsorption of basic compounds is suggested as being dependant on a surface pH 1 to 2 units lower than the pK_b of the adsorbate. It is important to recall, in the light of previous statements, that clay surface pH may be between 0.5 and 1.5 pH units lower than the suspension pH [156]. Indeed, Bailey et al. [155] estimated montmorillonite surface pH to be as much as 4 units more acid than that of the suspension. This variance between surface and suspension pH may also be exhibited by organic matter [157].

The effects of pH on adsorption by clays are mostly restricted to changes in the adsorbate, whereas the clay colloid itself is only insignificantly influenced. Soil organic matter, in contrast, has a high CEC, which decreases with increasing acidity because of hydrogen ion association with the functional groups. This phenomenon tends to offset any increase in the cationic character of the pesticide. The pH dependence of these acidic functional groups strongly influences the behavior of cationic and basic pesticides [106, 151, 158, 159]. The adsorption of anionic pesticides, at pH's at which they are undissociated, is closely related to soil organic matter levels [11, 106, 160]. McGlamery and Slife [108] found that atrazine adsorption by humic acids was pH dependent and increased under acid conditions, whereas adsorption onto macroorganic matter may be less susceptible to changes in pH [12].

It is evident from this discussion that the effects of pH upon adsorption are inconsistent and depend to a large degree on the nature of both adsorbent and adsorbate [154].

Changes in adsorption in acid environments may effect pesticide losses due to plant uptake. Corbin et al. [161], using high organic matter soils, showed that the phytotoxicity of dicamba, 2,4-D, prometone, and amitrole increased with increasing pH up to 6.5. Conversely, as the soil reaction decreased down to pH 4.3 toxicity of dalapon, paraquat, diquat, and vernolate increased. Variation of pH between 4.3 and 7.5 had no effect on the availability of chloramben, picloram, isocil, diuron, and nitralin.

Horrobin [162] observed that nonbiological s-triazine hydrolysis was slow at neutral pH but increased with increasing acidity or alkalinity. In support of this Armstrong et al. [27] measured atrazine hydrolysis in aqueous solution and found transformation at pH 2 and 12 complete in 10 days; at pH 4 and 11 hydrolysis took 100 days; and at pH 6 and 10 it took 1000 days. Addition of sterilized soil stimulated hydrolysis due both to the H^+ ions around the soil particles increasing acidity and to the adsorption of atrazine onto colloidal surfaces [163]. A pH-related decay of atrazine has been observed by others [164] and it is concluded that despite their relative persistence, nonbiological hydrolysis may be an important method of triazine dissipation in acid soils. Under acid conditions (pH 4.7) nonbiological loss of diazinon occurs [165] and acid catalysed breakdown of Ronnel adsorbed on bentonite [25] and the s-triazines [16, 29] have been reported. Bailey and White [182] state that surface acidity is the most important colloid factor in determining whether acid catalyzed degradation occurs.

It is apparent that pH changes may stimulate different segments of the microbial community, resulting in the rapid decay of certain pesticides. For instance, most soil bacteria are active in near neutral environments, while the actinomycetes prefer alkaline soils [166]. Conversely, fungi have an optimum pH somewhat on the acid side of neutral [167]. Corbin and Upchurch [168], in an investigation into the microbial detoxication of a range of herbicides, observed that dicamba and 2,4-D were rapidly degraded at pH 5.3, but not at pH 7.5. The authors attributed the microbial decay of these compounds to fungi. In contrast, dalapon and amitrole disappeared most rapidly at pH 6.5, were somewhat persistent at pH 5.3, and presumably were not readily metabolized by acidophilic fungi. Reaction may affect microbial activity as well as type. Gunderson and Jensen [169], studying the breakdown of dinitrophenols, showed that *Corynebacterium simplex* was only able to utilize DNOC as a nitrogen source, at alkaline pH levels (7.3-8.5).

III. CLIMATIC FACTORS

A. Temperature

In frozen soils pesticide loss is negligible [92, 170, 171], but increases with increasing temperature in nonfrozen soils. Burnside et al. [171] observed that in arctic and temperate zones triazines disappeared more slowly during the winter than in the summer months. Even in subtropical climates rates of pesticide loss may decrease during the winter [172]. Scifres et al. [48] recorded that picloram applied in the autumn had a longer carryover period than that applied in the spring.

Volatilization losses, as a result of temperature variation, may be due to two factors. Clearly temperature rises effect water evaporation and some pesticides undergo codistillation from the soil [194]. In addition, Bailey and White [173] have suggested that temperature affects adsorption by altering the solubility of the pesticide such that higher temperatures result in desorption. As adsorption processes are exothermic and desorption endothermic, one would

expect a temperature increase to reduce adsorption with a corresponding
increase in solute solubility. This is born out by most workers
[12, 106, 151], but there are notable exceptions. Freed et al. [174]
reported an increase in EPTC adsorption as the temperature rose. Of
course, the effect of temperature on adsorption may be different at
clay as opposed to organic matter sites [107] and accounts, in part,
for these apparent discrepancies. The adsorption of triazines by
humic acids increases with increasing temperature [108] and reports
of enhanced pesticide adsorption in organic soils may be due to
temperature induced changes in the structure and porosity of the
organic matter [58, 110]. Exchange reactions, such as those exhibited by the bipyridylium herbicides, tend to be independent of temperature fluctuations [106, 151], although Faust and Zarins [175]
observed an increase in the adsorption of diquat with a rise in
temperature. Vapor losses for some pesticides appear to be negligible and independent of temperature changes [131, 176].

Microbial activity is stimulated by temperature increases and
some ecological groups tend to dominate within certain temperature
ranges. Accordingly, microorganisms may be divided into three major
groups: mesophiles (optimum activity between 25° and 35°C), psychro-
philes (<20°C) and thermophiles (45°-65°C). Microbial breakdown of
dicamba [177], atrazine [178], amiben and dinoben [132] increases
with temperature. This increase may be related to optimum temperature for enzyme activity or to the increase in solubility of the
pesticide as discussed above. Interlamellar absorption of pesticide,
often rendering it unavailable for degradation, may be reduced as
the temperature rises.

Nonbiological decay of DDT [36, 58], atrazine [164], and potassium azide [179] are all stimulated by a rise in temperature.

B. Water

The solvent properties and reactivity of water ensure that it
effects both biological and nonbiological pesticide loss in a number
of ways.

Movement of pesticide within the soil profile is principally
effected by percolation of rain and irrigation water. The greater
the quantity of water entering the soil the more rapid are the
leaching rates [49, 171], although the converse is true for the intensity of rainfall (water flux). Accordingly, Harris [180] observed
that the downward movement of both dicamba and diphenamid was greater
when water was applied in 0.25-in. increments than when applied in
1-in. increments. In contrast, others have shown that in some instances leaching is more closely related to soil type rather than
to quantity of water [181].

During periods of drought pesticide persistence may be extended
because at low water levels competition for adsorption sites is less
intense and more of the pesticide becomes adsorbed onto the soil
colloids. In addition a decrease in water level leads to higher
concentrations of pesticide and a subsequent crystallizing out of
the solute. Under these conditions adsorption of pesticides is predominantly by clay particles whereas, at higher soil water levels,
organic matter adsorption takes place [63, 180]. Harris [40],
investigating the behavior of a number of insecticides under varying
water regimes, showed that in moist soils the bioactivity of heptachlor, diazinon, DDT, and parathion declined with increasing organic
matter. No such relationship was seen in dry soils. Similar phenomena have been reported for aldrin, lindane [183], and dieldrin
[71]. At high water levels, desorption of pesticides from mineral
soils is commonly observed [34]. Call [184] found it possible to
predict the sorption coefficient of the fumigant ethylene dibromide
using moisture content alone. The accuracy of these correlations
was reasonably consistent over a wide range of soil types, including
coarse sands, silts, and clays. Earlier, Wade [91, 185] had shown
a decrease in ethylene dibromide adsorption with increases in soil
water.

It is considered probable that within certain pesticide groups
there exists a relationship between water solubility and extent of
adsorption. This connection has been demonstrated by Bailey et al.

[155] for the substituted ureas and s-triazines (excepting atrazine).
However, their results with the urea herbicides are in direct con-
tradiction to those of Wolf et al. [186], Yuen and Hilton [187]
and Hilton and Yuen [188] who found that the adsorption of these
compounds was inversely related to their solubilities. Hance [114]
was unable to discover any relationship at all between the solubility
of ureas and soil adsorption. Harris and Warren [151] found no
solubility-sorption relationship for diquat, CIPC, DNBP, and atrazine
on either organic or inorganic adsorbents. Leopold et al. [97]
provided evidence for an inverse relationship between the adsorption
by activated carbon of chlorinated phenoxy herbicides and their
solubility.

Clearly, soil water has a profound effect on adsorption and the
toxicity of a pesticide is dependent upon the affinity of the soil
particle, for that compound together with the ability of the pesticide to compete with water molecules for adsorption sites. Good com-
petitors prove to be poor soil pesticides and the effectiveness of
DDT and heptachlor is caused, in part, by their lack of competi-
tiveness with water.

Although pesticide movement in relation to water is predominantly
in a downward direction, upward movement, presumably caused by cap-
illarity has been demonstrated for dicamba and diphenamid [180],
endothal [189], and phenols [190]. Surface runoff may also cause
loss of pesticide from the soil environment [191, 192] by acting as
a solvent or as a transporter of particulate matter on which pesticide is adsorbed. After heavy rains a good deal of dieldrin may be
lost by sediment transport [193].

Water affects the vapor density of both lindane and dieldrin
and, in consequence, there is greater volatilization of these insecticides from wet than from dry soils. Codistillation of aqueous
pesticide suspensions has been described by Acree et al. [194] and
soil moisture is cited by some workers as the major factor effecting
organochlorine volatilization from soil [58]. Lichtenstein and
Schulz [195] showed that the disappearance of aldrin was effected

by soil water whereas Bowman et al. [126] established that the loss
of a number of organochlorines was more rapid from wet than from dry
soils.

The effect of water on oxygen levels and the subsequent influence
on aerobic and anaerobic microbial activities are discussed elsewhere.
The effect of water, per se, on microbial activity is clearly to
serve as a liquid medium in which transport of microorganisms, extracellular enzymes, substrates, and metabolic by-products may occur.
Soil water is also a reservoir of oxygen (albeit a poor one) and
dissolved minerals and allows the maintenance of microbial cell
wall integrity.

Lichtenstein et al. [208], investigating insecticide persistence
in dry and wet loam soils, discovered that dieldrin represented only
3-10% of the aldrin/dieldrin residue recovered from the dry soil
but 53% of that recovered from the wet soil. Increased microbial
activity was proposed as accounting for this difference as it was
for a similar effect shown by parathion [196].

In dry soils nonbiological decomposition may be very slow [34]
as water plays a key role in the chemical breakdown of pesticides.
It may be important in the isomerization of organophosphates and the
self-alkylation of demeton [197]. Water is also a good medium for
oxidation reactions, especially in the case of dithiocarbamates and
the ethylenediamine group of pesticides [198]. The hydrolytic transformation of dazomet in soil occurs rapidly and the product of this
reaction, methylisothiocyanate, is the active fungicidal agent [199,
200]. Vapam undergoes a similar hydrolysis [200]. Water may also
act as a reagent by dissociation into hydroxide and hydrogen ions,
giving rise to alkaline and acid conditions that may vary between
pH 3 and pH 10.5. It is believed that water associated with clay
surfaces is in a more dissociated state than free water and may
account for the acid-catalyzed hydrolyses of some adsorbed pesticides
[25, 164, 165]. Many agrochemicals, including diquat, malathion,
endosulfan, TCA, and 2,4-D, undergo alkaline hydrolysis, whereas
others, such as captan, are hydrolyzed at neutrality [201].

C. Oxygen

Soil oxygen levels are inversely related to soil water content
and as a result poor aeration is usually associated with improper
drainage. Because small pores have a greater tenacity for water,
the aeration status of fine textured soils (clay) is often poor,
whereas that of coarse textured soils (sand) is usually good. The
already poor solubility of oxygen gas in water decreases with increasing temperature: 69.4 mg/liter at 0°C, 43.4 mg/liter at 20°C,
and 30.8 mg/liter at 50°C [202]. In the presence of large numbers
of actively respiring microorganisms the dissolved oxygen may be
rapidly consumed and subsequent replacement, by diffusion from air,
is very slow.

Even at water levels below saturation, anaerobic microenvironments are common in the soil. For instance, the center of soil
aggregates may be either anaerobic or have very low oxygen levels,
whereas the external surface of that same aggregate may be aerobic.
In areas of high microbial activity, where easily degraded organic
matter is plentiful, oxygen may be consumed at a faster rate than it
can be replaced. In addition, plant root respiration frequently
results in lower oxygen levels in soil than are found above ground.

The microbial degradation of a high number of pesticides, in
both aerobic and anaerobic environments, is reported in detail elsewhere in these volumes [1, 2]. It is of interest to note that microbial degradation under anaerobic conditions may be somewhat faster
[76, 203-205a] than that found in aerobic conditions. Guenzi and
Beard [206] compared the microbial conversion of DDT to DDD in aerobic
and anaerobic soils. In anaerobic soils <1% of the DDT was recovered
after 12 weeks, whereas in aerobic soils 75% of the DDT was still
present after six months. Microbial breakdown of DDT was seen by
Burge [207] to be inhibited by as little as 2% oxygen. In a recent
study by Yoshida and Castro [205] it was recorded that the degradation of γ-BHC in flooded rice soils was in all instances faster
than that observed in upland soils.

Many organic pesticides are unstable in oxygen-containing environments and the nonbiological oxidation of aldrin [208], amitrole
[201], and phorate [128] have been reported. In oxygen-poor environments organic matter components may act as reducing agents [209].

D. Radiation

Many pesticides are subject to light-stimulated transformations
if in aqueous solution or suspension and in the presence of oxygen.
This is because of the transparency of water to light of certain wave-
lengths that will, in turn, energize oxidation, reduction, elimination, hydrolysis, substitution, and isomerization reactions [210].

Aqueous solutions of 4-CPA undergo oxidation, reduction, and
hydrolysis if exposed to sunlight and air. Under similar conditions
photooxidation of monuron [211] and the decomposition of PCP have
been reported [212, 213]. Sheets [176] demonstrated the rapid decomposition of amiben in aqueous solution on exposure to sunlight or
light from fluorescent sun lamps. A much slower rate of photochemical
alteration was observed when dry amiben was exposed to light. Similarly, solutions of DDT are dehydrochlorinated in sunlight and air
to p,p'-dichlorobenzophenone (DBP) [214], whereas solid DDT is more
resistant. When exposed to air in darkness DDT is almost stable.
DDT in hexane [215] and methanol [216] solutions is readily decomposed. It has been shown that the presence of riboflavin stimulates
light degradation of amitrole [217, 218]. As a result, the phytotoxicity of amitrole to barley seedlings may be reduced by application of riboflavin [219], although Naylor [220] has questioned this
observation. The phytotoxicity of amiben to cucumber may be alle-
viated by exposure to sunlight [177].

It is evident that photochemical transformations can only occur
on or near the soil surface where light can penetrate but, although
light induced decomposition of pesticides is common *in vitro*, evidence concerning photodecomposition in soil is infrequently recorded.
Walter et al. [50] suggested that the loss of fluorodifen at the soil
surface was partially the result of photodecomposition. Taylorson
[221] noticed an increased loss of CDEC from soil after ultraviolet

radiation but could not show that it was caused by photodecomposition. Others have shown that dieldrin [222-224] and trifluralin [225-227] losses are rather slower and smaller from soil itself than from soil-free environments. Funderburk et al. [35] exposed diquat and para-quat-treated soil, kaolinite and montmorillonite to ultraviolet light and found that some loss, caused by photodecomposition, occurred. Losses from the herbicides alone (without soil adsorption) were considerably greater. Comes and Timmons [228] found that the toxicity of atrazine, simazine, fenuron, monuron, and diuron to oats was reduced when these herbicides were exposed on the soil surface to sunlight for 25 days. Ultraviolet light stimulation of DDT breakdown in soils has been demonstrated [36]. Sunlight-induced photolysis of aldrin in hexane produces a ketone compound that has been detected in soil [229]. Jordan et al. [230] found that ultraviolet light and sunlight decomposed monuron, atrazine, simazine and ametryne absorbed on filter papers, and it is probable that some photolysis of these herbicides occurs on soil surfaces. In contrast, other pesticides, such as MCPA [231] and siduron [232], appear unaffected by sunlight.

The indirect effects of sunlight may include the enhancement of degradation and volatilization rates resulting from an increase in soil temperature.

IV. OTHER FACTORS

A. Microbial Type

In the breakdown of naturally occurring organic materials considerable microbial specificity is evident. For example, cellulose degraders are predominantly fungal, chitin hydrolysis is performed mostly by actinomycetes and the destruction of lignin is confined almost entirely to one fungal family, the Polyporaceae.

This kind of substrate specificity also exists, to some extent, in pesticide-microbe interactions and is itself influenced by environmental factors (pH, temperature, oxygen, etc.) that affect the presence or absence of certain groups of microorganisms. This is illustrated by the degradation of the persistent organochlorine insecticide

dieldrin, with which four microbial genera are frequently implicated: *Trichoderma, Pseudomonas, Bacillus* [233], and *Aerobacter* [234].
Other pesticides are recorded as having a rather limited number of
organisms that can degrade them including paraquat [235], endothall
[236], and metabromuron [237]. According to Hirch and Alexander [238]
Nocardia and *Pseudomonas* will degrade halogenated aliphatics but not
fluorinated compounds, and Sheets et al. [44] have suggested that
conditions favoring fungal development may stimulate the biodegradation of fenac, TBA, and methoxyfenac.

B. Pesticide Formulation

The rate of entrance of a pesticide into the bulk of the soil
greatly affects volatilization and photodecomposition. If the pesticide is applied wet it will move into the soil profile, away from
the zone where radiation and temperature effects are greatest, and
into zones where biological decay may occur. Liquid formulations
often exhibit considerable loss by volatilization before they can
penetrate the soil. In contrast, granular applications, although
exposed to the sun and wind for longer periods of time, may show reduced volatility [24]. Oil-water emulsions, sometimes used in atrazine applications, have been suggested to be less persistent than
when water alone is used as a carrier [239]. Addition of surfactants
may increase the loss of a pesticide due to leaching [239a].

C. Pesticide Structure

In recent years a branch of pesticide research has been involved
with the relationship between pesticide structure and biodegradability
Perhaps the best examples of this relationship are those displayed
by the chlorinated aliphatic acids. With this group of herbicides
the number, position, and type of halogen substituants affects the
rate of microbial decomposition. Literature concerning pesticide
structure and decomposition has been extensively reviewed in recent
years by Kaufman [241] and Kearney et al. [242].

D. Prior and Posttreatment of Soil

Addition of easily degraded organic matter (manure) to a soil, either before or after application of pesticide, stimulates microbial activity and may hasten the decay of persistent pesticides. If the soil has received a prior treatment of the same or similar pesticide, then microbial enrichment or adaptation to that type of compound may have occurred and subsequent pesticide applications may be degraded more rapidly [145].

Cultivation of the soil after pesticide application stimulates aeration and microbial activity, leading to more rapid detoxification. Movement of soil also exposes pesticide that had previously been situated in buried layers to factors affecting photochemical decomposition and volatilization.

E. Plant Effects

The uptake of pesticides by plants and the subsequent harvesting of that crop may be a major route of pesticide loss from soil. Sikka and Davis [243] showed that soil samples taken over a period of six months, after being sprayed with atrazine, contained smaller residues if cropped than if left fallow.

Indirect effects of plants on pesticide persistence probably include shading, leaf runoff, and root zone microbial stimulation (the rhizosphere effect).

F. Depth

As the pesticide passes downward through the soil profile it moves from a degrading environment to a nondegrading one. On the soil surface the pesticide is subject to photodecomposition and volatilization pressures. In the A horizon organic matter content, temperature, and aeration all favor microbial decay, whereas in the B horizon degradation factors are limited.

Roeth et al. [178] measured atrazine adsorption and degradation, microbial population, organic matter, and clay content at various

depths in silty clay-loam and silt-loam soils. They found that adsorption, microbial populations, and organic matter decreased with
depth and, in a laboratory experiment, reported that atrazine degradation was two to three times greater in soil taken from 0- to
9-in. depths than in that from zones further than 9 in. from the
surface. The greater persistence of trifluralin with increasing
depth has been associated with a decrease in volatility [244].

V. CONCLUSION

This review has only sampled the vast quantity of work concerned
with pesticide-soil interactions that has accumulated over the past
twenty years. Nevertheless, it is apparent that despite the volume
of material available to the author large gaps in our knowledge
still remain to be filled. It is, in fact, debatable whether many
of the problems associated with soil biology can ever satisfactorily
be solved because of the physical, chemical, and biological complexity
of the medium.

What, then, is the practical value of pesticide-soil research?
To answer this question we need only to consider the ecological
shadows that are cast by the misuse of pesticides. Microbes are no
longer considered infallible in their ability to degrade each and
every organic compound with which they are faced. Some pesticides,
in fact, may remain in the soil environment for long periods of time
in an essentially unchanged and highly toxic form. In addition it
is evident that organic compounds may become involved in complex food
chains of which man often represents the highest link. Dramatic
figures concerning the accumulation of the organochlorine insecticides
in mammals and birds are commonly quoted [245] and when one considers
the rapid rise in the quantities of pesticide being manufactured
the concern of both scientific and nonscientific sections of the
populace for the preservation of environmental quality becomes
understandable.

Statisticians tell us that the earth's population will be doubled by the turn of the century. The increasing demands of this population and, in consequence, man's survival will depend to a large degree on his ability to change the environment without upsetting the delicate balance of nature. This will, in all probability, necessitate an expanding use of and reliance upon pesticides. To gain the greatest value with the least environmental destruction detailed quantitative and qualitative information concerning pesticide reactions in the soil environment is essential. Only then may agrochemicals be used for the optimum benefit of mankind.

VI. PESTICIDE NOMENCLATURE

Common and Chemical Names of Pesticides Referred to in the Text

Common name	Chemical name
Aldrin	1,2,3,4,10,10-Hexachloro-1,4,4a,5,8,8a-hexahydro-1,4-endo,exo-5,8-dimethanonaphthalene
Ametryne	2-Ethylamino-4-isopropylamino-6-methylthio-s-triazine
Amiben	3-Amino-2,5-dichlorobenzoic acid
Amitrole	3-Amino-1,2,4-triazole
Atrazine	2-Chloro-4-ethylamino-6-isopropylamino-s-triazine
γ-BHC	γ-Isomer of 1,2,3,4,5,6-hexachlorocyclohexane
Captan	N-Trichloromethylmercapto-4-cyclohexane-1,2-dicarboximide
CDEC	2-Chloroallyldiethyldithiocarbamate
Chloroxuron	N'-4-(4-Chlorophenoxy)phenyl-N,N-dimethylurea
Ciodrin	0,0-Dimethyl 0-[1-methyl-2-(1-phenylcarbethoxy)vinyl]phosphate
CIPC (chloropropham)	Isopropyl-m-chlorocarbanilate
4-CPA	4-Chlorphenoxyacetic acid
2,4-D	2,4-Dichlorophenoxyacetic acid
Dalapon	2,2-Dichloropropionic acid
DCNA	2,6-Dichloro-4-nitroaniline
DDD	1,1-Dichloro-2,2-bis(p-chlorophenyl)ethane
DDE	1,1-Dichloro-2,2-bis(p-chlorophenyl)-ethylene

Common name	Chemical name
DDT	1,1,1-Trichloro-2,2-bis(p-chlorophenyl)-ethane
Demeton	Mixture of 0,0-diethyl S- (and 0)-[2-(ethylthio)-ethyl]phosphorothioates
Diallate	S-2,3-Dichloroallyl-N,N-diisopropylthio-carbamate
Diazinon	0,0-Diethyl 0-(2-isopropyl-4-methyl-6-pyrimidinyl)phosphorothioate
Dicamba	2-Methoxy-3,6-dichlorobenzoic acid
Dichlorobenil	2,6-Dichlorobenzonitrile
Dieldrin	1,2,3,4,10,10-Hexachloro-6,7-epoxy-1,4,4a,5,6,7,8,8a-octahydro-1,4-endo,exo-5,8-dimethanonaphthalene
Diquat	2,2'-Bipyridylium 1,1'-ethylene dibromide
Dimethoate	0,0-Dimethyl S-(N-methylcarbamoylmethyl) phospordithioate
Dinoben	3-Nitro-2,5-dichlorobenzoic acid
Diphenamid	N,N-Dimethyl-2,2-diphenylacetamide
Diuron	3-(3,4-Dichlorophenyl)-1,1-dimethylurea
DMTT(dazomet)	Tetrahydro-3,5-dimethyl-2H-1,3,5-thia-diazine-2-thione
DNBP(dinoseb)	4,6-Dinitro-o-sec-butylphenol
DNOC	2-Methyl-4,6-dinitrophenol(3,5-dinitro-o-cresol)
Endosulfan	6,7,8,9,10,10-Hexachloro-1,5,5a,6,9,9a-hexahydro-6,9-methano-2,4,3-benzodioxa-thiepen-3-oxide
Endothal	3,6-Endoxohexahydrophthalic acid
Endrin	1,2,3,4,10,10-Hexachloro-6,7-epoxy-1,4,4a,5,6,7,8,8a-octahydro-1,4-endo,endo-5,8-dimethanonaphthalene
EPTC	Ethyl N,N-di-n-propylthiolcarbamate
Ethylene dibromide	1,2-Dibromoethane
Fenac	2,3,6-Trichlorophenylacetic acid
Fenuron	3-Phenyl-1,1-dimethylurea
Fluorodifen	4-Nitrophenyl-2-nitro-4-trifluoromethyl-phenyl ether
Heptachlor	1,4,5,6,7,8,8-Heptachloro-3a,4,7,7a-tetra-hydro-4,7-methanoindene
Heptachlor epoxide	1,4,5,6,7,8,8-Heptachloro-2,3-epoxy-2,3,3a,7a-tetrahydro-4,7-methanoindene
Isocil	5-Bromo-3-isopropyl-6-methyluracil
Lindane	γ-1,2,3,4,5,6-Hexachlorocyclohexane
Linuron	3-(3,4-Dichlorophenyl)-1-methoxy-1-methyl-urea
Malathion	0,0-Dimethyl-S-1,2-bis(ethoxycarbonyl) ethyl phosphorodithioate
MCA	Monochloroacetic acid
MCPA	[(4-Chloro-o-tolyl)oxy]acetic acid

Common name	Chemical name
Metabromuron	3-(p-Bromophenyl)-1-methoxy-1-methylurea
Methoxyfenac	2-Methoxy-3,6-dichlorophenylacetic acid
Monuron	3-(p-Chlorophenyl)-1,1-dimethylurea
Paraquat	4,4'-Bipyridylium 1,1'-dimethyl dichloride
Parathion	O,O-Diethyl O-p-nitrophenyl phosphoro-thioate
PCP	Pentachlorophenol
Phorate	O,O-Diethyl S-(ethylthiomethyl) phosphoro-dithioate
Phosphamidon	Dimethyl 2-chloro-2-diethylcarbamoyl-1-methyl vinyl phosphate
Picloram	4-Amino-3,5,6-trichloropicolinic acid
Prometone	2,4-Bis(isopropylamino)-6-methoxy-s-triazine
Prometryne	2,4-Bis(isopropylamino)-6-methylmercapto-s-triazine
Propanil	3',4'-Dichloropropionanilide
Pyrazon	5-Amino-4-chloro-2-phenyl-3(2H)-pyrida-zinone
Ronnel	O,O-Dimethyl-o-2,4,5-trichlorophenyl-phosphorothioate
Siduron	1-(2-Methylcyclohexyl)-3-phenylurea
Simazine	2-Chloro-4,6-bis(ethylamine)-s-triazine
2,4,5-T	2,4,5-Trichlorophenoxyacetic acid
TBA	2,3,6-Trichlorobenzoic acid
TCA	Trichloroacetic acid
TCBC	Trichlorobenzylchloride
Triallate	S-2,3,3-Trichloroallyl N,N-diisopropyl-thiocarbamate
Trietrazine	2-Chloro-4-diethylamino-6-ethylamino-s-triazine
Trifluralin	a,a,a-Trifluoro-2,6-dinitro-N,N-diiso-propyl-p-toluidine
Vapam	Sodium N-methyldithiocarbamate
Vernolate	s-Propyldipropylthiocarbamate

REFERENCES

1. A. D. McLaren and G. H. Peterson, Eds., *Soil Biochemistry*, Vol. 1, Dekker, New York, 1967.
2. A. D. McLaren and J. Skujins, Eds., *Soil Biochemistry*, Vol. 2, Dekker, New York, 1971.
3. S. M. Lambert, P. E. Porter, and R. H. Schieferstein, *Weeds*, *13*, 185 (1965).
4. L. Pauling, *Proc. Natl. Acad. Sci., U.S.*, *16*, 123 (1930).
5. L. Pauling, *Proc. Natl. Acad. Sci., U.S.*, *16*, 578 (1930).

6. J. L. White and M. M. Mortland, in *Pesticides in the Soil: Ecology, Degradation and Movement* (Proceedings of a Symposium), p. 95, Michigan State University, 1970.
7. G. E. Coats, H. H. Funderburk, J. M. Lawrence, and D. E. Davis, *Weed Res.*, *6*, (1966).
8. J. B. Weber, R. C. Meek, and S. B. Weed, *Soil Sci. Soc. Amer. Proc.*, *33*, 382 (1969).
9. J. B. Weber and D. C. Scott, *Science*, *152*, 1400 (1966).
10. S. B. Weed and J. B. Weber, *Soil Sci. Soc. Amer. Proc.*, *33*, 379 (1969).
11. D. C. Scott and J. B. Weber, *Soil Sci.*, *104*, 151 (1967).
12. R. E. Talbert and O. H. Fletchall, *Weeds*, *13*, 46 (1965).
13. J. J. Linscott, O. C. Burnside, and T. L. Lavy, *Weed Sci.*, *17*, 170 (1969).
14. R. L. Hollist and C. L. Foy, *Weed Sci.*, *19*, 11 (1971).
15. B. Yaron, A. R. Swoboda, and G. W. Thomas, *J. Agri. Food Chem.*, *15*, 671 (1961).
16. J. D. Russell, M. I. Cruz, and J. L. White, *J. Agri. Food Chem.*, *16*, 21 (1968).
17. R. Grover, *Weed Sci.*, *19*, 417 (1971).
18. A. R. Swoboda and G. W. Thomas, *J. Agri. Food Chem.*, *16*, 923 (1968).
19. J. Deli and G. F. Warren, *Weed Sci.*, *19*, 67 (1971).
20. R. A. Gray and A. J. Weierich, *Weed Sci.*, 77 (1968).
21. L. C. Erickson, *Weeds*, *13*, 100 (1965).
22. T. W. Donaldson and C. L. Foy, *Weeds*, *13*, 195 (1965).
23. D. J. Greenland, *Soils Fert.*, *28*, 415 (1965).
24. K. C. Marshall, in *Soil Biochemistry* (A. D. McLaren and J. Skujins, Eds.), Vol. 2, p. 409, Dekker, New York, 1971.
25. C. Rosenfield and W. Van Valkenburg, *J. Agri. Food Chem.*, *13*, 68 (1965).
26. M. M. Mortland and K. V. Raman, *J. Agri. Food Chem.*, *15*, 163 (1967).
27. D. E. Armstrong, G. Chesters, and R. F. Harris, *Soil Sci. Soc. Amer. Proc.*, *31*, 61 (1967).
28. D. E. Armstrong and G. Chesters, *Environ. Sci. Technol.*, *2*, 683 (1968).
29. M. Cruz, J. L. White, and J. D. Russell, *Israel J. Chem.*, *6*, 315 (1968).
30. W. R. Payne and G. W. Bailey, *Agron. Abstr.*, p. 68 (1969).
31. J. D. Lopez-Gonzales and C. Valenzuela-Calahorro, *J. Agri. Food Chem.*, *18*, 520 (1970).
32. J. G. Konrad, G. Chesters, and D. E. Armstrong, *Soil Sci. Soc. Amer. Proc.*, *33*, 259 (1969).
33. B. T. Boroman, R. S. Adams, and S. W. Fenton, *J. Agri. Food Chem.*, *18*, 723 (1970).
34. C. I. Harris, *J. Agri. Food Chem.*, *15*, 157 (1967).
35. H. H. Funderburk, N. S. Negi, and J. M. Lawrence, *Weeds*, *14*, 240 (1966).
36. R. D. Baker and H. G. Applegate, *Agron. J.*, *62*, 509 (1970).
37. J. B. Weber and H. D. Coble, *J. Agri. Food Chem.*, *16*, 475 (1968).

38. R. G. Burns and L. J. Audus, *Weed Res.*, *10*, 49 (1970).
39. K. Groves and K. S. Chough, *J. Agri. Food Chem.*, *18*, 1127 (1970).
40. C. R. Harris, *J. Econ. Entomol.*, *59*, 1221 (1966).
41. L. C. Liv, H. Cibes-Viade, and F. K. S. Koos, *Weed Sci.*, *18*, 470 (1970).
42. B. E. Day, L. S. Jordan, and V. A. Jolliffe, *Weed Sci.*, *16*, 209 (1968).
43. J. V. Parochetti and G. F. Warren, *Weed Sci.*, *16*, 13 (1968).
44. T. J. Sheets, J. W. Smith, and D. D. Kaufman, *Weed Sci.*, *16*, 217 (1968).
45. F. T. Lindstrom, L. Boersma, and H. Gardiner, *Soil Sci.*, *106*, 107 (1968).
46. W. J. Hanson and R. N. Nex, *Soil Sci.*, *76*, 209 (1953).
47. P. C. Kearney, C. I. Harris, D. D. Kaufman, and T. J. Sheets, *Advan. Pest Control Res.*, *6*, 1 (1965).
48. C. J. Scifres, O. C. Burnside, and M. K. McCartney, *Weed Sci.*, *17*, 486 (1969).
49. R. P. Upchurch and W. C. Pierce, *Weeds*, *5*, 321 (1957).
50. J. P. Walter, E. F. Eastin, and M. G. Merkle, *Weed Res.*, *10*, 165 (1970).
51. H. R. Sherburne, V. H. Freed, and S. C. Fang, *Weeds*, *4*, 50 (1956).
52. E. G. Rodgers, *Weed Sci.*, *16*, 117 (1968).
53. G. Voss and H. Geissbuhler, *Residue Rev.*, *37*, 133 (1971).
54. A. P. Edwards and J. M. Bremner, *J. Soil Sci.*, *18*, 64 (1967).
55. E. Aelbers and K. Homburg, *Meded. Landbhogesch. Gent.*, *24*, 893 (1959).
56. W. T. Scudder, *Florida Agri. Exp. Sta. Tech. Bull.*, *657*, 23 (1963).
57. O. C. Burnside, C. R. Fenster, G. A. Wicks, and J. V. Drew, *Weed Sci.*, *17*, 241 (1969).
58. W. D. Guenzi and W. E. Beard, *Soil Sci. Soc. Amer. Proc.*, *34*, 443 (1970).
59. R. Grover and R. J. Hance, *Can. J. Plant Sci.*, *49*, 378 (1969).
60. R. G. Nash and M. L. Beall, *Science*, *168*, 1109 (1970).
61. R. S. Tames and R. J. Hance, *Plant Soil*, *30*, 221 (1969).
62. W. E. Odum, G. M. Woodwell, and C. F. Wurster, *Science*, *164*, 576 (1969).
63. A. Walker and D. V. Crawford, in *Isotopes and Radiation in Soil Organic Matter Studies*, p. 91, I.A.E.A., Vienna, 1968.
64. J. W. Butcher, E. Kirknes, and M. Zabik, *Rev. Ecol. Biol. Sol.*, *6*, 291 (1969).
65. C. D. Gish, *Pest. Monit. J.*, *3*, 241 (1970).
66. G. M. Woodwell, *Sci. Amer.*, *216*, 24 (1967).
67. E. A. Boykins, *Atlantic Nat.*, *21*, 18 (1966).
68. E. A. Boykins, *Bio. Sci.*, *17*, 37 (1967).
69. B. N. K. Davis, *Ann. Appl. Biol.*, *61*, 29 (1968).
70. G. A. Wheatley and J. A. Hardman, *J. Sci. Food Agri.*, *19*, 219 (1968).
71. R. J. Roberts, *J. Econ. Entomol.*, *56*, 781 (1963).
72. C. I. Chacko and J. L. Lockwood, *Can. J. Microbiol.*, *13*, 1123 (1967).

73. W. H. Ko and J. H. Lockwood, *Rev. Ecol. Biol. Sol.*, *7*, 465 (1970).
74. J. L. Lockwood, in *Pesticides in the Soil: Ecology, Degradation and Movement*, p. 47, Proceedings of a Symposium, Michigan State University, 1970.
75. Y. -O. Shin, J. J. Chodan, and A. R. Walcott, *J. Agri. Food Chem.*, *18*, 1129 (1970).
76. W. H. Ko and J. L. Lockwood, *Can. J. Microbiol.*, *14*, 1075 (1968).
77. J. L. Mortenson and F. L. Himes, in *Chemistry of Soil*, 2nd. ed. (F. E. Bear, Ed.), p. 206, Reinhold, New York, 1964.
78. S. J. Toth, in *Chemistry of Soil*, 2nd ed. (F. E. Bear, Ed.), p. 142, Reinhold, New York, 1964.
79. M. M. Kononova, in *Soil Organic Matter*, Pergamon, Oxford, 1966.
80. M. Schnitzer, *Soil Sci. Soc. Amer. Proc.*, *33*, 75 (1969).
81. A. D. Rovira and E. L. Greacen, *Austral. J. Agri. Res.*, *8*, 659 (1957).
82. C. I. Harris and T. J. Sheets, *Weeds*, *13*, 215 (1965).
83. R. P. Upchurch, *Residue Rev.*, *16*, 47 (1966).
84. C. A. Edwards, *Residue Rev.*, *13*, 83 (1966).
85. G. S. Hartley, in *The Physiology and Biochemistry of Herbicides* (L. J. Audus, Ed.), p. 111, Academic, London, 1964.
86. R. P. Upchurch and W. C. Pierce, *Weeds*, *6*, 24 (1958).
87. J. D. H. Williams, *Weed Res.*, *8*, 327 (1968).
88. R. J. Hance, *Can. J. Soil Sci.*, *49*, 357 (1969).
89. P. J. Doherty and G. F. Warren, *Weed Res.*, *9*, 20 (1969).
90. P. Massini, *Weed Res.*, *1*, 142 (1961).
91. J. R. Peterson, R. S. Adams, and L. K. Cutkomp, *Soil Sci. Soc. Flm. Proc.*, *35*, 72 (1971).
92. P. Wade, *J. Sci. Food Agri.*, *5*, 184 (1954).
93. E. P. Lichtenstein and K. R. Schulz, *J. Econ. Entomol.*, *52*, 124 (1959).
94. R. S. Adams and P. Li, *Soil Sci. Soc. Amer. Proc.*, *35*, 78 (1971).
95. L. H. Liv, H. Cibes-Viade, and F. K. S. Koos, *Weed Sci.*, *18*, 470 (1970).
96. G. F. Warren, *Proc. North Carolina Weed Control Conf.*, *13*, 5 (1956).
97. A. E. Leopold, P. VanSchaik, and M. Neal, *Weeds*, *8*, 48 (1960).
98. R. P. Upchurch and D. D. Mason, *Weeds*, *10*, 9 (1962).
99. G. Macnamara and S. J. Toth, *Soil Sci.*, *109*, 234 (1969).
100. B. A. G. Knight and T. E. Tomlinson, *J. Soil Sci.*, *18*, 223 (1967).
101. G. T. Felbeck, Jr., in *Soil Biochemistry* (A. D. McLaren and J. Skujins, Eds.), Vol. 2, p. 36, Dekker, New York, 1971.
102. H. M. Hurst and N. A. Burges, in *Soil Biochemistry* (A. D. McLaren and G. H. Peterson, Eds.), Vol. 1, p. 260, Dekker, New York, 1967.
103. J. A. Leenheer and P. G. Moe, *Soil Sci. Soc. Amer. Proc.*, *33*, 267 (1969).
104. M. Schnitzer and S. I. M. Skinner, *Soil Sci. Soc. Amer. Proc.*, *29*, 400 (1965).
105. V. C. Farmer and R. I. Morrison, *Geochem. Cosmoch. Acta.*, *28*, 1537 (1964).

106. J. B. Weber, P. W. Perry, and R. D. Upchurch, *Soil Sci. Soc. Amer. Proc.*, *29*, 678 (1965).
107. J. D. Sullivan and G. T. Felbeck, *Soil Sci.*, *106*, 42 (1968).
108. M. D. McGlamery and F. W. Slife, *Weeds*, *14*, 237 (1966).
109. E. P. Dunigan and T. H. McIntosh, *Weed Sci.*, *19*, 279 (1971).
110. M. H. B. Hayes, M. Stacey, and J. Standley, *Trans. 9th Int. Congr. Soil Sci.*, *3*, 247 (1968).
111. M. Damanakis, D. S. H. Drennan, J. D. Fryer, and K. Holly, *Weed Res.*, *10*, 264 (1970).
112. R. L. Wershaw, P. J. Burcar, and M. C. Goldberg, *Environ. Sci. Technol.*, *3*, 271 (1969).
113. T. R. Kemp, L. P. Stolz, J. W. Herron, and W. T. Smith, Jr., *Weed Sci.*, *17*, 44 (1969).
114. R. J. Hance, *Weed Res.*, *5*, 108 (1965).
115. G. T. Felbeck, Jr., *Advan. Agron.*, *17*, 327 (1965).
116. M. H. B. Hayes, *Residue Rev.*, *31*, 132 (1970).
117. R. Grover, *Weeds*, *14*, 148 (1966).
118. E. P. Lichtenstein, T. W. Fuhremann, and K. R. Schulz, *J. Agri. Food Chem.*, *16*, 348 (1968).
119. G. A. Tompkins, T. H. McIntosh, and E. P. Dunigan, *Soil Sci. Soc. Amer. Proc.*, *32*, 373 (1968).
120. O. C. Burnside and R. Behrens, *Weeds*, *9*, 145 (1961).
121. R. L. Darding and J. F. Freeman, *Weed Sci.*, *16*, 226 (1968).
122. C. R. Harris and W. W. Sans, *J. Agri. Food Chem.*, *15*, 861 (1967).
123. H. P. Hermanson and C. Forbes, *Soil Sci. Soc. Amer. Proc.*, *30*, 748 (1966).
124. D. T. Smith and W. F. Meggitt, *Weed Sci.*, *18*, 260 (1970).
125. R. P. Thompson (1969), cited by J. B. Weber, *Residue Rev.*, *32*, 93 (1970).
126. M. C. Bowman, M. S. Schechter, and R. L. Carter, *J. Agri. Food Chem.*, *13*, 360 (1965).
127. C. R. Harris, *J. Econ. Entomol.*, *62*, 1437 (1969).
128. L. W. Getzin and R. K. Chapman, *J. Econ. Entomol.*, *53*, 47 (1960).
129. E. Koren, C. L. Foy, and F. M. Ashton, *Weed Sci.*, *16*, 172 (1968).
130. C. H. Keys and H. A. Friesen, *Weed Sci.*, *16*, 341 (1968).
131. A. E. Smith, *Weed Res.*, *10*, 331 (1970).
132. R. E. Talbert, R. L. Runyan, and H. R. Baker, *Weed Sci.*, *18*, 10 (1970).
133. L. K. Porter and W. E. Beard, *J. Agri. Food Chem.*, *16*, 344 (1968).
134. G. G. Briggs and J. E. Dawson, *J. Agri. Food Chem.*, *18*, 97 (1970).
135. J. G. Konrad and G. Chesters, *J. Agri. Food Chem.*, *17*, 226 (1969).
136. W. P. Anderson, A. B. Richards, and J. W. Whitworth, *Weed Sci.*, *16*, 165 (1968).
137. J. M. Thompson (1965), cited by M. H. B. Hayes, *Residue Rev.*, *31*, 132 (1970).

138. J. P. Martin, in *Pesticides and their Effects on Soils and Water*, p. 95, A.S.A. Special Publ., No. 8, Soil Sci. Soc. Amer., Madison, Wisconsin, 1966.

139. R. G. Burns, M. H. El-Sayed, and A. D. McLaren, *Soil Biol. Biochem.*, *4*, 107 (1972).

140. R. G. Burns, A. Pukite, and A. D. McLaren, *Soil Sci. Soc. Amer. Proc.*, *36*, 308 (1972).

141. R. Bartha, *J. Agri. Food Chem.*, *19*, 385 (1971).

142. H. D. Dubey and J. F. Freeman, *Soil Sci.*, *97*, 334 (1964).

142a. R. J. Hance, *Soil Biol. Biochem.*, *6*, 39 (1974).

143. L. L. McCormick and A. E. Hitbold, *Weeds*, *14*, 77 (1966).

144. R. G. Burns, *Bull. Environ. Contam. Toxicol.*, *6*, 316 (1971).

144a. R. G. Burns, *Proc. 11th Br. Weed Control Conf.*, *3*, 1203 (1972).

145. L. J. Andus, in *The Physiology and Biochemistry of Herbicides* (L. J. Andus, Ed.), p. 163, Academic, London, 1964.

146. F. M. Fowkes, H. A. Benesi, L. B. Ryland, W. M. Sawyer, K. D. Dettling, E. S. Loeffler, F. B. Folckemeyer, M. R. Johnson, and Y. P. Sun, *J. Agri. Food Chem.*, *8*, 202 (1960).

147. G. E. Lailach, T. D. Thompson, and G. W. Brindley, *Clays and Clay Minerals*, *16*, 275 (1968).

148. M. J. Frissel and G. H. Bolt, *Soil Sci.*, *94*, 284 (1962).

149. J. B. Weber, *Amer. Mineral.*, *51*, 1657 (1966).

150. J. B. Weber, S. B. Weed and T. M. Ward, *Weed Sci.*, *17*, 417 (1969).

151. C. I. Harris and G. F. Warren, *Weeds*, *12*, 120 (1964).

152. M. J. Frissel, *Verslag Landbouwk. Onderzoek*, *76*, 3 (1961).

153. R. J. Hance, *Weed Res.*, *9*, 108 (1969).

154. H. Geissbühler, C. Haselback, and H. Aebi, *Weed Res.*, *3*, 140 (1963).

155. G. W. Bailey, J. L. White, and T. Rothberg, *Soil Sci. Soc. Amer. Proc.*, *32*, 222 (1968).

156. R. D. Harter and J. L. Ahlrichs, *Soil Sci. Soc. Amer. Proc.*, *31*, 30 (1967).

157. A. D. McLaren, *Enzymologia*, *21*, 356 (1960).

158. B. V. Tucker, D. E. Pack, J. N. Ospensen, A. Omid, and W. D. Thomas, Jr., *Weed Sci.*, *17*, 48 (1968).

159. J. B. Weber, P. W. Perry, and K. Ibaraki, *Weed Sci.*, *16*, 134 (1968).

160. D. L. Coffey and G. F. Warren, *Weed Sci.*, *17*, 16 (1969).

161. F. T. Corbin, R. P. Upchurch, and F. L. Selman, *Weed Sci.*, *19*, 233 (1971).

162. S. Horrobin, *J. Chem. Soc.*, p. 4130 (1963).

163. J. G. Konrad, D. E. Armstrong, and G. Chesters, *Agron. J.*, *59*, 591 (1967).

164. S. R. Obien and R. E. Green, *Weed Sci.*, *17*, 5P9 (1969).

165. N. Sethunathan and I. C. MacKae, *J. Agri. Food Chem.*, *17*, 221 (1969).

166. S. A. Waksman, *Principles of Soil Microbiology*, 2nd ed., Williams & Wilkins, Baltimore, Maryland, 1932.

167. J. H. Warcup, *Trans. Brit. Mycol. Soc.*, *34*, 376 (1951).

168. F. T. Corbin and R. P. Upchurch, *Weeds*, *15*, 4 (1967).

169. K. Gundersen and H. L. Jensen, *Acta Agri. Scand.*, *6*, 100 (1956).
170. C. A. Edwards, *Residue Rev.*, *13*, 83 (1964).
171. O. C. Burnside, E. L. Schmidt, and R. Behrens, *Weeds*, *9*, 477 (1961).
172. G. A. Buchanan and E. G. Rogers, *Proc. S. Weed Conf.*, *16*, 393 (1963).
173. G. W. Bailey and J. L. White, *J. Agri. Food Chem.*, *12*, 324 (1964).
174. V. H. Freed, J. Vernetti, and M. Montgomery, *Proc. W. Weed Control Conf.*, *19*, 21 (1962).
175. S. D. Faust and A. Zarins, *Residue Rev.*, *29*, 151 (1969).
176. T. J. Sheets, *Weeds*, *11*, 186 (1963).
177. R. R. Hahn, O. C. Burnside, and T. L. Lavy, *Weed Sci.*, *17*, 3 (1969).
178. F. W. Roeth, T. L. Lavy, and O. C. Burnside, *Weed Sci.*, *17*, 202 (1969).
179. J. V. Parochetti and G. F. Warren, *Weed Sci.*, *18*, 555 (1970).
180. C. I. Harris, *Weeds*, *12*, 112 (1964).
181. W. E. Rauser and C. M. Switzer, *Hormolog.*, *4*, 13 (1963).
182. G. W. Bailey and J. L. White, *Residue Rev.*, *32*, 29 (1970).
183. C. A. Edwards, S. D. Beck, and E. P. Lichtenstein, *J. Econ. Entomol.*, *50*, 622 (1957).
184. F. Call, *J. Sci. Food Agri.*, *8*, 137 (1957).
185. P. Wade, *J. Sci. Food Agri.*, *6*, 1 (1955).
186. D. E. Wolf, R. S. Johnson, G. D. Hill, and R. W. Varner. *Proc. N.C. Weed Cont. Conf.*, *15*, 7 (1958).
187. Q. H. Yuen and H. W. Hilton, *J. Agri. Food Chem.* 10.,386 (1962).
188. M. W. Hilton and Q. H. Yuen, *J. Agri. Food Chem.*,11, 230 (1963).
189. R. D. Comes, D. W. Dohmont, and H. P. Alley, *J. Amer. Soc. Sugar-beet Technol.*, *11*, 287 (1961).
190. F. T. Phillips, *J. Sci. Food Agri.*, *15*, 458 (1964).
191. H. L. Trichell, H. L. Morton, and M. G. Merkle, *Weeds*, *16*, 447 (1968).
192. A. P. Barrett, E. W. Hauser, A. W. White, and J. H. Halliday, *Weeds 15*, 133 (1967).
193. J. H. Caro and A. W. Taylor, *J. Agri. Food Chem.*, *19*, 379 (1971).
194. F. Acree, Jr., M. Beroza, and M. C. Bowman, *J. Agri. Food Chem.*, *11*, 278 (1963).
195. E. P. Lichtenstein and K. R. Schulz, *J. Econ. Entomol.*, *54*, 517 (1961).
196. E. P. Lichtenstein and K. R. Schulz, *J. Econ. Entomol.*, *57*, 618 (1964).
197. D. F. Heath, *J. Chem. Soc.*, 1643 (1958).
198. G. D. Thorn and R. A. Ludwig, *Can. J. Chem.*, *38*, 872 (1954).
199. D. E. Munnecke and J. P. Martin, *Phytopathology*, *54*, 941 (1964).
200. N. J. Turner and M. E. Corden, *Phytopathology*, *53*, 1388 (1963).
201. H. P. Burchfield and J. Schechtman, *Contrib. Boyce Thompson Inst.*, *19*, 411 (1958).
202. N. A. Lange, in *Handbook of Chemistry* 9th ed., McGraw-Hill, New York, 1956.
203. O. Agundis and R. Behrens, *Weed Soc. Amer. Abstr.*, 70 (1966).

204. T. Golab, R. T. Herberg, J. V. Gramlich, A. P. Ravn, and G. W.
      Probst, *J. Agri. Food Chem.*, *18*, 838 (1970).
205. T. Yoshida and T. F. Castro, *Soil Sci. Soc. Amer. Proc.*, *34*,
      440 (1970).
205a. Z. H. Bhuiya and D. F. Rothwell, *Pl. Soil*, *39*, 193 (1973).
206. W. D. Guenzi and W. E. Beard, *Soil Sci. Soc. Amer. Proc.*, *32*,
      522 (1968).
207. W. D. Burge, *J. Agri. Food Chem.*, *19*, 375 (1971).
208. E. P. Lichtenstein and K. R. Schulz, *J. Econ. Entomol.*, *53*,
      192 (1960).
209. C. Steelink and G. Tollin, in *Soil Biochemistry* (A. D. McLaren
      and G. H. Peterson, Eds.), Vol. 2, p. 147, Dekker, New
      York, 1967.
210. D. G. Crosby, *Residue Rev.*, *25*, 1 (1969).
211. D. G. Crosby and C. S. Tang, *J. Agri. Food Chem.*, *17*, 1041
      (1969).
212. K. Munakata and M. Kuwahara, *Residue Rev.*, 25 13 (1969).
213. N. Hamadmad, cited by D. G. Crosby in *Pesticides in Soil:
      Ecology, Degradation and Movement*, Proceedings of a Sym-
      posium, p. 86, Michigan State University, 1970.
214. E. R. Fleck, in *Pesticides and their Effects on Soil and Water*,
      p. 18, A.S.A. Special Publications No. 8, Soil Sci. Soc.
      Amer., Madison, Wisconsin, 1966.
215. A. R. Mosier, W. D. Guenzi, and L. L. Miller, *Science*, *164*,
      1083 (1969).
216. J. R. Plimmer, U. I. Klingebiel, and B. E. Hummer, *Science*,
      167, 67 (1970).
217. P. Castelfranco, A. Oppenheim, and S. Yamaguchi, *Weeds*, *11*,
      111 (1963).
218. P. Castelfranco and M. S. Brown, *Weeds*, *11*, 116 (1963).
219. J. L. Hilton, *Plant Physiol.*, *37*, 238 (1962).
220. A. W. Naylor, *J. Agri. Food Chem.*, *12*, 21 (1964).
221. R. B. Taylorson, *Weeds*, *14*, 155 (1966).
222. G. L. Henderson and D. G. Crosby, *J. Agri. Food Chem.*, *15*,
      888 (1967).
223. J. Robinson, A. Richardson, B. Bush, and K. E. Elgar, *Bull.
      Environ. Contam. Toxicol.*, *1*, 133 (1966).
224. J. D. Rosen, D. J. Sutherland, and G. R. Lipton, *Bull. Environ.
      Contem. Toxicol.*, *1*, 133 (1966).
225. C. G. Messersmith, O. C. Burnside, and T. L. Lavy, *Weed Sci.*,
      19, 285 (1971).
226. G. W. Probst and J. B. Tepe, in *Degradation of Herbicides*
      (P. C. Kearney and D. D. Kaufman, Eds.), Dekker, New
      York, 1969.
227. W. L. Wright and G. F. Warren, *Weeds*, *13*, 329 (1965).
228. R. D. Comes and F. L. Timmons, *Weeds*, *13*, 81 (1965).
229. M. J. Zabik, R. D. Schuetz, W. L. Burton, and B. E. Pape, *J.
      Agri. Food Chem.*, *19*, 308 (1971).
230. L. S. Jordan, B. E. Day, and W. A. Clerx, *Weeds*, *12*, 5 (1964).
231. D. G. Crosby and E. Leitis, *J. Agri. Food Chem.*, *17*, 1041
      (1969).

232. I. J. Belasco and W. P. Langsdorf, *J. Agri. Food Chem.*, *17*, 1004 (1969).
233. F. Matsumura and G. M. Boush, *Science*, *156*, 959 (1967).
234. G. Wedemeyer, *Appl. Microboil.*, *16*, 661 (1968).
235. C. M. Tu and W. B. Bollen, *Weed Res.*, *8*, 38 (1968).
236. H. L. Jensen, *Can. J. Microbiol.*, *3*, 151 (1957).
237. B. G. Tweedy, C. Loeppky, and J. A. Ross, *J. Agri. Food Chem.*, *18*, 851 (1970).
238. P. Hirsch and M. Alexander, *Can. J. Microbiol.*, *6*, 241 (1960).
239. F. W. Slife (1967), cited by T. J. Sheets, *Residue Rev.*, *32*, 287 (1970).
239a. E. Koren, *Weed Sci.*, *20*, 230 (1972).
240. J. V. Parochetti, E. R. Hein, and S. R. Colby, *Weed Sci.*, *19*, 28 (1971).
241. D. D. Kaufman, in *Pesticides and their Effects on Soil and Water*, p. 85, A.S.A. Special Publ. No. 8, Soil Sci. Soc. Amer., Madison Wisconsin, 1966.
242. P. C. Kearney, D. D. Kaufman, and M. Alexander, in *Soil Biochemistry* (A. D. McLaren and G. H. Peterson, Eds.), Vol. 1, p. 318, Dekker, New York, 1967.
243. H. C. Sikka and D. E. Davis, *Weeds*, *14*, 289 (1966).
244. K. E. Savage and W. L. Barrentine, *Weed Sci.*, *17*, 349 (1969).
245. E. H. Dustman and L. F. Stickel, in *Pesticides and their Effects on Soil and Water*, p. 109, A.S.A. Special Publ. No. 8, Soil Sci. Soc. Amer., Madison Wisconsin, 1966.

CHAPTER 5

HUMUS-ENZYME SYSTEMS AND SYNTHETIC, ORGANIC
POLYMER-ENZYME ANALOGS

J. N. Ladd and J. H. A. Butler
Division of Soils, CSIRO
Glen Osmond, South Australia

I. INTRODUCTION

The activities of many enzymes in soils have been measured or
detected [1-4], but the origin of these enzymes, the states in

143

which they occur, and their roles in the multiplicity of biochemical transformations taking place in the soil continue to pose intriguing questions. Skujins [1] has discussed the many difficulties of elucidating the distribution and state of soil enzymes. It seems reasonable to assume that a high proportion of those enzymes active against added high molecular weight substrates, e.g., proteins or cellulose, occur in the soil outside living cells. Such an assumption is more difficult to justify for those enzymes active against substrates of low molecular weight.

Extracellular enzymes that persist in an active state in the soil but that cannot be extracted in high proportions are considered to be stabilized by chemical and physical association with soil colloids. Past studies have emphasized the role of inorganic clay minerals in binding and stabilizing proteins including enzymes [5-13]. It is somewhat surprising that only recently has attention been directed toward the possible occurrence of active humic-enzyme complexes in soils [1, 14-18, 227], especially because humic compounds have been considered to play an important role in conferring stability on soil nitrogenous components [19-21] and since a significant proportion of humic acid-N is accounted for as amino acid-N after hydrolysis of peptide bonds [22-26].

Although a high proportion, presumably, of enzymatic protein is rapidly denatured or degraded in soil after release from living cells, it may be that opportunities will exist for some enzyme molecules to become bound to humic compounds (either by covalent linkages during formation of the humic polymers or perhaps by ionic or hydrogen bonding to the preformed humic compounds) in such a way that some enzyme activity is retained and that the enzymes acquire enhanced stability to biological attack.

In this chapter, therefore, we have not only recorded the properties of humus-enzyme systems, but have also discussed evidence that directly or indirectly relates to the hypothesis that humus-enzyme complexes represent important components of soil enzyme systems. Also, we shall include information on the properties of enzymes (or proteins) variously bonded to (a) naturally occurring compounds such as lignin, tannins, and melanin pigments and (b) synthetic organic polymers. In recent years increasing attention has been given to the preparation of a great variety of water-insoluble, organic polymer-enzyme derivatives, the properties of which exhibit many common features. It is anticipated that insoluble, active, humus-enzyme systems may also possess properties resembling those established for synthetic, organic polymer-enzymes, especially those derivatives in which the organic polymer is polyanionic as is humus.

The interpretation of much of the information presented is deliberately speculative. We hope that the obvious lack of knowledge in some areas will provide incentives for continued studies on the occurrence, properties and role of humus-enzyme systems in the natural soil environment.

II. NATURE OF SOIL HUMIC COMPOUNDS AND RELATED SUBSTANCES

A. Humic and Fulvic Acids

The nature of humic and fulvic acids is far from clear [27-33]. Humic and fulvic acids contain C, H, O, H, and S; are variable in composition; range appreciably in molecular weight; and almost certainly do not have a regular structure. A substantial part of the polymers is aromatic [34, 35], carrying carboxyl, phenolic, and probably carbonyl and alcoholic functional groups [28-30]. Despite a number of attempts [36-38], the presence of quinone groups has yet to be established with any certainty.

The numbers of functional groups vary depending upon the source of the humic and fulvic acids, but as no really satisfactory methods are available for their measurement [28, 32, 29], values quoted must be regarded as approximate. However, because estimates show that humic and fulvic acids contain 35-47% oxygen, of which 49-100% can be accounted for as functional groups [32], there must be

considerable potential to bind to enzyme protein (by hydrogen, electrostatic, or covalent bonds) involving hydroxyl, carboxyl, and carbonyl groups. Table 1 shows the range of contents of functional
groups of humic and fulvic acids found by a number of authors.

TABLE 1

Contents of Functional Groups of Polymers

Polymer	Oxygen (%)	Phenolic hydroxyl (mEq/g)	Carboxyl (mEq/g)	References
Humic acid	35-37	2.9-5.7	1.5-3.0	[32]
Fulvic acid	44-48	2.7-6.7	6.1-9.1	[32]
Lignin	30	0.4-1.5	0.1-0.4	[40]
Tannin (hydrolyzable)	43	14	0	[41]
Melanin (*Sepia*)	24	6.5	2.3-3.3	[42]

B. Tannins

Tannins are amorphous, high molecular weight, polyphenolic substances of plant origin and, in the tanning industry, are defined
as those substances that can bond to protein and render it resistant
to decomposition. There are two distinct classes of tannins: hydrolyzable and condensed. Hydrolyzable tannins are polyesters of
gallic acid (1) and related derivatives and a central glucose residue, e.g., corilagin (2) [41]. They are readily hydrolyzed to a
phenolic acid and a sugar. On hydrolysis, gallotannins yield gallic
acid (1), and ellagitannins yield phenolic derivatives related to
hexahydroxydiphenic acid (3) or ellagic acid (4) [43].

Condensed tannins are considered to consist of condensates of
catechin or related compounds (5). Treatment with acid causes further polymerization rather than hydrolysis. The mode of condensation is as yet unknown, but an ether link has been suggested [44].
Thus, tannins as a whole can be regarded as partly aromatic polymers,
carrying a substantial number of aliphatic and phenolic hydroxyl
groups (Table 1).

(1)

(2)

(3)

(4)

(5)

C. Lignin

Lignin has not been assigned a definite structure. Lignins
from different plant species vary appreciably and the vigorous isolation procedures generally used probably yield a final product of
modified structure. Lignin molecules appear to be made up of derivatives of p-hydroxycinnamyl alcohol (6), coniferyl alcohol (7), and
related structures. These building units may be linked in a somewhat random manner by ether and carbon-to-carbon bonds, between
C-5 and the carbons or oxygens of the propane side chain [45].
Structure (8) illustrates the type of bonds that may be involved
but does not purport to be the structure of lignin [46].* Such a
structure would typify a complex condensate, with aliphatic and
phenolic hydroxyl, methoxyl, and some carbonyl groups. The presence
of significant numbers of carboxyl groups seems to be a matter of
conjecture. Table 1 shows the range of contents of functional
groups of several lignins. At least one-half of the oxygen content
(about 30%) of lignin can be accounted for as oxygen present in
functional groups [45].

OH

5

CH = CH-CH$_2$OH

(6)

OH

CH$_3$O

5

CH = CH-CH$_2$OH

(7)

---

*From Braun and Braun [46] by courtesy of Academic Press, New
York.

(8)

D. Melanins

Melanins are dark-colored, organic pigments of unknown and variable structure occurring in many animals and in some plants and fungi [42, 47-49, 228]. Synthetic melanins, closely resembling the natural materials, can be obtained by chemical or enzymatic oxidation of tyrosine, dihydroxyphenylalanine (DOPA), or histamine. Natural melanins occur in close combination with protein and can be separated into a pigment plus amino acids. Using diffusion measurements, Schimdli [47] estimated the molecular weight of the human hair pigment nucleus to be about 70,000. Piattelli et al. [48] have good evidence to show that the protein is covalently linked to the indole nucleus via cysteine units. On the basis of degradation studies of a number of melanins from different sources, Nicholaus et al. [49] suggested that there are two types of melanins: those containing indole units (9), apparently of animal origin, and those containing catechol units (10), perhaps of plant and fungal origin. Those containing catechol units perhaps should not be classed as melanins.

Methylation and decarboxylation studies performed by Piatelli and Nicolaus [42] show that *Sepia* melanin contains a considerable number of both carboxyl and phenolic hydroxyl groups. Table 1 shows the approximate functional group contents of *Sepia* melanin calculated from the results of these authors.

(9)   (10)

III. INTERACTIONS OF HUMUS AND NATURAL ANALOGS WITH AMINO ACIDS AND PROTEIN

The interactions of phenols, quinones, tannins and humic compounds with amino acids and protein will be discussed in some detail
because of their relevance to the manner in which humus-enzyme complexes may be formed.

A. Phenols and Quinones with Amino Acids

It is well known that phenols are readily oxidized enzymatically
or chemically to quinones with or without the participation of amino
acids to produce colored oxidation products [50-54]. The initial
reaction involves essentially three stages, with the consumption
of 1 mole of oxygen per mole of phenol oxidized (Fig. 1).

The rate of the nucleophilic substitution reaction appears to
be controlled by the nature of the substituents on the nitrogen
atom. Glycylglycylglycine reacts faster than glycylglycine, which
reacts faster than glycine. This effect has been referred to as
the "peptide effect." The ε-amino group of lysine reacts in the
same manner but less rapidly [52].

Further reactions of the nitrogen-containing products result
in the formation of black, insoluble colloids from which the amino
acids can be recovered in only very low yields after acid hydrolysis [52, 55]. During condensation, oxygen is taken up and carbon
dioxide and ammonia are released [50, 53, 56].

Thiol compounds react readily with quinones without utilizing
oxygen to produce colorless, fairly stable products, apparently
with no subsequent condensation [51, 54] [Eq. (1)].

$$(1)$$

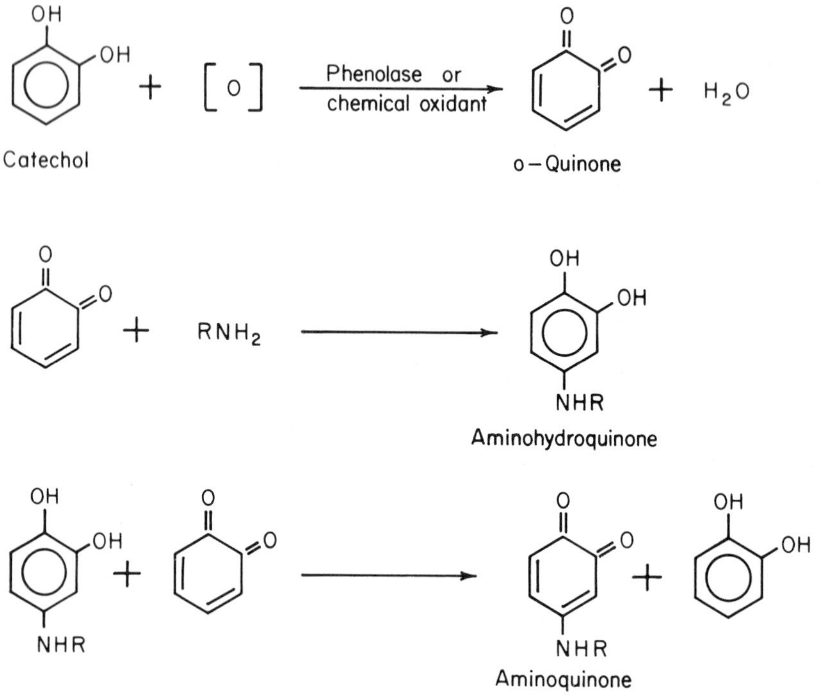

Fig. 1. Oxidation of catechol in the presence of an amine [52].

B. Phenols and Quinones with Protein

The interaction of phenols and quinones with protein can take place by either of two mechanisms, reversibly by hydrogen bonding or irreversibly by covalent bonding.

Hydrogen bonding takes place between the hydrogen of the phenolic group and the oxygen of the peptide bond (Fig. 2) producing a particularly strong bond, according to Flett [57]. Loomis and Battaile [58] consider that a protein may bond more than one-third of its weight of phenolic material in this manner without the participation of the amino group. Hydrogen bonds are certainly very

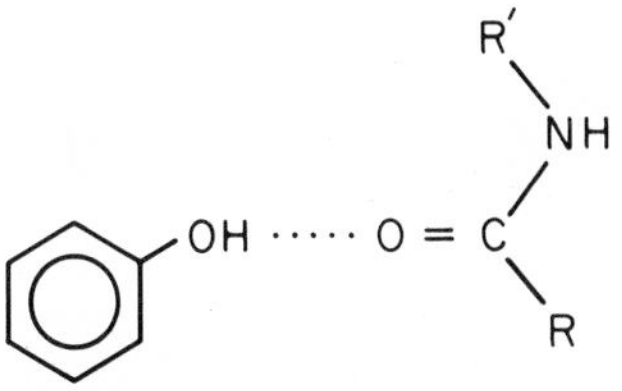

Fig. 2. Hydrogen bonding of the phenolic hydroxyl to the oxygen of the peptide bond.

important but there are many indications that covalent bonds are also formed, irreversibly linking the phenol to the protein.

The reaction of phenols and quinones with protein to form covalent bonds appears to be quite complex. The nature of the reaction is dependent upon the pH [59] and the ratio of phenol to protein [52, 60]. Up to pH 7, protein combines with unpolymerized p-benzoquinone. At slightly higher pH's, autoxidation of quinone increases and reaction of protein with monomeric quinone decreases. At still slightly higher pH's, protein combines with polymerized quinone and, beyond pH 8, autoxidation of p-benzoquinone takes over.

Theis [61] suggested that the initial linkage takes place between ε-lysylamino groups of the protein and the quinone to form a structure like (11). However, as with amino acids, terminal amino and sulfhydryl groups, if available, react much more readily.

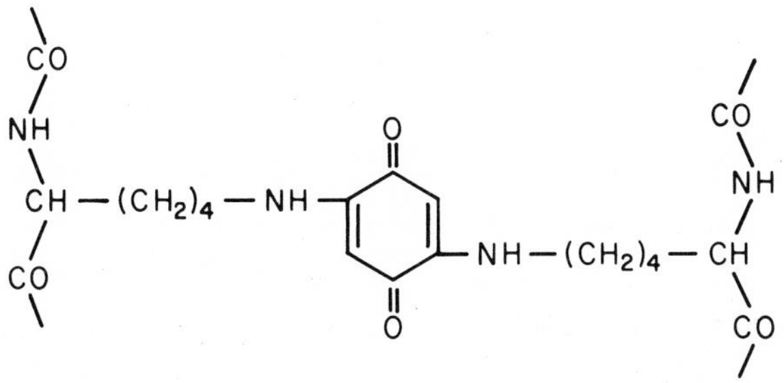

(11)

(12)

Pierpoint [60] studied the reaction of bovine serum albumin
with chlorogenoquinone (12) and considered that, in the presence of
excess albumin, a protein-S-phenolic compound is obtained without
a significant increase in molecular weight. With excess quinone,
he obtained brown polymeric material that strongly sorbed to DEAE-
Sephadex gel, and a red protein derivative, considered from its
electrophoretic behavior to contain more carboxyl groups than albumin. No significant increase in molecular weight had occurred.
Albumin, previously reacted with formaldehyde, succinic anhydride, or
2,4,6-trinitrobenzene sulfonic acid to block amino groups no longer
reacted with chlorogenoquinone. The significance of quinone-protein
interactions in a wider context has been discussed by Pierpont [62].

C. Tannins with Protein

Tannins react with proteins to produce three apparently unrelated effects, tanning, enzyme inhibition, and astringency [63].
Because tannins resemble humic materials in many ways, a brief out-
line of the tanning reaction is included (see review by Gustavson
[64]). The structure of the protein, collagen, consists of ordered
and disordered regions. The latter are particularly susceptible to
decomposition. During tanning, the disordered regions acquire biological stability by reacting with tannins until heavily cross-
linked. The tannin molecule must be large enough and have sufficient phenolic groups to cross-link at several points, but not too
large to penetrate readily into the collagen structure [44]. Experiments with model compounds containing the amide grouping [65-67]

indicate that peptide bonds of the collagen molecule are hydrogen bonded to phenolic groups of the tannin.

Tannins form resistant complexes with other proteins besides collagen [68-70]. Basaraba and Starkey [70] measured microbiological degradation of mixtures of chestnut tannin (condensed) with gliadin, and walnut tannin (hydrolyzable) with both gelatine and gliadin. Different pH's and different ratios of tannin to protein were used. Decomposition was inhibited in all cases. The resistance of the complex was much greater at pH 4.0 than at pH 7.0, reflecting the greater dissociation of the complex at higher pH's. Benoit et al. [71] found that tannins had little effect on the decomposition of peptone, phenylalanine, and lysine. This suggests that the tannin and protein were hydrogen bonded rather than covalently linked. Condensed tannins produced more stable complexes with protein than do hydrolyzable tannins [64, 70, 72, 73].

Lewis and Starkey [73] studied complexes of a number of tannins with several proteins and found that the rate of decomposition of a tannin-protein complex was related to that of the original tannin. Feeney [74] examined the resistance to proteolysis of protein complexed to tannins. The degree of complex formation depended on the ratio of tannin to protein and the reaction period. Casein, complexed with oak leaf tannin, was not hydrolyzed by trypsin at pH 7.6. However, at pH 9.2 significant hydrolysis took place and increased as the ammount of tannin in the complex decreased. Interpretations are complicated because both enzyme and substrate are able to complex with the tannin. Loomis and Battaile [58] consider the pH effects an indication that the binding of protein involves hydrogen bonding between un-ionized phenolic groups of both hydrolyzable and condensed tannins and substituted amide groups of the protein. With hydrolyzable tannins, un-ionized carboxyl groups also form strong hydrogen bonds. Where phenolic substances are able to hydrogen bond internally, e.g., in the hydrolyzable tannins, the ability to hydrogen bond to other groups, such as protein, is reduced. This may be one reason why hydrolyzable tannins form less stable complexes with protein than do condensed tannins.

Experiments with hydrogen bond breaking compounds also emphasize the importance of hydrogen bonding in the interaction of tannins with protein. Gustavson [75] has shown that 8 M urea removed
54-59% of condensed tannin and 81-95% of hydrolyzable tannin from
leather. Brown and Wright [76] demonstrated by electrophoresis
that tea infusion greatly reduced the electrophoretic mobility of
casein. When 7 M urea was added, the effect of the tea infusion
was removed, indicating that the tea polyphenols had hydrogen bonded
to the protein.

Despite the importance of hydrogen bonds, the failure of urea
to break completely condensed tannin-protein complexes [75] leaves
little doubt that a second, more stable bond, presumably covalent,
is formed between condensed tannins and protein.

D. Lignins with Protein

In 1932, Waksman and Iyer [77] and Hobson and Page [78] demonstrated the resistance of lignin-protein complexes to decomposition.
Waksman and Iyer [77] found that a mechanical mixture of lignin and
protein depressed ammonia formation by bacteria but not by *Trichoderma* fungi. A complex isolated by acid precipitation from a previously alkaline solution of lignin and protein was even more resistant. Ammonia released from a given amount of casein in the
complex decreased with increasing amounts of lignin. Their hypothesis that stabilization resulted from the formation of a Schiff
base type linkage [Eq. (2)] between lignin and protein is somewhat
doubtful because peptone, glutamic acid, and glycine, which presumably could react similarly, were not protected by lignin.

$$RNH_2 \; + \; R_2C=O \longrightarrow R_2C=N\text{-}R \qquad\qquad (2)$$

Protein   Lignin   Lignoprotein

Norman [79] also cast doubt on the Schiff base theory of Waksman
and Iyer [77]. He considered that only a few peptide linkages

would be blocked by the limited number of lignin carbonyls and protein amino groups able to react.

Hobson and Page [78] considered that their biologically stable
preparations of egg albumen and oxidized lignin involved more than
coprecipitation of oppositely charged colloids. The involvement of
the phenolic hydroxyl group in these complexes is suggested by the
results of Bennett [80], who showed that methylation of the phenolic
groups of oxidized lignin prevented it from fixing ammonia. Lynch
and Lynch [81] also showed that lignin-protein complexes were resistant to microbial decomposition, although neither the complexes
nor the lignin alone was as resistant as a humic acid preparation.
Estermann et al. [10] prepared lignin-lysozyme complexes that were
extremely resistant to decomposition by chymotrypsin, mixed soil
cultures, and pure cultures of three different bacteria.

E. Humic Acids with Protein

Mattson [82] showed that proteins in solution can be precipitated by humic acid and proposed a salt-type linkage between carboxyl groups of the humic acid and amino groups of the protein.
The same year, Waksman and Iyer [77] proposed that humic acid was
a lignoprotein complex in which protein was bound by a Schiff base
linkage. Presently, it appears that a substantial proportion of
the amino acids recovered after acid hydrolysis of humic acid are
derived from peptides or proteins [53, 55, 83-86], but very little
is definitely known of the bond between humic acid and the nitrogenous moieties. Waksman and Iyer [87] precipitated peat humus
with acid in the presence of different amounts of casein. As the
humus did not appear to affect the rate of decomposition of the
casein in the precipitate, they suggested that the peat humus was
already saturated with protein, implying mere coprecipitation in
this case.

Loginow [88] studied the coprecipitation of humic acids with
gelatine and ovalbumen and found that the degree of precipitation
of protein was independent of the concentration of humic acid, at

least within the range 1-5 g/liter. At a weight ratio of protein to humic acid of greater than 2.5:1, precipitation occurred at a pH between 5 and 6. It appeared that the pH solubility character-istics of the major component of the mixture controlled the solu-bility of the complex. Loginow [88] claimed that because precipi-tation of gelatine and humic acid by $CaCl_2$ was the same at pH 6 and 9, coprecipitation of protein with humic acids was independent of the charge on the protein. He also concluded that the humic-protein complex could be soluble and that the complex was formed by adsorption processes. Because there was no measure of actual com-plex formation, only of precipitation, and because the situation was complicated by the presence of Ca^{2+} ions, it is difficult to draw firm conclusions regarding the type of bonding that may have been involved. A similar investigation was carried out by Mayaudon [89] who found that a humic acid previously hydrolyzed to remove protein, complexed with plant protein at pH 2 in the presence of Ca^{2+}. At higher pH's (6-9) much of the complex appeared to disso-ciate. Thus, he proposed ionic bonding of negatively charged humic acid with positively charged protein at low pH's. Residual protein, hydrogen bonded to the humic acid, was of greater biological sta-bility than the protein complexed by ionic bonds.

Simonart et al. [85], using phenol as a hydrogen bond breaking solvent, were able to dissolve a small amount of proteinaceous ma-terial, which suggests that a substantial part of soil humic protein is held covalently. However, phenol may not be completely effective in this case. Recently, Khan and Schnitzer [90] reported that ex-haustive methylation permitted the separation of soil fulvic acid into a number of ethers and esters of phenolic and benzene carboxylic acids and suggested that these compounds were hydrogen bonded to form the fulvic polymer.

IV. INTERACTIONS OF HUMIC COMPOUNDS AND RELATED SUBSTANCES WITH ENZYMES

A. Effect of Tannins on Enzyme Activity

Lyr [91] showed that tannin, at concentrations of between 2×10^{-6} and 3×10^{-4} M, inhibited xylanase, polygalacturonase, peroxidase, and laccase activities by 50%. Guerritore et al. [92] clearly demonstrated that tannic acid in a concentration of 10 μg/ml, which did not precipitate proteins, completely inhibited malic, glucose-6-phosphate and isocitric dehydrogenases. Inhibition was removed by the addition of polyvinylpyrrolidone to a concentration of 45 mg/ml, suggesting that the inhibition in this case was due to hydrogen bonding of the tannic acid to the enzyme.

Boudet and Gadal [93] also showed that tannin from oak leaves inhibited enzyme activity and concluded that the inhibition of β-amylase was caused by irreversible, nonspecific blocking by tannin of the active sites of the enzyme.

In the same year, Goldstein and Swain [72] carried out an extensive study of the effect of tannins on several enzymes and demonstrated significant inhibition of alcohol dehydrogenase, lactate dehydrogenase, peroxidase, catalase, and β-glucosidase. Unlike many earlier workers, they used low molecular weight assay substrates because many of the high molecular weight substrates bind tannins and confound the results obtained. Using β-glucosidase and tannic acid, Goldstein and Swain [72], as did Guerritore et al. [92], produced up to 58% inhibition of the enzyme without precipitation. They were also able to regenerate the activity of enzyme tannin precipitates by adding nonionic polymers or nonionic and cationic detergents. This, they state, strongly suggests that, at least initially, the protein and tannin were linked by hydrogen bonds and ionic forces. As did Lewis and Starkey [73], Goldstein and Swain [72] showed that condensed wattle tannin produced a more stable complex, with enzyme protein than did tannic acid (a hydrolyzable

tannin). Presumably other types of bonds may be involved. Again
Tamir and Alumot [94] found that condensed tannin (from carobs) was
a much more effective inhibitor of trypsin than a hydrolyzable tannin, m-digallic acid. However, amylase was inhibited to a similar
extent and lipase was most strongly inhibited by m-digallic acid.
Polyvinylpyrrolidone reactivated trypsin and lipase but not α-amylase,
suggesting that the trypsin and lipase-tannin complexes were hydrogen bonded, whereas with α-amylase, the bonding took some other form.
In all cases inhibition was noncompetitive. These authors used
high molecular weight substrates in all cases and undoubtedly, with
trypsin acting on casein, interaction of the tannin with the substrate casein must have affected the results obtained.

Firenzuoli et al. [95], using low molecular weight substrates,
demonstrated complete inhibition of malate dehydrogenase, isocitrate
dehydrogenase, and glucose-6-phosphate dehydrogenase by 5 μg/ml of
tannic acid without the formation of a precipitate. Inhibition
could be reversed by polyvinylpyrrolidone or Tween 80. Tannic acid
was at least ten times as effective an inhibitor as chlorogenic
acid, pyrogallate, or abietic acid.

Albergina [96] found that oxidized chlorogenic acid inhibited
a number of enzymes and implicated essential NH_2 or =NH groups of
the enzymes in their interaction with the inhibitor. Williams [97]
and Byrde [98] both have reviewed studies on the effects of phenolic compounds upon enzyme activity. In many cases, inhibition
was implied rather than demonstrated directly.

B. Effect of Melanins on Enzyme Activity

Akino [99, 100] reported that melanin prepared from dihydroxyphenylalanine (DOPA) inhibited the enzyme hyaluronidase. In a
more extensive study, Akino [102] found that the degree of inhibition depended markedly upon the pH of the preincubation mixture.
He observed no inhibition at pH 4.6 and maximum inhibition at pH
7 to 8. Inhibition was prevented by addition of NaCl with the
melanin, but after a 15-min preincubation of melanin with enzyme,

inhibition was irreversible. The pH effect suggests the occurrence
of electrostatic bonding between melanin and enzyme. However, the
irreversibility of the inhibition implies that a more permanent bond
is formed also. A break in the temperature inhibition curve, according to Akino [101], reinforces the suggestion that two types of
bonds are involved. The enzymes α- and β-amylase, catalase, ribo-
nuclease, and trypsin were also irreversibly inhibited by melanin.
Kuo and Alexander [102] also found that DOPA melanin inhibited a
number of enzymes. When enzyme and inhibitor were preincubated,
melanin in a concentration of 100 μg/ml inhibited chitinase by 52%,
a *Bacillus subtilis* protease by 55%, and glucanase by 34%. When
substrate and inhibitor were preincubated together, less inhibition
was obtained subsequently, probably because the substrate binding
of melanin that otherwise would complex with the enzyme. Low molecular weight aromatic products produced during melanin formation
were only slightly inhibitory to enzymes.

C. Effect of Humic and Fulvic Acids on Enzyme Activity

Saalbach [103] found that a chernozem humic acid increased
aldolase and phosphatase activity in rye seedlings. This led to
the determination of the direct effect of humic acid solutions on
aldolase, amylase, invertase, and phosphatase activities. Very low
concentrations (0.0125 μg/ml) of humic acid stimulated aldolase and
phosphatase activity, whereas higher concentrations (0.125-12.5
μg/ml) inhibited aldolase, amylase, and saccharase activity but
had no effect on phosphatase activity.

Scheffer et al. [104] determined the effect of a synthetic
humic acid prepared by oxidative polymerization of hydroquinone.
The preparation, at a concentration of 0.4 μg/ml, inhibited the
activities of two acid phosphatases by 50%, whereas at 2 mg/ml [104]
the synthetic humic acid stimulated the activity of an alkaline
phosphatase by 50%. The vastly different concentrations involved
suggest very different mechanisms of action. It is possible that
stimulation may have been caused by residual hydroquinone in the

synthetic humic preparation, because hydroquinone at 1.4 µg/ml
caused a 50% stimulation of alkaline phosphatase but had no effect
on acid phosphatase.

Ladd et al. [105] and Ladd and Butler [106] reported that concentrations of 2 and 20 µg/ml of several soil humic acids brought
about 50% inhibition of the proteolytic enzyme Pronase hydrolyzing
the substrates carbobenzoxylglyclleucine and albumin, respectively.
Pronase hydrolysis of the high molecular weight substrate albumin
was inhibited to a lesser extent, presumably because the albumin,
in relatively high concentration, competes effectively with the
enzyme for binding to humic acid. Inhibition was immediate, reversible, and competitive. Ladd and Butler [14] also demonstrated that
soil humic acids and synthetic humic acids prepared from p-benzoquinone and catechol inhibited carboxypeptidase, chymotrypsin, and
trypsin, and stimulated papain, ficin, and thermolysin, but had no
effect on phaseolain and tyrosinase. Subtilopeptidase was stimulated by low concentrations but inhibited at higher concentrations
of humic acid (cf. Saalbach [103] with aldolase). Inhibition or
stimulation was consistent for a given enzyme regardless of the
substrate used, suggesting that the effect of the humic acid was
primarily on the enzyme, not on the substrate.

Monovalent and divalent cations, at concentrations of 10^{-1}
and 10^{-2} M, respectively, almost completely removed the effects of
humic acids on the activities of the enzymes tested [15]. The concentrations of inorganic salts required to abolish the effects of
humic acids were several orders of magnitude greater than those of
the humic acids, based on their carboxyl contents. The authors
suggested that humic acids reversibly bind enzymes as cations by
a cation exchange mechanism and that inorganic cations, in sufficiently high concentrations, displace the enzymes from the complexes.
Butler and Ladd [107] had previously implicated the carboxyl group
in the binding of enzyme to humic acid. They found that diazo-
methane-methylated humic acids in which both the carboxyl and phenolic groups were blocked no longer influenced enzyme activity and

showed that the influence of partially hydrolyzed methylated humic acids, in which some carboxyl groups were free, depended upon the extent of hydrolysis. A methylated humic acid, hydrolyzed to free all carboxyl groups but to leave phenolic groups blocked, had the same effects on enzyme activity as the original unmethylated sample. Thus, carboxyl but not phenolic groups were involved. Ladd and Butler [108] demonstrated the involvement of enzymatic amino groups by showing that trypsin and carboxypeptidase, specifically acetylated at their amino groups, were unaffected by concentrations of soil humic acids that markedly inhibited the unacetylated enzymes. This finding also eliminated the possibility that the inhibition of carboxypeptidase by humic acid was caused by the removal of the essential Zn atom from the enzyme.

Somewhat in contrast to Schnitzer's [109] suggestion that fulvic acids may influence plant growth through metal binding, there seems to be no doubt that the action of humic acids on proteolytic enzyme activity is not one of metal binding. Chymotrypsin has no metal requirement but is inhibited. Thermolysin is stabilized by Ca^{2+}, yet humic acid stimulates rather than inhibits thermolysin activity. Pronase is inhibited by humic acids and stabilized by Ca^{2+}, but if the inhibition is caused by the removal of Ca^{2+}, it is anticipated that the extent of the inhibition will increase with time rather than be immediate as found by Ladd and Butler [14]. Nor was the stimulation of ficin or papain the result of the removal of inhibitory heavy metal ions, since assays were run in the presence of cysteine and EDTA to maintain the essential sulfhydryl groups of the enzymes. Butler and Ladd [110] also compared the effects of humic and fulvic acids upon four proteolytic enzymes. The humic acids behaved similarly and as a group, had a greater effect on enzyme activity than did fulvic acids, owing in part to differences in molecular weight. However, humic acid fractions of a given molecular weight range generally had a greater effect than fulvic acids of the same range. The authors consider that the results may indicate that the more aromatic and condensed humic acid molecule is more rigid and can distort the bound enzyme to a greater extent than can fulvic acid.

Mato and Mendez [111] and Mato et al. [112] also showed that humic acid inhibited enzymes. Commercial and soil humic acids at concentrations of 17 and 40 μg/ml, respectively, produced 50% inhibition of indoleacetic acid oxidase. Later, they found that three soil fulvic acids inhibited indoleacetic acid oxidase to an extent directly related to their phenolic group content but apparently unrelated to their carboxyl content.

The interaction of natural anionic polymers with protein (enzymatic and nonenzymatic) does not present a consistent picture. It appears from the pH behavior, reversibility studies, and experiments with various selective blocking reagents that at least three types of bonding are involved: ionic, hydrogen bonding, and covalent bonding. These bonds play a greater or lesser role depending upon the polymers involved and the conditions used. In short-term experiments, many of the bonds may be ionic. With high molecular weight reactants and low pH's, hydrogen bonding becomes more important (particularly with tannins), and in longer-term experiments covalent bonds probably start to contribute. Evidence for ionic bonds comes from the ready reversibility of the reaction after, for example, the addition of competing cations. The importance of hydrogen bonding has been indicated by pH effects and from the use of hydrogen bond breaking compounds such as urea and polyvinylpyrrolidone.

V. PREPARATION AND PROPERTIES OF SYNTHETIC ORGANIC POLYMER-ENZYME DERIVATIVES

Within the last 10 to 15 years increasing interest has been shown in the properties of enzymes insolubilized by attachment to organic polymeric carriers or by entrapment within the lattices of cross-linked organic matrices, as evidenced by several reviews pertinent to this subject [113-124].

A. Preparation

Water-insoluble, organic polymer-enzyme derivatives have been prepared by four principal methods: (a) adsorption of enzymes on-to synthetic ion-exchange resins [125-130], (b) physical immobili-zation of the enzymes within gels of pore sizes sufficiently small to prevent escape of the enmeshed enzymes [131, 142], (c) formation of enzymatic polymers in which enzyme molecules are covalently cross-linked by suitable bifunctional reagents [143-146], (d) covalent bonding of enzymes to some suitable water-insoluble organic matrix [116, 142, 143, 147-221]. From the current evidence available on the mode of formation of humic compounds, it can be visualized that humic-enzyme derivatives may arise by analogous mechanisms, either by covalent bonding to quinones during humic synthesis or by ionic and hydrogen bonding to the preformed humic polymers.

Many properties of synthetic, organic polymer-enzyme systems exhibit similar features despite the different procedures adopted in the preparation of the derivatives. The possibility that desorp-tion of ionically bound enzymes or leakage of entrapped enzymes from within a gel lattice may lead to heterogeneous systems, the kinetics of which are difficult to interpret, has tended to limit the number of studies employing methods (a) and (b) above. Most attention has been directed toward those preparations in which the enzyme has been covalently bonded to some suitable organic carrier.

Many enzymes, especially hydrolases acting on peptide bonds, have been covalently bonded to organic matrices (Table 2). Func-tional groups of the enzymes available for bonding to organic poly-mers include terminal and basic amino groups, carboxyl groups, sulfhydryl groups, the phenolic groups of tyrosine, and the imidazole group of histidine [113, 118]. In many cases, little is known of which groups on the enzyme surface have reacted with the organic polymer moiety [117], although it is presumed that tyrosine and histidine residues are primarily involved in reactions involving diazotization and that terminal and lysine amino groups are the primary sites of reactions involving nucleophilic substitutions.

TABLE 2

Enzymes Covalently Bonded to Organic Polymer Matrices

Group	Enzyme	Reference
Oxidoreductases	Alcohol dehydrogenase	[149, 159]
	Glucose-6-phosphate dehydrogenase	[209]
	Lactic dehydrogenase	[154, 184]
	Glucose oxidase	[154, 136, 197]
	Catalase	[145, 146, 163]
	Peroxidase	[199]
Transferases	Hexokinase	[192, 209]
	Creatine kinase	[179, 184]
	Pyruvate kinase	[184]
Hydrolases	Lipase	[148]
(acting on	Acetylcholinesterase	[134, 181]
ester bonds)	Cholinesterase	[133, 196]
	Alkaline phosphatase	[206]
	Acid phosphatase	[129]
	Deoxyribonuclease	[196]
	Ribonuclease	[147, 163]
(acting on	α-Amylase	[180, 201, 211, 212]
glycosyl bonds)		
	β-Amylase	[168, 193, 211, 212]
	Glucoamylase	[130]
	β-Fructofuranosidase	[219]
	β-Galactosidase	[184]
	Diastase	[147, 149, 152, 159, 165, 202]
(acting on	Leucine aminopeptidase	[213]
peptide bonds)	Carboxypeptidase	[147]
	Pepsin	[147, 149, 152, 159, 203]
	Rennin	[220]
	Trypsin	[125, 142, 144, 153-155, 163, 166, 168, 173, 177, 185, 198, 200, 204, 208, 214, 215, 221]

TABLE 2 (continued)

Group	Enzyme	Reference
Hydrolases (acting on peptide bonds)	α-Chymotrypsin	[125, 150, 163, 168, 171, 172, 174, 177, 184, 185, 205, 210, 221]
	Papain	[143, 161, 165, 176, 188, 189, 194, 202, 204, 221]
	Ficin	[117, 164, 167, 179]
	Subtilopeptidase-A	[119, 204]
	Bromelain	[119, 187]
	Pronase	[217, 218]
(acting on C-N bonds other than peptide)	Urease	[158, 216]
	Aminoacylase	[126-128]
(acting on acid anhydride bonds)	Apyrase	[182, 183, 195, 196]
Lyases	Aldolase	[137]
	Enolase	[138]

Enzymes have been coupled to (a) polysaccharides, such as cellulose and dextrans [150, 162-164, 167, 168, 171, 174, 175, 179, 180, 183, 184, 186, 187, 192, 193, 195, 196, 199, 201, 205-211, 213, 214, 220, 221], (b) collodion [161, 188, 189, 194], (c) copolymers of ethylene and maleic anhydride [154, 155, 166, 177, 182, 196, 198, 200, 206-215], (d) copolymers of methacrylic acid and methacrylic acid-3-fluoro-4,6 dinitroanilide [149, 151, 152-156, 206], (e) copolymers of polystyrene and methacrylic acid [165, 202], (f) copolymers of amino acids [143, 153, 157, 158, 172, 177, 185, 203, 217, 218], (g) copolymers of acrylamide and acrylamide derivatives [142, 211, 212], and (h) copolymers of starch and methylenedianiline [204].

Methods used for polymer preparation and conversion to forms
that react with enzymes have been summarized elsewhere [113, 114,
117-119, 121, 123], the main considerations being that the coupling
reaction should neither cause denaturation of the enzyme nor involve a high proportion of functional groups essential for enzyme
activity. The nature of the reactive group on the organic matrix
by which coupling is effected has an important influence on the
properties of the final enzyme derivative, in that it is this group
that determines whether the matrix, after attachment of the enzyme,
.is charged or not. Hydrophilic carriers apparently are more effective in binding enzymes and stabilizing bound enzymes than those
with a predominance of hydrophobic features [113, 121].

Protein-to-carrier ratios of different preparations range
widely. Goldstein [119] has reported that derivatives of ethylene-
maleic anhydride copolymers may contain up to 80% by weight of
bound protein [154]. Cellulose-enzyme derivatives contain approximately 5-10% protein and derivatives of starch-methylene dianiline
copolymers contain about 10% protein [204].

B. Properties

Enzymes attached within the pores or on the surface of insoluble organic matrices function in a microenvironment quite different
from that of enzymes in free solution. Direct interaction between
the organic matrix and the enzyme or between the organic matrix and
the substrate and products affects the properties of the overall
system. Thus, although immobilized enzymes still obey Michaelis-
Menten kinetics [134, 139, 155, 164, 179, 187, 196, 205, 210, 216,
219], attachment of enzymes to solid supports affects their activities toward substrates of different molecular weight and charge,
their specificity of action and their stabilities toward such physical factors as pH and temperature.

1. Kinetics of Organic Polymer-Enzyme Derivatives

Almost invariably, the specific activity of an enzyme is lowered as a result of the enzyme becoming attached to or entrapped

within an insoluble organic matrix. Important factors influencing
the kinetics of the insolubilized derivatives are (a) rates of
diffusion of the substrate to and of the products from the active
site of the enzyme; (b) steric restrictions imposed by the carrier,
either as a result of restricted movement of substrate to the otherwise available active site of the enzyme or because of the orienta-
tion of the enzyme in relation to the carrier surface (the manner
of attachment of the enzyme involving functional groups being so
located that the active site becomes partially or completely inac-
cessible to an otherwise available substrate); and (c) charge-charge
interactions between ionic groups of the substrate and of the sup-
porting organic matrix.

In addition, conformational changes may be induced in the tertiary structure of the enzyme owing to bonding forces between groups
on the surfaces of the enzyme and the organic polymer carrier. It
is possible, too, that the mode of attachment may involve groups,
a proportion of which are part of the active site of the enzyme but
that are present also as unessential groups at other locations on
the enzyme's surface. In these cases, provided an excess of activated organic polymer is not employed, a proportion only of the enzyme is likely to be inactivated [123].

a. Diffusion Effects. The kinetics of enzymes attached to
electrically neutral carriers are similar to those of free enzymes,
when assayed against low molecular weight substrates, i.e., in the
absence of charge interactions and steric restrictions, insolubilized
and soluble enzymes exhibit similar pH-activity profiles and
Michaelis constants (K_m) [113, 143, 153, 179]. Nevertheless, small
but significant increases in the K_m values of enzymes bound to organic carriers have been reported and have been attributed to diffusion effects [167, 179, 205, 219]. As a result of enzyme activity
and a slower diffusion of substrate due to the presence of the
carrier, the substrate concentration in the immediate vicinity of
the attached enzyme is lower than that in the bulk solution. Kay
and Lilly [205] have found that K_m values for the hydrolysis of un-

charged acetyltyrosine ethyl ester (ATEE) by a chymotrypsin-DEAE
cellulose derivative were decreased to values similar to that obtained with the free enzyme, after grinding the insoluble enzyme
preparation to a fine powder.

Increased K_m values resulting from diffusion effects [115] are
related to the diffusion layer thickness and the diffusion constant
of the substrate, according to the equation

$$K'_m = K_m + \frac{xV_{max}}{D}$$

where K'_m is the apparent Michaelis constant, x is the diffusion
layer thickness, and D is the diffusion coefficient of the substrate.

Rates of diffusion of products away from the immediate environment of the active site of the attached enzyme also may influence
the behavior of the system. Thus, Goldman et al. [161, 188, 189]
have found that the pH-activity profile of the hydrolysis of benzoyl-
arginine ethyl ester (BAEE) by papain bound to the electrically
neutral collodion matrix differed from that obtained with free papain. The activity of the insolubilized enzyme was low at neutral
pH where the native enzyme was optimally active, and high at alkaline pH. The effect was diminished by grinding the papain-collodion
membrane and abolished by increasing the buffer concentration or by
forcing the substrate through the membrane under pressure. The results were explained in terms of a lowered pH (by 2-4 units) within
the papain membrane because it slowed the diffusion of hydrogen
ions, formed during substrate hydrolysis, away from the insolubilized
enzyme. Similar effects have been reported by Axen and Ernback [221].

In a theoretical treatment of the diffusion phenomenon, it was
shown [190] that when substrate diffusion became rate-limiting, a
membrance-bound enzyme did not attain its maximum velocity (V_{max})
unless acting on a poor substrate, i.e., when the breakdown of substrate was negligible compared with its rate of diffusion into the
membrane.

b. Steric Effects. Steric effects, induced by the carrier, become important when the molecular size of the substrate is similar
to the pore size of the matrix within which the enzyme is bound.
The effects have been demonstrated by comparing the activities of
(a) free and bound enzymes toward both high and low molecular weight
substrates and of (b) enzymes bound to matrices of different pore
sizes. Thus, the lowering of enzyme activities after attachment of
proteolytic enzymes to insoluble organic carriers is much less when
assayed with low molecular weight substrates than when proteins are
used [117, 143, 153, 168, 217, 218]. Steric effects were also
apparent when water-insoluble α-amylase [201] and derivatives of
papain [145] and trypsin [144] cross-linked with glutaraldehyde
were used. Porath et al. [174] found that increasing proportions
of agarose in agarose-chymotrypsin derivatives caused a marked decline in specific activities toward casein but had no effect on
their ATEE-hydrolyzing abilities.

Haynes and Walsh [144] found that the inhibition of insolubilized trypsin was inversely related to the size of the inhibitor used
and that only a limited number of sites was available to each inhibitor. Levin et al. [154] also found that the large molecular weight
inhibitor from soybeans had little effect on the activities of the
insoluble polytyrosyltrypsin and maleic acid ethylene-trypsin derivatives when assayed with BAEE but completely inhibited their
activities toward protein. Native trypsin was completely inhibited
in its action on all substrates. Thus, the high molecular weight
inhibitor appears to reach those active sites of the insolubilized
enzymes that are also accessible to casein but not some additional
sites accessible to BAEE.

c. Charge Effects. The organic polymer moieties of many enzyme
derivatives carry a net charge and interactions between the matrix
and charged substrates have important effects on the kinetics of
the reaction, in particular on the K_m values and pH-activity profiles [120]. It is anticipated that in this regard the behavior
of humus-enzyme systems would be similar to that determined with

other polyanionic-enzyme systems, e.g. where carboxymethylcellulose
or ethylene-maleic acid copolymers are used as carriers.

At equilibrium, the concentration of hydrogen ions within the
microenvironment of an insoluble, charged organic matrix will differ
from that in the bulk solution, being of relatively high concentrations at or near the surfaces of a polyanionic matrix and of relatively lower concentration within a polycationic matrix. Hence,
an enzyme attached to or entrapped within a charged matrix will
function at a pH different from that measured in free solution.
Consequently, at low ionic strengths, pH-activity profiles of polyanionic derivatives of enzymes will be displaced toward more alkaline values relative to those of the native enzymes [143, 154, 155,
160, 164, 171, 172, 177, 183,198]. Conversely, pH-activity profiles
of polycationic enzyme derivatives are displaced toward more acidic
values compared with those of the free enzymes [116, 172]. This
is illustrated in Fig. 3, using negatively and positively charged
derivatives of chymotrypsin. With these systems the anomalies
were removed at high ionic strengths.

Recently, Goldstein et al. [204] have shown that the pH-activity
profiles of the electrically neutral, starch-methylenedianiline
derivatives of three proteolytic enzymes were also displaced toward
the alkaline region compared with those of the respective native
enzymes and that the effects were independent of the ionic strengths
of the medium. The authors [204] have suggested that the pK_a
values for the active sites of the bound enzymes have been altered
and that the negligible effects of ionic strength on the pH-activity profiles reflect more localized charge interactions than previously observed with polyelectrolyte-enzyme derivatives discussed
above.

Substrates possessing a charge opposite to that of the sup-
porting organic carrier will concentrate within the microenvironment
of the matrix, whereas substrates with a like charge will be in
lower concentrations within the matrix than in the bulk solution.
This phenomenon is reflected in differences in the apparent K_m values

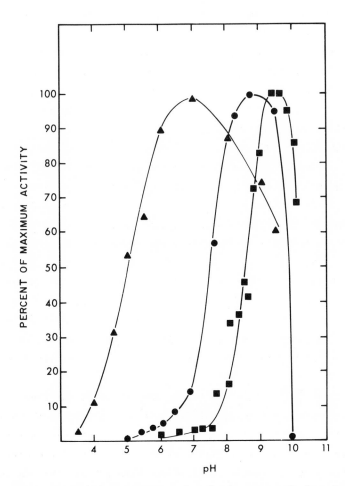

Fig. 3.   pH-Activity curves at low ionic strength for chymotrypsin (●), a polyanionic ethylene-maleic acid copolymer derivative of chymotrypsin (IMECH■), and a polycationic poly-L-ornithyl
derivative of chymotrypsin (POCH▲), using acetyl-L-tyrosine ethyl
ester as substrate.   (From Goldstein and Katchalski [116] by courtesy
of Springer-Verlag, Berlin.)

of free and polyelectrolyte-bound enzymes, the K_m constants of bound
enzymes increasing when the charges of the matrix and substrate are
like [195] and decreasing when they are opposite [155, 160, 179].
At high ionic strengths, K_m values of free and bound enzyme systems
are approximately equal. Similarly, when either the substrate or
matrix is uncharged, K_m values of the bound enzyme systems approximate those of the respective free enzymes [161, 177, 194], provided
diffusion effects are not great. Data pertinent to each of these
situations are given in Table 3.

The effects of charged matrices on the pH-activity profiles
and K_m values of insolubilized enzyme systems have been established
using generally low molecular weight substrates. Possible electrostatic interactions between charged organic supports and charged
high molecular weight substrates, e.g., proteins may affect both the
activities and also the specificities of the bound enzymes. Levin
et al. (1954) prepared a series of polyanionic trypsin derivatives
in which the proportion of enzyme bound to the organic polymer
moiety varied from 1:20 to 3:1. The specific rates of hydrolysis
of negatively charged proteins increased with decreasing proportions
of carrier in the preparations. Also, marked decreases in caseino-
lytic activity accompanied increases in the charge density on the
carrier.

Changes in the specificity of enzymes resulting from attachment to organic polymers, have been established for both soluble
[198] and insoluble [154, 160, 169, 178, 203] trypsin derivatives.
Restrictions on the specificity of action of the enzyme derivatives
are considered to be caused by charge interactions between the organic polymer carrier and different regions of the high molecular
weight substrates.

2. Stabilities of Organic Polymer-Enzyme Derivatives

Factors determining the stability of enzymes bound to organic
carriers have not as yet been clearly defined [114, 117]. Hydrophilic surfaces tend to confer greater stability. However, even
when the organic matrix is hydrophilic overall, localized hydrophobic

TABLE 3

Michaelis Constants (K_m) of Free Enzymes and Organic Polymer-Enzyme Derivatives

Enzyme	Organic polymer carrier	Charge on carrier	Substrate	Charge on substrate	K_m (M)
ATP-creatine phosphotransferase	None		ATP	−	6.5×10^{-4}
	Aminobenzyl-cellulose	0	ATP	−	8.0×10^{-4}
	Carboxymethyl-cellulose	−	ATP	−	7.0×10^{-3}
Ficin	None		BAEE	+	2.0×10^{-2}
	Carboxymethyl-cellulose	−	BAEE	+	2.0×10^{-3}
Chymotrypsin	None		ATEE	0	2.7×10^{-4}
	Carboxymethyl-cellulose	−	ATEE	0	5.6×10^{-4}
Trypsin	None		BAA	+	6.8×10^{-3}
	Ethylene-maleic anhydride copolymer	−	BAA	+	2.0×10^{-4}
Papain	None		BAEE	+	1.9×10^{-2}
	p-Aminophenylalanine-p-leucine copolymer	0	BAEE	+	No change from free enzyme

[a]From Hornby et al. [179] by courtesy of The Biochemical Society, London.

interactions between the enzyme and carrier surfaces may lead to
instability and denaturation of the enzyme [123].

   a. Effects of Lyophilization and Storage. Trypsin [154] and
chymotrypsin [159], bonded to a copolymer of ethylene and maleic
anhydride, retained 70-90% of their activities after lyophilization
as did Sephadex-bound derivatives of trypsin, chymotrypsin, and
papain [221]. By contrast, lyophilization inactivated trypsin and
papain derivatives of a p-aminophenylalanine-leucine copolymer
[113, 143] and trypsin and subtilopeptidase-A derivatives of a
starch-methylene dianiline resin [204].

   Insolubilized enzymes, either as buffered suspensions or as
lyophilized powders, often retain activity for considerable periods

TABLE 4

Effect of Lyophilization and Storage
on the Stabilities of Organic Polymer-Amylase Derivatives

Enzyme	Organic polymer carrier	Residual activity (%) after:		Reference
		Lyophili- zation	Storage (4°C, 3 months)	
α-Amylase	Polyacrylamide (azide coupled)	84	85	[212]
	Polyacrylamide (diazo coupled)	28	73	
	Polyacrylamide (isothiocyanato coupled)	44	67	
β-Amylase	Polyacrylamide (diazo coupled)	–	73	
		–	51	
β-Amylase	Cellulose (diazo coupled)	–	100	[193]
	Cellulose (isothiocyanato coupled)	–	89	

of time, the extent of which varies with the enzyme, the nature of
the organic carrier, and the manner in which the two moieties are
coupled. Table 4 compares the stabilities of α- and β-amylases
coupled to cellulose and polyacrylamide carriers.

The stability on storage has also been determined for various
insoluble organic polymer derivatives of catalase [146], urease
[158, 216], ficin [164], pepsin [203], Pronase [217, 218], chymotrypsin [163, 174, 175], α-amylase [180], papain [189], trypsin
[153, 173], phosphomonoesterase [129], glucose oxidase [134], lac-
tic dehydrogenase [134], β-fructofuranosidase [219], glucose-6-
phosphate dehydrogenase [209], and hexokinase [209]. Westman [198]
has also demonstrated that a soluble, ethylene-maleic anhydride
copolymer derivative of trypsin was much more stable than native
trypsin, retaining 65% of the initial activity after 17 days in
solution.

b. Effect of Temperature. The stabilities of free and bound
enzymes after preincubation at various temperatures have been widely
investigated [129, 134, 142, 143, 154, 159, 164, 180, 181, 187,
189, 193, 204, 212, 213, 216]. Generally, insolubilization of the
enzymes enhances their thermal stabilities, but exceptions have
been noted. Some selected results are given in Table 5.

α-Amylase, covalently linked to microcrystalline cellulose,
was comparatively stable when subjected to heat denaturation at
45°C. The half-life of the activity of the bound enzyme was ten
times greater than that of the native α-amylase [180]. Further
studies with β- and γ-amylases, attached by different techniques
to cellulose [193], or with α- and β-amylases bound to cross-linked
polymers of polyacrylamide [212] again demonstrated the greater
heat stability of the insolubilized enzyme derivatives. There were
differences also in the heat stabilities of amylases attached to
different matrices or attached by different means to the same type
of matrix [193, 212]. These observations may be related to

TABLE 5

Effect of Temperature on the Stabilities of Organic Polymer-Enzyme Derivatives

Enzyme	Organic polymer carrier	Preincubation conditions	Residual activity (%)	Reference
α-Amylase	Cellulose	45°C, pH 6.9, 20 min	90	[180]
	None		17	
Urease	Nylon	75°C, pH 7.0, 75 min	65	[216]
	None		17	
Ficin	Carboxymethyl-cellulose	66°C, pH 6.5, 37 min	70	[164]
	None		46	
Trypsin	Ethylene-maleic anhydride copolymer	100°C, pH 4.3, 10 min	32	[154]
	Ethylene-maleic anhydride copolymer	pH 8.0	33	
	None	pH 4.3	80	
	None	pH 8.0	0	
Phosphomonoesterase	Carboxymethyl-cellulose	43°C, pH 4.3, 10 min	59	[129]
	None		31	
Acetylcholinesterase	Silastic resin	60°C, 5 min	128	[181]
	None		8	

differences either in the number or in the nature of the amino acid side chains of the enzyme, which are linked during derivative formation, thus preserving to different extents the tertiary structure of the enzyme against disruptive thermal vibrations [123].

Ficin linked to carboxymethylcellulose [164] showed greater heat stability than the free enzyme, whereas bromelain, similarly linked [187], was as sensitive to heat denaturation as the native enzyme. Another sulfhydryl enzyme, papain, either bound within collodion membranes [189], covalently bonded to polypeptide or protein carriers [143], or insolubilized by cross-linking enzyme molecules themselves [143], was less stable than free papain at temperatures of 65°-80°C. Trypsin bonded to an anionic organic polymer was less stable to heat than native trypsin at pH 4.3 but more stable at pH 8.0 [154]. Phosphomonoesterase adsorbed to carboxymethylcellulose [129], or acetylcholinesterase entrapped within a Silastic resin [121], showed enhanced thermal stabilities relative to those of the free enzymes.

c. Effect of pH. Goldstein [114] has reported that the attachment of enzymes to polyanionic organic polymers enhances their stabilities in the alkaline pH range, whereas polycationic derivatives of enzymes show improved stabilities at acidic pH's. Bar-Eli and Katchalski [153] have shown that an insoluble polytyrosyltrypsin derivative was highly stable after incubation at pH 7.0-9.0 for 25 hr at 25°C, retaining 80% of its initial activity, whereas similarly treated, native trypsin was inactivated. Similar trends were reported using trypsin bound to ethylene-maleic anhydride copolymers [154], polyacrylamides [123], and a starch-methylenedianiline resin [204]. In these systems, increased stabilities at neutral to alkaline pH's were caused, at least in part, by decreased autodigestion of the bound trypsin, because anchoring the enzyme to an insoluble carrier removed the opportunity for enzymes to encounter each other. Autodigestion of organic polymer-trypsin derivatives may be further decreased when lysine residues of the enzyme are involved in the

coupling to the organic carrier. A similar effect of alkaline pH's
on diastase stability has been reported [202].

At acidic pH's, free trypsin was more stable than its insoluble derivatives [153, 154, 204], especially at elevated temperatures
[154]. Papain bonded to electrically neutral collodion was more
stable than free papain [189], whereas the stability of papain
linked to a starch-methylene dianiline resin was unchanged [204].
Similarly bound subtilopeptidase-A showed enhanced stability [204].

Goldstein et al. [204] have concluded that the stability of
insolubilized enzymes is determined primarily by the nature of the
amino acid residues bonded to the organic carrier and by their role
in maintaining the tertiary structure of the enzyme, and that immobilization of the enzyme per se is of secondary importance.

d. Effect of Denaturating Compounds and Other Agents. Tosa et
al. [128] showed that after pretreatment with 6 M urea, a DEAE-
Sephadex-aminoacylase complex actually increased in activity by 30%,
whereas 6 M urea caused a greater than 80% loss of activity of the
native enzyme. They considered that the gain in activity resulted
from the urea converting the insolubilized enzyme from a rigid to
a more flexible structure.

Trypsin bound to Sephadex [208] retained much of its activity
after storage in 8 M urea for 7 days, whereas native trypsin was
completely inactivated. Similarly, an ethylene-maleic anhydride
derivative of trypsin was less sensitive to urea than to free
trypsin [154], although an opposite effect has been reported [163]
using a cellulose-trypsin derivative. Silman et al. [143] have reported that soluble and insolubilized papain were equally sensitive
to denaturation by 4 M guanidine hydrochloride.

Attachment of the sulfhydryl enzymes bromelain and ficin to
carboxymethylcellulose [164, 187] protected the enzymes from inactivation by oxidation. Thus Hornby et al. [164] have reported that
the ficin derivative retained full activity after 21 days with or
without cysteine whereas the activity of ficin in free solution
declined by 34% and 90%, respectively.

Phosphomonoesterase adsorbed to carboxymethyl cellulose was less sensitive to surface inactivation than the native enzyme [129], and aminoacylase, adsorbed to DEAE Sephadex, was more resistant toward proteases than the unbound enzyme [128].

VI. RELEVANCE OF HUMUS-ENZYME SYSTEMS TO THE SOIL ENVIRONMENT

Felbeck [222] has reported that amino acids released by acid hydrolysis of unfractionated humic acids constitute 10-11% of the weight of the humic preparations, although values may range widely depending upon the source and extractant used. The hydrolyzable amino acid content of humic acid fractions increases with the molecular weight of the fraction [223, 224] and may reasonably account for about 15% of the weight of many humic fractions of molecular weights near 150,000 (as determined by Sephadex-gel filtration procedures). If, in these cases, the amino acids are released by hydrolysis of peptide bonds in a protein moiety, the molecular weight of the latter must average about 22,500. This is similar to that of several proteolytic enzymes. Therefore, it is feasible that humic acid fractions of high molecular weight could contain a protein (enzyme) component, as an alternative to lower molecular weight peptides. Enzymes of high molecular weight may not be so easily accommodated as humic acid-enzyme complexes on the basis of average amino acid contents of humic preparations. However, humic preparations, even when fractionated according to molecular size, may conceivably contain some components with an amino acid content considerably higher than that of the average for the fraction.

Studies of the functional groups of humic compounds and of the mechanisms of humic synthesis suggest that proteins could be bound in humus-enzyme derivatives by ionic, hydrogen, or covalent bonding. Linkage of quinones by nucleophilic substitution to sulfhydryl and to terminal and lysyl-ε-amino groups of the enzyme may lead to active derivatives, provided that these groups do not form part of the active site of the protein or are not essential for the maintenance

of the tertiary structure of the enzyme. Nucleophilic substitution
is commonly used in the preparation of active, synthetic, organic
polymer-enzyme derivatives. It would be of considerable interest
to covalently bond selected enzymes to quinones, and, after formation of black, insoluble polymer-enzyme complexes, to determine the
effects of derivative formation on enzyme properties, such as the
relative activities toward high and low molecular weight substrates,
K_m values, pH-activity profiles, and stabilities toward biological
and physical agents. Rowell (personal communication) reacted trypsin and Pronase with p-benzoquinone, under conditions that led to
the formation of brown, soluble, and insoluble enzyme complexes.
Compared with the respective native enzymes, the enzyme complexes
exhibited increased stability at 25°C and at elevated temperatures,
decreased K_m values, and pH-activity profiles that were displaced
toward more alkaline pH's.

Detailed studies of the effects of extracted soil humic acids
on enzyme activity have been carried out by Ladd and Butler [14, 15,
105-110], using a range of proteolytic enzymes. In these systems,
the enzymes were reversibly bound to the humic acids by ionic linkages, and (as with similarly bound synthetic, organic polymer-
enzyme derivatives) it is difficult to determine the proportions
of residual activity due to free enzyme and to the humus-enzyme
complex. Steric effects, which feature prominently in studies with
covalently linked organic polymer-protease derivatives, appear to
play a less important role in the reversibly bound humic acid-pro-
tease systems [106]. At present, the extent to which enzymes may
be bound covalently, ionically, or by hydrogen bonding to humic
compounds in the soil is unknown. The proportion of soil enzyme
activity extractable by buffers is generally low, suggesting that
the amounts of enzymes bound exclusively by ionic linkages to
humic compounds are also low.

In regard to the formation and persistence of active humus-
enzyme derivatives in soils, little inference can be drawn from
data demonstrating correlations between soil enzyme activity and

organic matter content. More direct evidence, based on the properties of extracted, isolated humus-enzyme preparations, is convincing,
however, only if artifact formation during extraction is eliminated.

Chalvignac and Mayaudon [16], by extracting a soil with 0.2 M
Na_2CO_3 solutions and precipitating with ammonium sulfate at 70%
saturation, obtained preparations containing humic compounds that
enzymatically decarboxylated tryptophane. The activity of the final
preparation, relative to that of the initial extract or soil, was
not given, but the inference is that the preparation contained an
active humic acid-tryptophane decarboxylase complex that constitutes a site of enzyme activity in soil. This study is most interesting. However, it is necessary to establish also that the humic
acids and enzyme were not coincidentally extracted from the soil
and coprecipitated by ammonium sulfate.

In perhaps an analogous investigation, Ladd [17], using a
Tris-borate buffer at pH 8.1, extracted humic compounds and enzymes
active toward peptide derivatives and proteins. It was later shown
that 70% saturated ammonium sulfate precipitated 53% of the extracted
enzyme(s) together with 49% of the brown humic material. Nevertheless, separation of the enzymes from a high proportion (77%) of the
humic compounds could be effected simply by precipitation of the
humic material as insoluble calcium salts. The regression of activity on humic content of the extracts was not statistically significant, suggesting that in this case, at least, a major proportion of the humic material was coincidentally removed from the soil
with the enzymes without, however, eliminating the possibility that
the enzymes were closely associated with some humic compounds,
either in the extract or when formerly in the soil [17]. Also,
Getzin and Rosefield [225] have extracted a soil with 0.2 M NaOH
to obtain an esterase preparation active against malathion. The
enzyme was partially purified by precipitating humates with $MnCl_2$.

Chalvignac and Mayaudon [16] showed that their extracts retained
some activity after either lyophilization or preincubation at elevated temperatures, but without a comparison with the native enzyme

under the same conditions, increased stability due to the presence
of humic compounds cannot be postulated. Similarly, Ladd [17]
showed that the activity of soil extracts toward a peptide derivative was stable to lyophilization and to the action of the proteolytic enzymes thermolysin and subtilisin. Activities declined when
the extracts were held at 50°C for 48 hr either from thermal denaturation or from proteolysis, and the further addition of a neutralized humic acid solution did not increase the enzyme stability.

Ladd and Butler (unpublished data) have found that a neutralized
humic acid (33 µg/ml) inhibited trypsin activity initially. After
storage at 30°C for 48 hr, the activity of the humic acid-trypsin
system exceeded that of trypsin alone, which declined rapidly because of autolysis. In a somewhat analogous fashion, ethylene-
maleic acid copolymer ionically bonded to trypsin, enhanced enzyme
stability slightly [198], although to a much lesser extent than
that obtained with covalently linked soluble and insoluble trypsin
derivatives of the same polymer.

Burns et al. [18, 227] have prepared urease-active fractions
from a soil, dispersed by a preliminary sonication treatment. The
preparations were clay-free as found by X-ray analysis, although
ash contents were not determined. Humic material could be extracted
from the insoluble urease preparations without a proportionate removal of enzyme. The activity of the brown enzyme preparations was
stable in the presence of Pronase, which attacked native urease.
The authors [18, 227] have concluded that the soil urease is present
in organic colloidal particles, in a manner that permits free pas-
sage of substrate and products but that excludes larger molecules,
such as Pronase.

Enzymes that can function extracellularly in the soil probably
are more likely to be present as complexes with soil humic compounds
than are those obliged to act intracellularly. Enzymes assayed
with high molecular weight substrates presumably are functioning
extracellularly. In other cases, extracellular action of enzymes
toward some low molecular weight substrates, e.g., phosphate esters

[226] and peptides (Ladd, Butler, and Brisbane, unpublished results),
may be deduced from the indirect evidence that relatively minor
variations in soil enzyme activity may be observed under laboratory
or field conditions that cause large fluctuations in microbial populations (although contributions from viable microorganisms not detected by the plating procedure adopted, from dead microorganisms,
or from living and dead plant cells cannot be eliminated).

   The duration of extracellular enzyme activities in soils depends upon the abilities of the enzymes to withstand denaturation
and destruction by microbial action. Evidence with organic polymer-
enzymes shows that derivative formation leads not only to enhanced
enzyme stability to physical and biological factors but also to restrictions on the range of substrates that the bound enzyme can
attack. For example, proteolytic enzymes when bound to an insoluble
organic matrix are not only protected from autolysis (and in the
case of trypsin, from inhibition by high molecular weight inhibitors)
but are also unable, because of steric effects, to hydrolyze proteins
as effectively as peptides.

   Thus, if humus-enzyme derivatives were formed in soils and behaved analogously to synthetic organic polymer-enzymes (and the
latter seems reasonable, considering the similar trends observed
with a great variety of matrix-bonded enzyme derivatives), it could
be anticipated that soil enzymes hydrolyzing, for example, proteins,
would have an apparent relatively short half-life. Such enzymes
would be either free or so bound to soil surfaces that they would
be unprotected from autolysis or attack by other proteases or, al-
ternatively, their activities toward high molecular weight substrates might be lost through stabilization of the enzyme protein
in a humic-enzyme complex. The stabilized enzymes may still hydrolyze low molecular weight peptides, however. If the stabilized
enzyme fraction contributes a major portion of the soil enzyme activity toward peptides, then the overall activity will appear to
be unresponsive to conditions that lead to relatively large changes
in activity toward high molecular weight proteins.

Ladd and Paul [229] have shown that, following the addition of
a glucose-sodium nitrate solution to an air-dried soil, activity
toward casein increased 12-fold within 5 days and then declined to
29% of the maximal activity after 28 days, whereas activities
toward a low molecular weight substrate, a phenylalanylleucine
dipeptide derivative, increased approximately twofold and showed
little decline within the same period. Although the patterns of
enzyme activity were compatable with those anticipated if humus
enzyme derivatives were formed, there is no direct evidence for this.
Indeed, intracellular peptidases may have been mainly responsible
for the increased hydrolytic activity toward the dipeptide derivative. In the complex soil environment, many proteolytic enzymes
may be synthesized and it is highly unlikely that all enzymes hydrolyzing the selected proteins and peptides of the assay will be
mutually inclusive. In this context, it would be interesting to
examine the formation, stabilities, and background activities of
proteolytic enzymes in soil using as substrates dimers, oligomers,
and polymers of a given amino acid. It would also be of interest
to determine whether, in general, extracellular soil enzymes hydrolyzing added high molecular weight substrates have shorter half-
lives than those assayed with low molecular weight compounds.

In conclusion, the formation of humus-enzyme derivatives in
soils appears to be feasible. However, direct, unequivocal evidence
for their presence has yet to be presented.

REFERENCES

1.   J. J. Skujins, in *Soil Biochemistry* (A. D. McLaren and G. H.
     Peterson, Eds.), Vol. 1, p. 371, Marcel Dekker, New
     York, 1967.
2.   G. Durand, *Rev. Ecol. Biol. Sol.*, *2*, 141 (1965).
3.   E. Hofmann and G. Hoffmann, *Advan. Enzymol.*, *28*, 365 (1966).
4.   J. P. Voets and M. Dedeken, *Meded. Rijkafac. Landbwetten-
     schappen (Ghent)*, *31*, 177 (1966).
5.   L. E. Ensminger and J. E. Gieseking, *Soil Sci.*, *53*, 205 (1942).
6.   A. D. McLaren, *J. Phys. Chem.*, *58*, 129 (1954).

7. A. D. McLaren, *Soil Sci. Soc. Amer. Proc.*, *18*, 170 (1954).
8. A. D. McLaren and E. F. Estermann, *Arch. Biochem. Biophys.*, *61*, 158 (1956).
9. S. Kiss, *Z. PflanzenErnähr. Düng. Bodenk.*, *81*, 117 (1958).
10. E. F. Estermann, G. H. Peterson, and A. D. McLaren, *Soil Sci. Soc. Amer. Proc.*, *23*, 31 (1959).
11. S. Aomine and Y. Kobayashi, *Soil Sci. Plant Nutr.* (Tokyo), *10*, 28 (1964).
12. Z. Ambroz, *Sb. vys. Sk. zemed. les Fai. Brne A*, *2*, 161 (1966).
13. L. H. Sorensen, *Experientia*, *25*, 20 (1969).
14. J. N. Ladd and J. H. A. Butler, *Austral. J. Soil Res.*, *7*, 253 (1969).
15. J. N. Ladd and J. H. A. Butler, *Soil Biol. Biochem.*, *2*, 33 (1970).
16. M. A. Chalvignac and J. Mayaudon, *Plant Soil*, *34*, 25 (1971).
17. J. N. Ladd, *Soil Biol. Biochem.*, *4*, 227 (1972).
18. R. G. Burns, M. H. El-Sayed and A. D. McLaren, *Soil Biol. Biochem.*, *4*, 107 (1972).
19. J. M. Brumner, in *Soil Nitrogen* (W. V. Bartholomew and F. E. Clark, Eds.), Vol. 10, p. 93, Amer. Soc. Agron., Inc., Madison, 1965.
20. J. Mayaudon, in *Isotopes and Radiation in Soil Organic Matter Studies*, p. 177, International Atomic Energy Agency, Vienna, 1968.
21. F. E. Broadbent, in *Isotopes and Radiation in Soil Organic Matter Studies*, p. 131, International Atomic Energy Agency, Vienna, 1968.
22. H. W. Scharpenseel and R. Krausse, *Z. PflanzErnähr. Düng. Bodenk.*, *96*, 11 (1962).
23. J. N. Ladd and P. G. Brisbane, *Austral. J. Soil Res.*, *5*, 161 (1967).
24. P. Simonart, L. Batistic and J. Mayaudon, *Plant Soil*, *272*, 153 (1967).
25. F. J. Sowden, *Can. J. Soil Sci.*, *50*, 233 (1971).
26. P. G. Brisbane, M. Amato, and J. N. Ladd, *Soil Biol. Biochem.*, *4*, 51 (1972).
27. F. Scheffer and B. Ulrich, in *Humus and Humusdungung*, Ferdinand Enke, Stuttgart, 1960.
28. P. Dubach and N. C. Mehta, *Soils Fert.*, *26*, 293 (1963).
29. F. Martin, P. Dubach, N. C. Mehta, and H. Deuel, *Z. Pflanz-Ernähr. Düng. Bodenk.*, *103*, 27 (1963).
30. G. T. Felbeck, *Advan. Agron.*, *17*, 327 (1965).
31. M. M. Kononova, in *Soil Organic Matter*, 2nd Engl. ed., Pergamon, Oxford, 1966.
32. F. J. Stevenson and J. H. A. Butler, in *Organic Geochemistry* (G. Eglinton and M. T. J. Murphy, Eds.), p. 534, Springer-Verlag, Berlin, 1969.
33. G. T. Felbeck, in *Soil Biochemistry* (A. D. McLaren and J. J. Skujins, Eds.), Vol. 2, p. 36, Dekker, New York, 1971.
34. M. V. Cheshire, P. A. Cranwell, C. P. Falshaw, A. J. Floyd, and R. D. Haworth, *Tetrahedron*, *23*, 1669 (1967).

35. M. Schnitzer and J. G. Desjardins, *Soil Sci. Soc. Amer. Proc.*,
     34, 77 (1970).
36. M. Schnitzer and S. T. M. Skinner, *Soil Sci. Soc. Amer. Proc.*,
     29, 400 (1963).
37. T. A. Kukharenko and L. N. Yekaterinina, *Pochvovedenie*, *7*,
     95 (1967); *Sov. Soil Sci.* (Engl. transl.), *7*, 933 (1967).
38. L. N. Yekaterinina and T. A. Kukharenko, *Pochvovedenie*, *3*,
     68 (1971); *Sov. Soil Sci.* (Engl. transl.), *7*, 173 (1971).
39. J. M. Thompson, *Proc. Soc. Anal. Chem.*, *3*, 182 (1966).
40. H. Ishikawa and K. Takaichi, *Japan. Wood Res. Soc.*, *2*, 162
     (1956).
41. O. T. Schmidt, D. M. Schmidt, and J. Herok, *Justus Liebigs
     Ann. Chem.*, *587*, 67 (1954).
42. M. Piatelli and R. A. Nicolaus, *Tetrahedron*, *15*, 66 (1961).
43. E. Haslam, in *The Chemistry of Vegetable Tannins*, Academic,
     London, 1966.
44. T. White, in *The Chemistry of Vegetable Tannins*, Symp. Soc.
     of Leather Trades Chemists, Croydon, 1956.
45. W. J. Schubert, in *Lignin Biochemistry*, Academic, London, 1965.
46. F. E. Brauns and D. A. Brauns, in *The Chemistry of Lignin:
     Supplement Volume*, Academic, New York, 1960.
47. B. Schimdli, *Helv. Chim. Acta*, *38*, 1078 (1955).
48. M. Piatelli, E. Fattorusso, S. Magno, and R. A. Nicolaus,
     Tetrahedron, *19*, 2061 (1963).
49. R. A. Nicolaus, M. Piattelli, and E. Fattorusso, *Tetrahedron*,
     20, 1163 (1964).
50. E. H. Trautner and E. A. H. Roberts, *Austral. J. Sci. Res.
     Sci. B*, *3*, 356 (1951).
51. H. S. Mason, *Advan. Enzymol.*, *16*, 108 (1955).
52. H. S. Mason, *Nature (London)*, *175*, 771 (1955).
53. K. Haider, L. R. Frederick, and W. Flaig. *Plant Soil*, *22*,
     49 (1965).
54. W. S. Pierpoint, *Biochem. J.*, *112*, 609 (1969).
55. J. N. Ladd and J. H. A. Butler, *Austral. J. Soil Res.*, *4*,
     41 (1966).
56. W. O. James, E. A. Roberts, H. Beevers, and P. C. DeKock,
     Biochem. J., *43*, 626 (1948).
57. M. St. C. Flett, *J. Soc. Dyers Colourists*, *68*, 59 (1952).
58. W. D. Loomis and J. Battaile, *Phytochemistry*, *5*, 423 (1966).
59. H. C. Stecker and J. H. Highberger, *J. Amer. Leather Chem.
     Assoc.*, *37*, 226 (1942).
60. W. S. Pierpoint, *Biochem. J.*, *112*, 619 (1969).
61. E. R. Theis, *J. Biol. Chem.*, *157*, 23 (1945).
62. W. S. Pierpoint, *Rep. Rothamsted Exp. Stn.*, Part 2, 199 (1970).
63. M. Mandel and E. T. Reese, *Ann. Rev. Phytopathol.*, *3*, 85
     (1965).
64. K. H. Gustavson, *J. Soc. Leather Trades Chem.*, *50*, 144 (1966).
65. W. Grassmann, *Collegium, Haltingen*, *809*, 530 (1937).
66. K. H. Gustavson, *J. Poly. Sci.*, *12*, 317 (1954).
67. G. Batzer and G. Weissenberger, *Makromolek. Chem.*, *17*, 320
     (1952).

68. W. R. C. Handley, *Plant Soil*, *15*, 37 (1961).
69. W. C. Porter and J. H. Schwartz, *J. Food Sci.*, *27*, 416 (1962).
70. J. Basaraba and R. L. Starkey, *Soil Sci.*, *101*, 17 (1966).
71. R. E. Benoit, R. L. Starkey, and J. Basaraba, *Soil Sci.*, *105*, 153 (1968).
72. J. L. Goldstein and T. Swain, *Phytochemistry*, *4*, 185 (1965).
73. J. A. Lewis and R. L. Starkey, *Soil Sci.*, *106*, 241 (1968).
74. P. P. Feeney, *Phytochemistry*, *8*, 2114 (1969).
75. K. H. Gustavson, *J. Amer. Leather Chemists Ass.*, *42*, 13 (1947).
76. P. J. Brown and W. B. Wright, *J. Chromatogr.*, *11*, 504 (1963).
77. S. A. Waksman and K. R. N. Iyer, *Soil Sci.*, *34*, 43 (1932).
78. R. P. Hobson and H. J. Page, *J. Agri. Sci.*, *22*, 497 (1932).
79. A. G. Norman, *Soil Sci. Soc. Amer. Proc.*, *7*, 7 (1942).
80. E. Bennett, *Soil Sci.*, *68*, 399 (1949).
81. D. L. Lynch and C. C. Lynch, *Nature (London)*, *181*, 1478 (1958).
82. S. Mattson, *Soil Sci.*, *33*, 41 (1932).
83. H. W. Scharpenseel, in *Radioisotopes in Soil-Plant Nutrition Studies*, p. 115, IAEA, Vienna, 1962.
84. J. N. Ladd and P. G. Brisbane, *Austral. J. Soil Res.*, *5*, 161 (1967).
85. P. Simonart, L. Batistic, and J. Mayaudon, *Plant Soil*, *27*, 153 (1967).
86. F. J. Sowden, *Can. J. Soil Sci.*, *50*, 233 (1970).
87. S. A. Waksman and K. R. N. Iyer, *Soil Sci.*, *36*, 57 (1933).
88. W. Loginow, *Roczn. Naukro In.*, *90A*, 417 (1965).
89. J. Mayaudon, in *Radioisotopes in Soil-Plant Nutrition Studies*, p. 177, IAEA, Vienna, 1968.
90. S. U. Khan and M. Schnitzer, *Can. J. Chem.*, *49*, 2302 (1971).
91. H. Lyr, *Enzymologia*, *23*, 231 (1961).
92. A. Guerritore, P. Vanni, E. Mastronuzzi, and V. Baccari, *Boll. Soc. Ital. biol. sper.*, *41*, 485 (1965).
93. A. Boudet and P. Gadal, *C. R. Acad. Sci.*, *(Paris)*, *260*, 4252 (1965).
94. M. Tamir and E. Alumot, *J. Sci. Food. Agric.*, *20*, 199 (1969).
95. A. M. Firenzuoli, P. Vanni, and E. Mastronuzzi, *Phytochemistry*, *8*, 61 (1969).
96. F. Albergina, *Life Sci.*, *3*, 49 (1964).
97. A. H. Williams, in *Enzyme Inhibition by Phenolic Compounds* (J. B. Pridham, Ed.), p. 87, Pergamon, Oxford, 1963.
98. R. J. W. Byrde, in *Perspectives of Biochemical Plant Pathology*, (S. Rich, Ed.), p. 663, Conn. Agr. Exp. Sta. Bull., 1963.
99. M. Akino, *Annot. Zool. Japan*, *25*, 48 (1952).
100. M. Akino, *Japan J. Zool.*, *11*, 63 (1953).
101. M. Akino, *Japan J. Zool.*, *12*, 527 (1960).
102. M. J. Kuo and M. Alexander, *J. Bact.*, *94*, 624 (1967).
103. E. Saalbach, *Trans. Intern. Congr. Soil Sci. 6th, Paris D*, 107 (1956).
104. F. Scheffer, W. Ziechmann, and W. Rochus, *Naturwiss.*, *49*, 131 (1962).

105. J. N. Ladd, P. G. Brisbane and J. H. A. Butler, *Trans. 9th Int. Congr. Soil Sci.(Adelaide) Australia*, *3*, 319 (1968).
106. J. N. Ladd and J. H. A. Butler, *Austral. J. Soil Res.*, *7*, 241 (1969).
107. J. H. A. Butler and J. N. Ladd, *Austral. J. Soil Res.*, *7*, 263 (1969).
108. J. N. Ladd and J. H. A. Butler, *Soil Biol. Biochem.*, *3*, 157 (1971).
109. M. Schnitzer, *Proc. Soil Sci. Soc. Amer.*, *33*, 75 (1969).
110. J. H. A. Butler and J. N. Ladd, *Soil Biol. Biochem.*, *3*, 249 (1971).
111. M. C. Mato and J. Mendez, *Geoderma*, *3*, 255 (1970).
112. M. C. Mato, R. Fabregas, and J. Mendez, *Soil Biol. Biochem.*, *3*, 285 (1971).
113. I. H. Silman and E. Katchalski, *Ann. Rev. Biochem.*, *35*, 873 (1966).
114. L. Goldstein, *Ferment. Advan.*, 3rd Symp. Pap. Int. Ferment., p. 391, 1968.
115. M. D. Lilly and A. K. Sharp, *Chem. Eng.*, Jan-Feb., 12 (1968).
116. L. Goldstein and E. Katchalski, *Fresenius' Z. Anal. Chem.*, *243*, 375 (1968).
117. E. M. Crook, *FEBS Symp.*, *19*,297 (1969).
118. A. S. Lindsey, *J. Macromol. Sci. Revs. Macromol. Chem.*, *C3* (1), 1 (1969).
119. L. Goldstein, in *Methods in Enzymology* (S. P. Colowick and N. O. Kaplan, Eds.), Vol. XIX, p. 935, Academic, New York, 1970.
120. A. D. McLaren and L. Packer, *Advan. Enzymol.*, *33*, 245 (1970).
121. S. A. Barker and R. Epton, *Proc. Biochem.*, *5* (8), 14 (1970).
122. K. Mosbach, *Sci. Amer.*,March 26 (1971).
123. R. Epton and T. H. Thomas, in *An Introduction to Water-Insoluble Enzymes* (Koch-Light Laboratories Ltd., Ed.), p. 1, 1971.
124. R. Goldman, L. Goldstein, and E. Katchalski, in *Biochemical Aspects of Reactions on Solid Supports* (G. R. Stark, Ed.), p. 1, Academic, New York, 1971.
125. M. A. Mitz and R. J. Schlueter, *J. Amer. Chem. Soc.*, *81*, 4024 (1959).
126. T. Tosa, T. Mori, N. Fuse, and I. Chibata, *Enzymology*, *31*, 214 (1966).
127. T. Tosa, T. Mori, N. Fuse, and I. Chibata, *Agri. Biol. Chem.*, *33*, 1047 (1969).
128. T. Tosa, T. Mori, and I. Chibata, *Agri. Biol. Chem.*, *33*, 1053 (1969).
129. J. Gryszkiewicz, E. Dziembor, and W. Ostrowski, *Bull. Acad. Pol. Sci.*, *XVIII*, 439 (1970).
130. M. J. Bachler, G. W. Strandberg, and K. L. Smiley, *Biotechnol. and Bioeng.*, *XII*, 85 (1970).
131. P. Bernfeld and J. Wan, *Science*, *142*, 678 (1963).
132. G. G. Guilbault and D. N. Kramer, *Anal. Chem.*, *37*, 1675 (1965).

133. E. K. Bauman, L. H. Goodson, G. G. Guilbault, and D. N. Kramer,
      Anal. Chem., *37*, 1378 (1965).
134. G. P. Hicks and S. J. Updike, *Anal. Chem.*, *38*, 726 (1966).
135. K. Mosbach and R. Mosbach, *Acta Chem. Scand.*, *20*, 2807 (1966).
136. S. J. Updike and G. P. Hicks, *Nature (London)*, *214*, 986 (1967).
137. P. Bernfeld, R. E. Bieber, and P. C. MacDonnell, *Arch. Bio-*
      chem. Biophys., *127*, 779 (1968).
138. P. Bernfeld and R. E. Bieber, *Arch. Biochem. Biophys.*, *131*,
      587 (1969).
139. P. Bernfeld, R. E. Bieber, and D. M. Watson, *Biochim. Biophys.*
      Acta, *191*, 570 (1969).
140. J. Dobo, *Acta Chim. Acad. Sci. Hung.*, *63*, 453 (1970).
141. K. Mosbach and P. O. Larsson, *Biotechnol. and Bioengin.*, *XII*,
      19 (1970).
142. K. Mosbach, *Acta Chem. Scand.*, *24*, 2084 (1970).
143. I. H. Silman, M. Albu-Weissenberg, and E. Katchalski, *Bio-*
      polymers, *4*, 441 (1966).
144. R. Haynes and K. A. Walsh, *Biochem. Biophys. Res. Comm.*, *36*,
      235 (1969).
145. E. F. Jansen and A. C. Olson, *Arch. Biochem. Biophys.*, *129*,
      221 (1969).
146. A. Schejter and A. Bar-Eli, *Arch. Biochem. Biophys.*, *136*,
      325 (1970).
147. N. Grubhofer and L. Schleith, *Z. Physiol. Chem.*, *297*, 108
      (1954).
148. H. Brandenberger, *Rev. Ferment. et Inds. Aliment.*, *11*, 237
      (1956).
149. G. Manecke and G. Günzel, *Makromolek. Chem.*, *51*, 199 (1961).
150. M. A. Mitz and L. J. Summaria, *Nature (London)*, *189*, 576 (1961).
151. G. Manecke and G. Günzel, *Makromolek. Chem.*, *51*, 199 (1962).
152. G. Manecke, *Pure Appl. Chem.*, *4*, 507 (1962).
153. A. Bar-Eli and E. Katchalski, *J. Biol. Chem.*, *238*, 1690 (1963).
154. Y. Levin, M. Pecht, L. Goldstein, and E. Katchalski, *Biochem.*,
      3, 1905 (1964).
155. L. Goldstein, Y. Levin, and E. Katchalski, *Biochem.*, *3*, 1913
      (1964).
156. G. Manecke, *Naturwissenschaften*, *51*, 25 (1964).
157. R. Axen and J. Porath, *Acta Chem. Scand.*, *18*, 2193 (1964),
158. E. Riesel and E. Katchalski, *J. Biol. Chem.*, *239*, 1521 (1964).
159. Y. Levin, M. Pecht, L. Goldstein, and E. Katchalski, *Bio-*
      chemistry, *3*, 1905 (1964).
160. L. Goldstein, Y. Levin, and E. Katchalski, *Biochemistry*, *3*,
      1913 (1964).
161. R. Goldman, H. I. Silman, S. R. Caplan, O. Kedem, and E.
      Katchalski, *Science*, *150*, 758 (1965).
162. N. Weliky and H. H. Weetall, *Immunochemistry*, *2*, 293 (1965).
163. B. P. Surinov and S. E. Manoilov, *Biokhimiya*, *31*, 387 (1965).
164. W. E. Hornby, M. D. Lilly, and E. M. Crook, *Biochem. J.*, *98*,
      420 (1966).
165. G. Manecke and H. J. Förster, *Makromolek. Chem.* *91*, 136 (1966).

166. E. B. Ong, Y. Tsang, and G. E. Perlmann, *J. Biol. Chem.*, *241*, 5661 (1966).

167. M. D. Lilly, W. E. Hornby, and E. M. Crook, *Biochem. J.*, *100*, 718 (1966).

168. R. Axen and J. Porath, *Nature (London)*, *210*, 367 (1966).

169. S. Lowey, L. Goldstein, and S. M. Luck, *Biochem. Z.*, *345*, 248 (1966).

170. A. Riman, B. Alexander, and E. Katchalski, *Biochem.*, *5*, 792 (1966).

171. R. P. Patel, D. V. Lopiekes, S. P. Brown, and S. Price, *Biopolymers*, *5*, 577 (1967).

172. L. Goldstein, Y. Levin, M. Pecht, and E. Katchalski, *Israel J. Chem.*, *5*, 90 (1967).

173. A. F. S. A. Habeeb, *Arch. Biochem. Biophys.*, *119*, 264 (1967).

174. J. Porath, R. Axen, and S. Ernback, *Nature (London)*, *215*, 1491 (1967).

175. G. Kay and E. M. Crook, *Nature (London)*, *216*, 514 (1967).

176. G. Manecke and G. Günzel, *Naturwissenschaften*, *54*, 647 (1967).

177. E. Katchalski, *7th Int. Cong. Biochem.*, *147* (1967).

178. S. Lowey, L. Goldstein, C. Cohen, and S. M. Luck, *J. Mol. Biol.*, *23*, 287 (1967).

179. W. E. Hornby, M. D. Lilly, and E. M. Crook, *Biochem. J.*, *107*, 669 (1968).

180. S. A. Barker, P. J. Somers, and R. Epton, *Carbohyd. Res.*, *8*, 491 (1968).

181. S. N. Pennington, H. D. Brown, A. B. Patel, and C. O. Knowles, *Biochim. Biophys. Acta*, *167*, 479 (1968).

182. H. D. Brown, A. B. Patel, S. K. Chattopadhyay, and S. N. Pennington, *Enzymologia*, *35*, 233 (1968).

183. H. D. Brown, A. B. Patel, S. K. Chattopadhyay, and S. N. Pennington, *Enzymologia*, *35*, 215 (1968).

184. G. Kay, M. D. Lilly, A. K. Sharp, and R. J. H. Wilson, *Nature (London)*, *217*, 641 (1968).

185. T. Wagner, C. J. Hsu, and G. Kelleher, *Biochem. J.*, *108*, 892 (1968).

186. W. E. Hornby, M. D. Lilly, and E. M. Crook, *Biochem. J.*, *107*, 669 (1968).

187. C. W. Wharton, E. M. Crook, and K. Brocklehurst, *Eur. J. Biochem.*, *6*, 565 (1968).

188. R. Goldman, O. Kedem, and E. Katchalski, *Biochemistry*, *7*, 4518 (1968).

189. R. Goldman, O. Kedem, I. H. Silman, S. R. Caplan, and E. Katchalski, *Biochemistry*, *7*, 486 (1968).

190. R. Goldman, O. Kedem, and E. Katchalski, *Biochemistry*, *7*, 518 (1968).

191. R. Goldman, O. Kedem, I. H. Silman, S. R. Caplan, and E. Katchalski, *Biochemistry*, *7*, 486 (1968).

192. R. Bohnensack, W. Agustin, and E. Hofmann, *Experientia*, 348 (1969).

193. S. A. Barker, P. J. Somers, and R. Epton, *Carbohyd. Res.*, *9*, 257 (1969).

194. I. Silman, *J. Gen. Physiol.*, *54*, 50 (1969).
195. K. P. Wheeler, B. A. Edwards, and R. Whittam, *Biochim. Biophys. Acta*, *191*, 187 (1969).
196. A. B. Patel, S. N. Pennington, and H. D. Brown, *Biochim. Biophys. Acta*, *178*, 626 (1969).
197. G. Broun, E. Selegny, S. Avrameas, and D. Thomas, *Biochim. Biophys. Acta*, *185*, 260 (1969).
198. T. L. Westman, *Biochem. Biophys. Res. Commun.*, *35*, 313 (1969).
199. N. Weliky, F. S. Brown, and E. C. Dale, *Arch. Biochem. Biophys.*, *131*, 1 (1969).
200. H. Fritz, M. Gebhardt, E. Fink, W. Schramm, and E. Werle, *Hoppe-Seyler's Z. Physiol. Chem.*, *350*, 129 (1969).
201. W. M. Ledingham and W. E. Hornby, *FEBS Lett.*, *5*, 118 (1969).
202. G. Manecke, G. Günzel, and H. J. Förster, *J. Polymer Sci.*, 607 (1970).
203. S. S. Rao, V. M. Patki, and A. D. Kulkarni, *Ind. J. Biochem.*, *7*, 210 (1970).
204. L. Goldstein, M. Pecht, S. Blumberg, D. Atlas, and Y. Levin, *Biochemistry*, *9*, 2322 (1970).
205. G. Kay and M. D. Lilly, *Biochim. Biophys. Acta*, *198*, 276 (1970).
206. R. A. Zingaro and M. Uziel, *Biochim. Biophys. Acta*, *213*, 271 (1970).
207. H. H. Weetall, *Biochim. Biophys. Acta*, *212*, 1 (1970).
208. D. Gabel, P. Vretblad, R. Axen, and J. Porath, *Biochim. Biophys. Acta*, *214*, 561 (1970).
209. K. Mosbach and B. Mattiasson, *Acta Chem. Scand.*, *24*, 2093 (1970).
210. R. Axen, P. A. Myrin, and J. C. Janson, *Biopolymers*, *9*, 401 (1970).
211. S. A. Barker, P. J. Somers, and R. Epton, *Carbohyd. Res.*, *14*, 323 (1970).
212. S. A. Barker, P. J. Somers, R. Epton, and J. V. McLaren, *Carbohyd. Res.*, *14*, 287 (1970).
213. R. Koelsch, J. Lasch, and H. Hanson, *Acta Biol. Med. Germ.*, *24*, 833 (1970).
214. H. Fritz, M. Gebhardt, R. Meister, K. Illchmann, and K. Hochstrasser, *Hoppe-Seyler's Z. Physiol. Chem.*, *351*, 571 (1970).
215. H. Fritz, M. Gebhardt, R. Meister, and H. Schult, *Hoppe-Seyler's Z. Physiol. Chem.*, *351*, 1119 (1970).
216. P. V. Sundaram and W. E. Hornby, *FEBS Lett.*, *10*, 325 (1970).
217. P. Cresswell and A. R. Sanderson, *Biochem. J.*, *119*, 447 (1970).
218. P. Cresswell and A. R. Sanderson, *Proc. Biochem. Soc.*, *117*, 43 (1970).
219. H. Filippusson and W. E. Hornby, *Biochem. J.*, *120*, 215 (1970).
220. T. Seki, T. A. Jenssen, Y. Levin, and E. G. Erdös, *Nature (London)*, *225*, 864 (1970).
221. R. Axen and S. Ernback, *Eur. J. Biochem.*, *18*, 351 (1971).
222. G. T. Felbeck, *Soil Sci.*, *111*, 42 (1971).

223. J. H. A. Butler and J. N. Ladd, *Austral. J. Soil Res.*, *7*,
     229 (1969).
224. T. J. Piper and A. M. Posner, *Soil Sci.*, *106*, 188 (1968).
225. L. W. Getzin and I. Rosefield, *Biochim. Biophys. Acta*, *235*,
     442 (1971).
226. J. R. Ramirez-Martinez and A. D. McLaren, *Enzymologia*, *31*,
     23 (1966).
227. R. G. Burns, A. H. Pukite, and A. D. McLaren, *Soil Sci. Soc.*
     Amer. Proc., *36*, 308 (1972).
228. H. Mason, in *Advances in Biology of the Skin*, *8*, 298 (1967).
229. J. N. Ladd and E. A. Paul, *Soil Biol. Biochem.*, *5*, 825 (1973).

CHAPTER 6

HUMUS BIOCHEMISTRY

K. Haider

Institut für Biochemie des Bodens
Forschungsanstalt für Landwirtschaft
Braunschweig-Völkenrode, Germany

J. P. Martin

Department of Soil Science and Agricultural Engineering
University of California
Riverside, California

and

Z. Filip

Department of Microbiology
Agricultural University
Prague, CSSR

I. INTRODUCTION

Humus is the structureless component of the soil organic fraction. It is primarily derived from the higher plants, which grow
upon the soil, and forms during the microbial decomposition of the
original plant constituents and of new substances synthesized by
the soil microorganisms. It is therefore a biological product.
When an organic residue is incorporated into the soil and environmental conditions are favorable, the microorganisms immediately be-
gin to utilize it as a source of food and energy. Readily available
constituents, such as cellulose, peptides, and the most simple organic components, are rapidly used for energy and the synthesis of
microbial tissues. More resistant components, especially lignins
and other plant phenolic compounds, are decomposed more slowly and
tend to accumulate in the soil in partially degraded or microbially
altered forms. Together with products of microbial synthesis they
form the brown-to-black structureless soil organic polymers that
with time become more and more resistant to further degradation
and constitute the main components of humus.

Humus formation is unique to the biological soil system. During
the degradation of organic residues not only reactions catalyzed by
specific microbial enzymes occur, but reactive substances formed
through microbial activity undergo chemical reactions that lead to
the formation of new organic substances. In this respect the soil
is different from a specific organism which carries on its metabolic processes almost exclusively through biochemical reactions.
This chapter will consider both biochemical and chemical reactions
involved in humus formation. Reactions of synthetic organic chemicals introduced into the soil and that might be incorporated into
the soil organic matter are excluded [1]. Biochemical reactions,
leading to high molecular sulfur or phosphorous components, will
be only briefly mentioned, because this topic was considered in
Volume 1 [2, 3]. For most studies prior to 1965, reference will
be made to review articles.

II. DEGRADATIVE REACTIONS IN THE SOIL

The first biochemical processes involved in the transformation
of plant, microbial, and other organic matter residues to soil humus
are degradative reactions. Through microbial decomposition of these
residues various structural units for humus polymer formation are
released. In addition, relatively simple organic compounds are
produced that are utilized by the microbes for the synthesis of
cells and numerous organic substances, including humus structural
units and humic-type polymers. It would be impossible in this review to cover in detail all degradative biochemical reactions involved in the microbial decomposition of organic residues. Those
degradative reactions especially pertinent to the formation of relatively stable organic complexes will be emphasized.

A. Degradation of Total Plant Material

Clark and Paul [4] have summarized reported data on the decomposition of various plant constituents and organic residues in soil.
The time required for the loss of half the added carbon in the form
of CO_2 from most residues varied from 3 days for glucose to 500
days for pine needles. Specific substances such as waxes and phenols
under the conditions of the studies decomposed still more slowly
[5-9]. Plant material labeled uniformly with ^{14}C has been extensively used to study the degradation and turnover of added plant
carbon in the soil [10-15]. Generally, about 60-70% of the added
carbon is rapidly released as CO_2. About one-third remains in the
soil after 1 year and about one-fifth is present after 5 years.
Even after 2 years, added plant carbon mineralizes several times
faster than the original soil carbon [10, 11]. A significant percentage of the newer carbon may be present in microbial tissues as
evidenced by a higher rate of CO_2 evolution after destruction of
the soil population by fumigation or irradiation and recolonization.
Rough calculations made by Jenkinson [10] suggested that about 10%

of the original plant carbon was in microbial tissues after 1 year
and about 4% after 4 years.

Analyses of the plant residues during decomposition indicated
that cellulose decomposes rapidly, whereas lignin type polymers are
more resistant and remain in relatively high concentrations for
longer periods of time [16-18]. Adding different concentrations of
plant carbon up to 2% did not alter the percentage of plant carbon
evolved as CO_2 or retained in the soil [10, 15, 19, 20]. Several
investigators [21-25] have reported that the addition of fresh organic material to the soil may accelerate the decomposition of the
soil humus [21]. This effect was referred to as a "priming action."
Most recent workers, however, have not noted this action to a high
degree [11, 26, 27].

B. Degradation of Carbohydrates

Various sugars, especially in the polysaccharide or polymerized
form, constitute the most abundant type of organic material in plant
residues. They serve as a readily available source of carbon and
energy for the synthesis of microbial cells and products, including
phenolic compounds and polymers, peptides, microbial polysaccharides,
and other organic compounds some of which may become structural
units of soil humus polymers.

Labeled or unlabeled glucose, the most readily metabolized carbohydrate, has often been used as a soil amendment to study its decomposition and conversion to cell substances and humic materials.
In a few days or weeks about 60-80% is converted to CO_2 and the
residue is stabilized in microbial tissues and products [14, 28-30].
When the first flush of activity is over, the CO_2 evolution curve
levels off and remains nearly parallel to the abscissa [31, 32].
Residue activity is found in the various humus fractions, including
amino acids and sugars released on 6 N HCl hydrolysis [29, 33, 34].
Studies on the use of differentially labeled ^{14}C-glucose to estimate glycolytic activity of soil microbes were reported by Mayaudon
[35] in Volume 2 of this series. Macura and Kubatova [35a]

investigated the utilization of sugar mixtures by the soil population. In the presence of glucose the rate of galactose and of lac-
tose utilization was reduced. It was concluded that catabolites
of glucose degradation inhibited the enzymes involved in degradation
of the other sugars.

Starch and cellulose are readily decomposed in soil. If cellulose is protected by lignin it is somewhat more stable than when
added in the isolated form. When cellulose is incorporated into
the soil, both bacteria and fungi attach themselves to the substrate
or penetrate into it. Digestion is largely localized at the microbe-
substrate interface and does not occur by diffusion of the hydrolyzing enzymes some distance away from the organisms. About half of
the organisms present in a normal soil community are able to degrade cellulose and even more of them degrade starch. For most of
these organisms cellulase is a constitutive enzyme but others only
produce the enzyme in the presence of cellulose. Cellobiose, formed
from the small amount of cellulose nearly always present in soil,
acts as an inducer [36, 37]. For details of the biochemistry of
cellulose decomposition by microbes the reader is referred to a
number of recent reviews. In a review by Jurasek et al. [38], detailed data on the morphological changes of the cellulose and plant
cell wall structure are included. Norkrans [39] lists the organisms
that degrade cellulose and includes the enzymes involved. Transformations of polysaccharides by soil microorganisms are reviewed
by Reese [40], who includes some of the literature on the decomposition of microbial cell wall polymers by bacteria and fungi.

The biological transformations of microbial residues in soil
have been reviewed by Webley and Jones [41]. Some fungal cell walls
are highly resistant to degradation. The stability is usually
associated with the presence of a melanin-type constituent because,
upon removal of this polymer, the polysaccharide cell wall structures are more readily degraded [42-45]. Also, the shielding of
cell wall components against rapid degradation by certain polysaccharides has been reported [46].

Polysaccharides constitute an important fraction of the soil humus. Processes involved in their biosynthesis, degradation, and stabilization have been reviewed [47, 48]. The ease of decomposition of plant and microbial polysaccharides in the soil varies greatly. Salt or complex formation with metal ions or clays may greatly increase resistance to decomposition [29, 49-53].

C. Degradation of Amino Acid Compounds

Amino acids, peptides, or proteins when incubated with soil are rapidly decomposed with the release of CO_2 and NH_3 but a small percentage is incorporated into tissues of microorganisms and into soil humic constituents. Mayaudon and Simonart [54] studied the decomposition of C-1 and C-2 ^{14}C-labeled glycine in soil; more of the C-1 carbon was released as CO_2. The ratio of oxidized C-1 to C-2 after 12 hr of incubation was about 5.6:1. The C-2 was to a greater degree incorporated into other compounds, especially amino acids, glucosamine, and certain sugars, and was noted in more than 20 different compounds. After 30 days about 90% of the C-1 and 70% of the C-2 carbon was lost as CO_2. The residual activity was resistant to further degradation. A greater stabilization of the indole unit of tryptophan compared to the aliphatic side chain has been reported [35]. Evidence of a greater stabilization of protein than of amino acids in the presence of humic acids has been noted [55-57].

An intact ^{14}C-labeled plant globulin isolated from spinach leaves lost about 45% of its carbon as CO_2 in 30 days when incubated in the soil, whereas a hydrolyzate of the same protein lost 71%. Coprecipitated globulin and 6 N hydrolyzed humic acid could not be separated into the two components by electrophoresis. The sorption of the protein on the organic colloids appeared to have partially stabilized it against decomposition. This may be analogous to the partial stabilization of organic substances by clay minerals such as montmorillonite [58]. A stabilization of proteins may also be related to an inhibition of proteolytic enzymes by humic acids as

observed for Pronase, a protease from *Streptomyces griseus*, by
Ladd and Brisbane [59] and Brisbane and Ladd [60]. The inhibiting
action appears to be dependent upon free hydroxy groups of the
humic acids, because inhibition was not observed when the hydroxy
groups were methylated [60, 60a]. The protection of proteins by
plant tannins observed by Basaraba and Starkey [61] is probably
also caused by free hydroxy groups that are linked through hydrogen
bonds to the peptide groups, as has been suggested for the tanning
of leaf proteins at senescence [62-65].

D. Degradation of Phenolic Constituents

Complex phenolic polymers appear to constitute the greatest
portion of the soil humus [65a]. Phenolic compounds and polymers
synthesized by plants and by microbes are important sources of these
phenolic units [66]. Small amounts of simple phenolic compounds

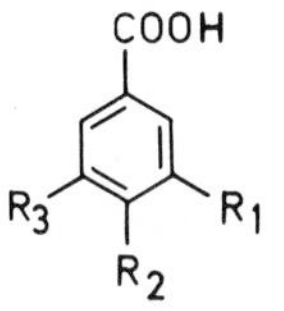

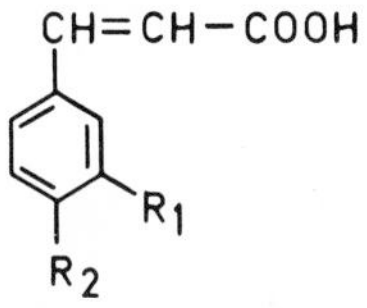

$R_1, R_3 = H$; $R_2 = OH$ (1) $R_1 = H$; $R_2 = OH$ (5)
$R_1 = OCH_3$; $R_2 = OH$; $R_3 = H$ (2) $R_1 = OCH_3$; $R_2 = OH$ (6)
$R_1, R_2 = OH$; $R_3 = H$ (3)
$R_1, R_3 = OCH_3$; $R_2 = OH$ (4)

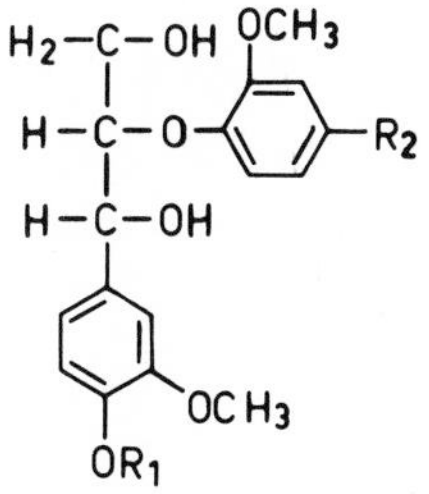

$R_1 = CH_3$; $R_2 = H$ (7)
$R_1 = H$; $R_2 = CH = CH - CH_2OH$ (8)
$R_1 = H$; $R_2 = H$ (9)

Fig. 1. Structures of some common phenols isolated from plants
or soils.

can be extracted from soil especially after weak hydrolysis treatment. Bruckert et al. [67], Whitehead [68], and Wang et al. [69,
70] (Fig. 1) isolated p-hydroxybenzoic (1), vanillic (2), protocatechuic (3), syringic (4), p-hydroxycinnamic (5), ferulic (6),
and other aromatic acids from soils by extraction with dilute alkaline solvents or with ether (Fig. 1). Most of these substances
were undoubtedly derived from lignin through microbial degradation.
Guenzi and McCalla [71, 72] isolated the same substances from plowed
and subtilled soils or from plant residues. McCalla [72] reported
concentrations of about 15 ppm for p-coumaric acid on an oven dry
basis for the subtilled soil. This corresponded to 0.04% of the
organic matter. Schnitzer and Skinner [73] obtained phenols by
more rigid extraction with ethanolic NaOH at pH 11 or by exhaustive
methylation of a podzol fulvic acid [74].

In pure culture common phenolic compounds are rapidly utilized
by specific microorganisms. Apparently however, few studies have
been made on the rate of decomposition of simple phenols in soil.
Batistic and Mayaudon [75] studied the stability of uniformly
^{14}C-labeled p-coumaric (5), vanillic (2), and ferulic acids (6)
in soil. They noted upon 150 days of aerobic incubation a bio-
stabilization of about 50% of the original activity and believed
that the greater part consisted of the added phenolic acids. They
suggested a stabilization through complex formation with the clay
and humic colloids. Wang et al. [76] also observed a stabilization
of labeled phenolic acids in soil but theorized a cofixation of
the phenols on humic substances. Kunc [76a] noted a series of oxygen uptake peaks during the incubation of vanillin-amended soil.
These were associated with the various steps in the microbial transformation or degradation of vanillin, namely vanillin to vanillic
acid to protocatechuic acid to ring fission. He concluded that a
succession of different groups of microorganisms may have been involved and that environmental factors can also exert an influence.

Degradative pathways of phenols by pure microbial cultures
have been extensively studied and were reviewed by Dagley [77] in

Volume 1 of this series and more recently by Evans [78] and Dagley
[79]. The microbes cleave the phenol ring directly or after the
introduction of additional hydroxyl groups, by microbial oxygenases.
For most microbes the presence of at least two hydroxyl groups in
the o position is necessary for ring cleavage. The mechanism of
oxidative ring fission occurs as the o or m cleavage [77-79]. Some
of the enzymes responsible for ring fission or oxygenation have been
obtained in crystalline form and have been well characterized [80].
Studies on inductive and regulatory phenomena concerned with phenol-
degrading enzymes have been reviewed by Ornston [81].

Most of the phenols in plants, either in free or condensed
form, have methoxyl groups as in vanillic (2), syringic (4), or
ferulic (6) acids or arylated hydroxyl groups as in veratrylglycerol-
β-guaiacyl (7) or o-coniferyl ether (8) (Fig. 1). These ether linkages can be readily cleaved by many microorganisms but the mechanisms are not well established. Trojanowsky et al. [82] reported
that peroxidases are involved in the cleavage of the methyl ether
linkages of the phenols shown in Fig. 1 by the white rot fungus
Pholiota mutabilis. Peroxidases are widely distributed in the white
rot lignin-degrading fungi [83-86]. Leonowitz and Trojanowsky [87]
observed an 80% demethylation of vanillic acid by enzymes of *P.
mutabilis* in the presence of H_2O_2 and a decrease of the total
methoxyl groups in lignin of about 12%. *Pseudomonas* spp. peroxidases
were shown to be active in the splitting of the methyl ether linkage
in syringic acid (Haider and El-Khanialy, unpublished). Fukuzumi
et al. [88] demonstrated that an NADH-dependent enzyme, which was
probably not a phenol oxidase and was isolated from a white rot
fungus, was responsible for the cleavage of the aryl ether linkage
of veratrylglycerol-β-guaiacyl ether (7). An ether bond cleavage
of both guaiacyl (9) and veratrylglycerol-β-guaiacyl ether (7)
was also established [89, 90]. Various white rot fungi [91, 92]
and Fungi Imperfecti [93, 94] rapidly demethylated methyl [14]C-
labeled vanillic, syringic, or ferulic acids by release of [14]CO_2.
The latter fungi, however, had only a limited capacity to degrade

these compounds further by ring fission. The demethoxylating ability of the soil population reduces the methoxyl content of the soil
humus.

Flavonoids are important phenolic constituents of mosses, ferns,
and higher plants. Some species contain as much as 1-5% of a particular flavonoid on a fresh weight basis. Börner [95, 96] found
appreciable amounts of phloridzin (10) (Fig. 2a) in apple roots.
Barz [97] and Grisebach and Zilg [98] reported that isoflavonoids
were excreted from plant roots into the surrounding culture medium.

Phloridzin (10) is degraded by *Aspergillus* sp., *Penicillium*
sp., *Pullularia pullulans*, and other fungi to phloroglucinol (11),
phloretic acid (12), p-hydroxybenzoic acid (13), and protocatechuic
acid (14) [99-102]. Westlake et al. [103] isolated about 100 different organisms capable of degrading rutin (15). *Aspergillus niger*
and *A. flavus* were found to be particularly active. They produced
a potent extracellular enzyme system capable of degrading rutin
with the formation of rutinose, phloroglucinolcarboxylic acid, and
protocatechuic acid [104]. Rumen organisms also degrade rutin [105].
The first step in the main degradative pathway appears to be an
opening between positions 2 and 3 and a release of carbon monoxide

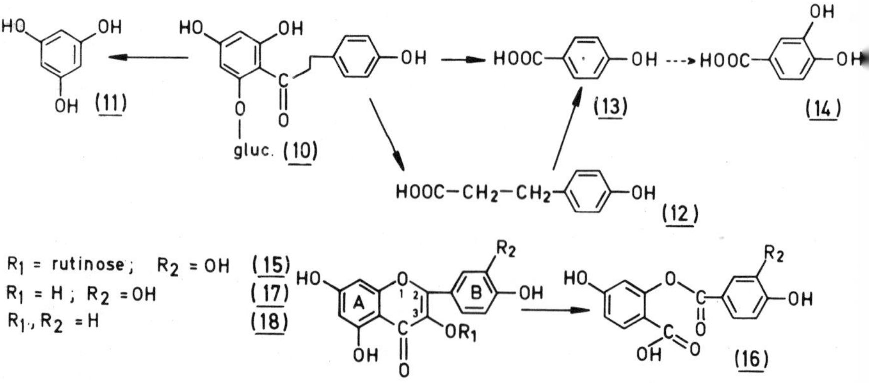

Fig. 2a. Degradation of some flavonoids by microorganisms.

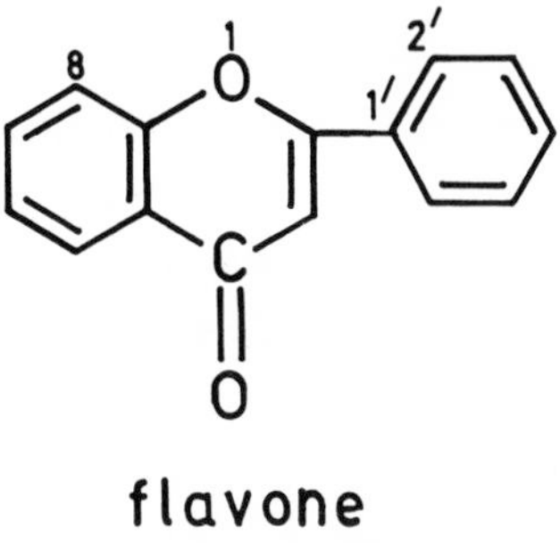

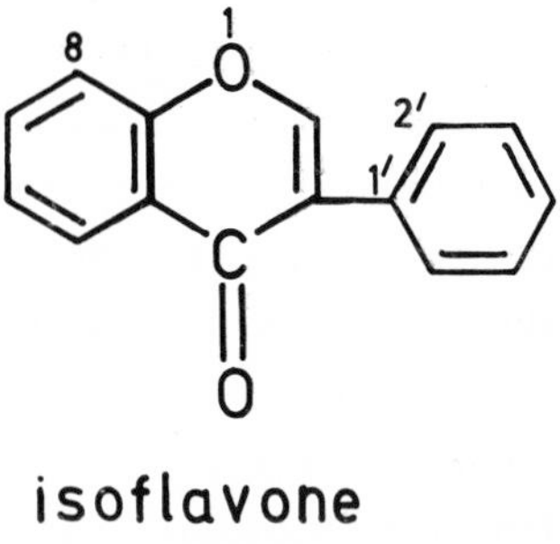

flavone   isoflavone

Fig. 2b.   Structure of flavone and isoflavone.

[106], because protocatechuoylphloroglucinolcarboxylic acid (16) could be identified as an intermediate. Similarly [107], the fla-vonoids quercetin (17) and kaempferol (18) are degraded to hydroxy-benzoic acids (ring B), phloroglucinol (ring A), and carbon monox-ide (C-3).

Barz [108] screened a large number of flavonoids and isofla-vonoids for degradability by a bacteria strain isolated from the rhizosphere. Both were utilized but a characteristic substrate specificity for this organism was evident. Only compounds with the basic skeleton of an isoflavone or flavone (Fig. 2b) with substit-uents in the 3,3', 4',5, and 7 positions were degraded. Compounds with substituents in the 2,2' and 8 positions in the case of iso-flavonoids and in the 2' and 8 positions of flavonoids, respectively, were not utilized. In addition, no intermediate decomposition products shown in Fig. 2a could be detected at any stage during the rapid decomposition. This indicated that the mechanism of de-composition in the bacteria was different from that in the fungi. In further studies on the decomposition of flavonoid compounds, Barz [109] isolated a *Fusarium oxysporium* strain from the rhizo-sphere that rapidly degraded a great number of benzoic and cinnamic acid compounds as well as flavonoids and isoflavonoids and related compounds. Phloroglucinolcarboxylic acid, carbon monoxide, and

benzoic acid derivatives were established as intermediates of
flavonoid decomposition.

Because lignin is a phenolic polymer, is relatively resistant
to microbial decomposition, and is present in such large amounts in
plant residues, and because lignin-type phenols are recovered during
the microbial decomposition of lignin and on chemical degradation
of humus polymers, the plant lignins are considered to be a very
important source of constituent units for soil humus formation.
The lignin molecules at many stages of decomposition, including
chunks of molecules as well as simple phenolic compounds, could
serve as structural units for the synthesis of the soil polymers.

Several recent reviews have dealt with the microbial decomposition of lignins [84, 86, 92, 110, 111, 111a]. Simple phenols
released during decomposition in culture solution or in soil include
vanillic acid, p-hydroxybenzoic acid, ferulic acid, 4-hydroxy-3-
methoxyphenylpyruvic acid, p-hydroxycinnamic acid, guaiacyglycerol,
dehydrodivanillin, coniferylaldehyde, and guaiacylglycerol-β-coni-
feryl ether. Although progress has been made the overall reactions
leading to the depolymerization of the macromolecule have not been
well established. Most of the experiments have been made with
model compounds or with modified lignin preparations, such as the
lignin left after growth of brown rot fungi and lignosulfonates
or "lignin powders." In most tests white rot fungi have been used.
This group of basidiomycetes is characterized [112] by the presence
of a high ratio of holocellulose to lignin in the residual woody
material following decomposition. The ratio ranges from 30 for
Grifola sp. to about 2-5 for *Stereum frustulosum*. Fungi associated
with a lower ratio are grouped with the brown rot fungi.

Most of the white rot fungi produce and excrete phenoloxidase
enzymes, but the former belief of Bavendamm [113] that only fungi
which excrete phenoloxidase degrade lignin is no longer acceptable.
Poria taxicola [114] does not excrete a phenoloxidase but decomposes
lignin. Sundman and Näse [115] studied lignin decomposition by
52 fungi, including wood rot and soil types. Excretion of

phenoloxidases was not closely correlated with ability to decompose lignin preparations. Haider and Domsch [17] studied a number of soil fungi belonging to the Imperfecti group. Many of these partially degraded lignin but apparently did not excrete phenol oxidases. These fungi appear to be important in the degradation and transformation of lignin in agricultural soils. They were partly classified as soft rot fungi [116-119] and range with respect to the intensity of lignin degradation in between the white and brown rot fungi. According to Seifert [116] they have a high demethoxylation ability. With similar organisms and by use of specifically ^{14}C-labeled polymers of lignin alcohols, namely, coniferyl, p-coumaryl, and sinapyl alcohols, the rate of degradation of distinct groups was examined by Haider and Martin [93] and Martin and Haider [94] and is shown for *Stachybotrys chartarum* in Table 1. The release of $^{14}CO_2$ is high from the methoxyl and C-3 atoms (carbinol group) of the side chains. The carbons of the aromatic nucleus and the C-1 and C-2 carbons of the side chains showed a higher stability

TABLE 1

Release of $^{14}CO_2$ from Differentially Labeled Coniferyl Alcohol in Model Lignin by *Pleurotus ostreatus* and *Stachybotrys chartarum*

	Percentage of added activity		
	P. ostreatus		*S. chartarum*
Labeled component[a]	10 days	28 days	28 days
^{14}C-1 side chain	4.0	17	9.7
^{14}C-2 side chain	2.5	16	1.8
^{14}C-3 side chain (carbinol)	4.5	42	19.8
$O^{14}CH_3$	3.8	50	13.2
^{14}C-1–^{14}C-6 (ring)	22.0	38	9.6

[a]The polymers (model lignins) were prepared by mushroom phenolase oxidation of a mixture of labeled coniferyl alcohol together with unlabeled p-coumaryl and sinapyl alcohols.

but were found in appreciable quantities in the solubilized material and in transformation products. Similar studies with white rot fungi, e.g., *Pleurotus ostreatus*, and the same labeled polymers showed a high rate of metabolism of the ring carbon atoms to CO_2. The rate of ring decomposition was higher than the rate of methoxyl and C-3 degradation. The C-2 and C-1 carbon atoms of the side chains were released as CO_2 in a later and more progressed stage of lignin degradation. These observations indicate that the white rot fungi may rapidly depolymerize the lignin polymer and use the aromatic units as a source of energy and for synthesis of cell constituents. In contrast, the observations of Fukuzumi and his colleagues [88, 90] on the enzymatic cleavage of the aryl ether bond of guaiacylglycerol-β-guaiacyl ether and related compounds by white rot fungi is of great importance. According to Freudenberg [121] about 50% of the phenylpropane units in coniferous lignin are linked by β-aryl ether linkages. Nimz [122], by chemical cleavage of the β-aryl ether linkage, obtained nearly 100% solubilization of lignin from coniferous and deciduous woods [122, 123]. The mixture of phenols contained monomer, dimer, and oligomer lignin degradation products.

During decomposition of lignin by brown rot fungi an appreciable decrease in the methoxyl content and an increase in solubility of the residual lignin also occurs. The greater solubility may partly be associated with an increase in the number of free hydroxyl groups [124]. Kirk et al. [124] working with lignin isolated from wood during decay by the brown rot fungus *Lenzites trabea* found additional hydroxyl groups in the phenols released on oxidative degradation. The introduction of the hydroxyl groups occurred in the o position to the side chain. A great number of soil bacteria are able to demethylate lignin without further degrading the polymers [125]. Jaschhof [126], however, isolated a series of *Xanthomonas* and *Micrococcus* spp. that relatively increased the methoxyl content of an alkaline lignin preparation on incubation for 100 days. A decrease in weight of 4-10% occurred, which the author [126] concluded was related to degradation of aliphatic side chains and not to splitting of the phenol-ether bonds.

A great number of soil bacteria are able to degrade simple phenols released upon the depolymerization of lignin. Even such lignans as α-conidendrin (19) [127] or such heartwood phenolic compounds as pinosylvin (20), pinobanksin (21), and pinocembrin (22) [128] (Fig. 3) may be decomposed. During decomposition of conidendrin by *Agrobacterium* sp. isovanillic acid (23) quickly accumulates, whereas upon prolonged incubation methoxy-p-benzoquinone (24) is found among the metabolites [129] (Fig. 3).

The heartwood phenolic compounds (20, 21, and 22) were partially transformed into new phenolic compounds by ascomycetes or oxidatively polymerized to red compounds by phenol oxidases of white rot basidiomycetes [128].

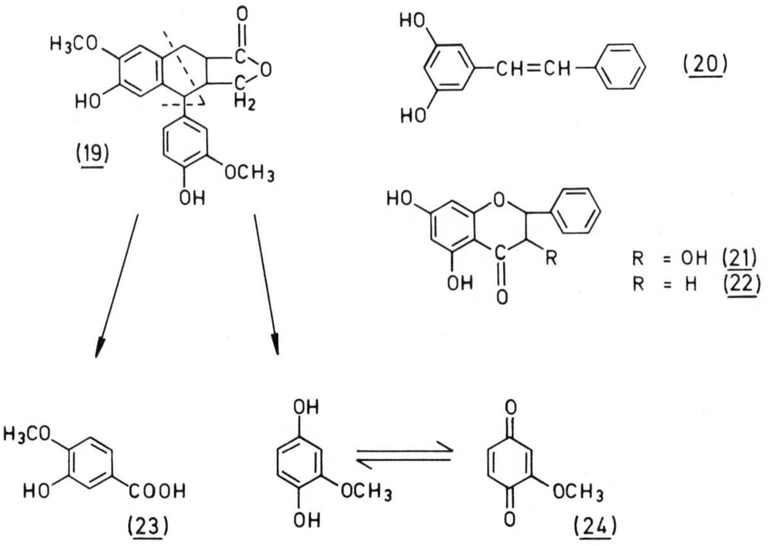

Fig. 3. Degradation of α-conidendrin and structure of heartwood phenolic compounds.

III. SYNTHETIC REACTIONS IN SOILS

The reactions involved in the microbial decomposition of organic residues within the soil are almost exclusively biochemical reactions. Through these reactions many of the constituent units for soil humus formation and cell synthesis are produced. The synthetic reactions leading to the large soil humus polymers are not completely dependent on the living cells, because reactive precursors produced by microorganisms can react to form polymers by strictly chemical reactions. This is especially true for the formation of humic acids, although the other important polymers of the soil organic fraction, the soil polysaccharides, are probably formed from altered plant and microbial polysaccharides and microbially synthesized polysaccharides through biochemical processes.

A. Conversion of Total Plant Material and Plant Constituents into Humic Substances

After examining published reports, Kononova [130] concluded that about 30% of the annual plant litter debris was converted to humic substances. A comparison of the quantities of new formed humus with the total humus reserves in the upper 1 m of soil in various climatic zones indicated that about 100-200 years would be required for the present accumulation. Paul et al. [131] and others [132, 133] have reported a mean residence time up to 100 years or more for organic matter in soils. Kononova [130] therefore assumes that the newly formed humus decomposes more rapidly than the older humus and is partly mineralized and partly transformed into still more stable forms. The same conclusions were made from soil incubation experiments with labeled plant materials or glucose. However, the mechanisms involved in this earlier stabilization are more or less speculative and contradictory. Even after prolonged incubation periods of soils with labeled plant material or glucose [14, 20, 33, 34, 134] the specific activity of the part of the humus that can be hydrolyzed by acid is always greater than that of the residue. Using various soil extraction procedures, Jansson and Persson [14] found that after incubation of soil with labeled glucose for 1 month, 40% of the remaining activity was released upon hydrolysis with 0.55 N H_2SO_4 and presumably was present in microbial tissues. Even after 2 years the distribution remained about the same. Using labeled barley straw, these authors [14] found 50% of the labeled carbon remaining after 1 month and 40% after 2 years. From 1 month to 2 years only a slight additional increase of activity in the humic acids and residual soil carbon was found. The percentage of activity in these fractions was greater than in ^{14}C-glucose-amended soils. Partially altered straw constituents and secondary microbial metabolic products probably accounted for some of the activity.

Mayaudon and Simonart [135, 136] studied the decomposition of ^{14}C-labeled glucose, hemicellulose, and cellulose in soils. The residual ^{14}C was distributed throughout the various soil organic matter fractions. The pattern of distribution, however, was more related to that of soil organic nitrogen than to the hydrolyzable soil organic carbon [137]. Probably much of the labeled carbon from readily decomposable substances is associated with nitrogen during the initial period of ample energy supply, intense microbial activity, and vigorous mineralization. When the readily available energy supply is exhausted the initial humus-forming processes slow down.

A similar view was presented by Swaby and Ladd [138], who theorized that specific properties of humic substances are formed in the microbial tissues at or shortly after death and later they are further modified by the soil system. Freytag [31] and Freytag and Igel [28] also found an increase of the ^{14}C content in the humic acid fraction after the addition of tagged glucose up to 12 days and afterwards a slow decrease. The addition of NPK shortened this period. By addition of the same labeled compound, Wagner and his colleagues [33, 34, 139-142] found that half of the activity contained in the humic acid fraction was hydrolyzable with acid and appreciable amounts were found in the amino acids of the

hydrolyzates. Using a combustion method designed to selectively
separate aliphatic from aromatic carbons [143], Wagner [34] reported
that about 57% of the labeled humic acid carbon was aromatic. It
was concluded [141] that certain microbial polymers, especially
those connected with cell wall structures, persisted in the soil.
A great number of soil organisms form dark colored polymers or
melanins. They belong to the fungi [66, 144, 145], the actinomycetes
[146], and the bacteria [147-148a]. Since the early part of the
century various investigators have suggested or presented some evidence that these substances may be similar to soil humic acids
[149-150]. In some fungal species the dark pigments may be restricte
to certain structures, such as spores, conidia, or sclerotia, and
may be present only in the surface tissues [42, 43, 151-154]. In
other species all the cells are pigmented and the high molecular
weight polymers are secreted into or also formed in the surrounding
media. This has been reported for *Azotobacter* by Bortels and Olivares [147], for *Streptomyces* sp. [146, 155-157] and for a great
number of fungi [66, 154, 158-161]. The chemical structure of
most of these dark brown-to-black polymers is not yet quite clear.
Most are apparently quite distinct from melanins occurring in animals, because they are not formed by an oxidative polymerization of
tyrosine through dihydroxyphenylalanine and its quinone but more
probably are formed through a polymerization of polyhydroxyphenols
and amino acid compounds. Nicolaus, Piatelli, and colleagues [162-
166] studied the degradation products of a great number of dark
pigments of fungi and higher plants and compared them with those
of animals. From plant and fungal pigments they obtained catechol,
benzoic, protocatechuic, and melittic acids, whereas the animal
melanins yielded indole compounds.

B. Relation of Microbial Pigment Formation
to the Synthesis of Humic Substances

Recently Martin and Haider [66] reviewed the literature on
the biosynthesis of phenols by different soil fungi belonging to the

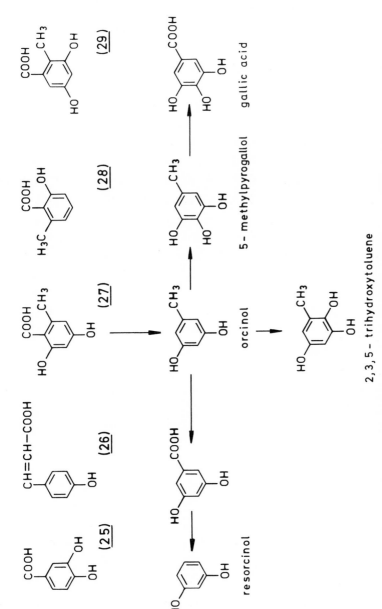

Fig. 4. Phenolic compounds formed from nonaromatic precursors (25-29) and transformation of orsellinic acid (27) by *Epicoccum nigrum* [93] and *Aspergillus sydowi* [168].

Imperfecti group and their transformation into dark colored polymers.
The phenols are synthesized from metabolites of glucose and originate either from shikimic acid or from a condensation of acetate and
malonate. Through these pathways p-hydroxycinnamic (25), protocatechuic (26), orsellinic (27), and 6-methylsalicylic (28) acids
are formed from nonaromatic precursors. Cresorsellinic acid (29)
(2-methyl-3,5-dihydroxybenzoic acid) is also found in *Epicoccum
nigrum* cultures but it could be a transformation product of a methylated orsellinic acid (Fig. 4). These phenols are transformed
by the fungi to numerous other phenolic compounds by decarboxylation,
hydroxylation, and oxidation of methyl groups as shown for orsellinic
acid in Fig. 4. Also, an oxidative cleavage of the side chain of
p-hydroxycinnamic acid and introduction of further hydroxy groups
to the aromatic nucleus leads to the formation of numerous hydroxy-
lated benzoic acids. In Table 2, the phenols and the organisms
that produce them are listed. *Epicoccum nigrum*, which according to
Domsch and Gams [167] is common on dead plant material in many soils,
synthesized about 24 different phenols [93]. They originate by
transformation of orsellinic and cresorsellinic acids and of small
amounts of cinnamic acid.

Stachybotrys atra and *S. chartarum* [94], also very common soil
fungi found especially during litter decomposition, synthesized
about 20 different phenols derived from orsellinic and p-hydroxycinnamic acids. Possibly 6-methylsalicylic acid is formed by *S.
chartarum*. *Aspergillus sydowi*, another soil fungus, synthesizes
in addition to the above phenols appreciable amounts of 6-methyl-
salicylic acid and transforms it to 3-hydroxybenzoic and 2,5-dihy-
droxybenzoic acids by hydroxylation of the C-5 atom, oxidation of
the methyl group to carboxyl, and decarboxylation [168].

Hendersonula toruloidea transforms the above-indicated primary
phenols and possibly several dimethyl phenols to about 45 different
phenolic compounds, which have been partly characterized [160].
The phenols are formed during the main growth phase of the organisms
in culture solutions containing glucose and organic or inorganic

TABLE 2

Phenols Isolated Directly from the Culture Media of
Epicoccum nigrum, *Stachybotrys chartarum*, *Aspergillus sydowi*,
and *Hendersonula toruloidea* or from the Polymers of These Fungi
after Reductive Degradation with Na-Amalgam

Phenolic compounds	*E. nigrum*	*S. chartarum*	*A. sydowi*	*H. toruloidea*
Acids				
Orsellinic	++++	++++	+++	+++
Cresorsellinic	+++	—	—	—
6-Methylsalicylic	—	—	+++	+++
3,5-Dihydroxybenzoic	++	++	++	++
2,5-Dihydroxybenzoic	—	—	++	++
2,6-Dihydroxybenzoic	—	—	++	—
2,4-Dihydroxybenzoic	++	—	—	—
p-Hydroxycinnamic	+	—	+++	—
Caffeic	—	—	++	—
p-Hydroxybenzoic	+	+	++	—
m-Hydroxybenzoic	—	—	++	++
Protocatechuic	+	+	++	—
2,3,4-Trihydroxybenzoic	—	—	+++	—
Gallic	—	+++	++	—
Toluenes				
3,5-Dihydroxy	++++	+++	++	+++
2,4-Dihydroxy	++	—	—	++
2,6-Dihydroxy	—	—	++	+
2,3,5-Trihydroxy	+++	++	++	++
2,4,5-Trihydroxy	++	—	—	—
2,3,6-Trihydroxy	—	—	++	—
2,4,6-Trihydroxy	—	—	+	+
3,4,5-Trihydroxy	+	+++	++	—
4-Methyl-2,6-dihydroxy	—	—	++	—
Phenols				
Resorcinol	++	++	++	++
Phloroglucinol	++	—	++	++
Pyrogallol	++	+++	++	—

nitrogen sources. After the glucose is consumed, the pH of the culture solutions increases from about pH 4.0-5.5 to 7.0-8.0 by the accumulation of ammonia formed during autolysis. Many of the free phenols disappear in the culture solution and in the cells with the formation of dark colored polymers. These polymers may be either precipitated directly by acidification of the culture medium or they may be extracted from the cells with dilute NaOH and then be precipitated by acidification. From 1 liter of medium about 1-2 g of polymer can be isolated from the solution and an additional 2-3 g can be extracted from the cells of *S. chartarum*. This corresponds to about 30% of the biomass formed in 1 liter of culture solution containing 30 g of glucose. The nitrogen content of the polymers ranged from 2 to 8%, depending on the organism and the N source and amount [169]. In the *S. chartarum* cell polymers, about 50% of the cell nitrogen was linked into the polymers [94]. The fungus polymers have been referred to as "humic acids" because they resemble soil humic acid polymers with respect to marked resistance to decomposition, elemental composition, exchange capacity, phenols released upon sodium amalgam reduction, and nitrogen and amino acids released upon 6 N HCl hydrolysis or by proteolytic enzymes [94, 168, 170].

     Some of the fungi if cultured on organic residues, such as cereal or bean straw, as the only carbon source showed an appreciable increase in the yield of polymers as compared to when they were cultivated on glucose. *Hendersonula toruloidea*, however, produced higher amounts in the glucose medium. If phenols, which can be isolated during microbial degradation of lignin, such as p-coumaric, ferulic, or sinapic acids, were added to glucose culture solutions, they were readily transformed by demethylation of the methoxy groups, introduction of additional hydroxy groups to the aromatic nucleus, and partial degradation of the three-carbon side chain.

     Many benzoic acid derivatives in addition to the phenols formed by the organisms from glucose could therefore be isolated from the culture solutions. In studies with specifically labeled phenols

[93, 94] a rapid transformation of the methoxyl and side chain carbons into CO_2 was noted whereas the ring carbons were only slowly
transformed. Ring ^{14}C was found primarily in the phenolic polymers. These observations as well as the disappearance of the free
phenols from the culture solution were evidence for a copolymeriza-
tion of the added phenols and their transformation products into
the polymers. Isolation of phenols following reductive degradation
of the polymers with sodium amalgam lead to the same conclusions
[93, 170]. Although the fungal polymers obtained from a glucose
culture solution yielded only phenols synthesized by the fungi, the
polymers obtained upon addition of lignin degradation products or
plant residues yielded, in addition, transformation products of
lignin phenols. The same phenols have been found after reductive
degradation of soil humic acids [171]. Similar observations were
made with numerous other soil fungi belonging to the Imperfecti
group [18]. Many of the fungi were able to degrade lignin and they
also formed phenols through biosynthesis from nonaromatic precursors.
Both the fungal and lignin derived phenols were incorporated into
the dark polymers formed.

C. Biochemistry of Microbial Phenolic Polymer Formation

Many of the reactions involved in polymer formation from the
fungal phenols appear to be autoxidative processes [93, 168]. Martin and Haider [94] demonstrated by using model mixtures that such
phenols as 2,3,5-, 2,4,5-, 2,3,6,- and 3,4,5-trihydroxytoluenes
react even under weakly acid or neutral conditions with the oxygen
of the air to form reactive quinones or radicals. These compounds
react with other phenols present in the mixture to form polymers.
The same was found for 2,3,4- and to a smaller extent for 3,4,5-
trihydroxybenzoic acids.

Musso and co-workers made numerous studies on the chemistry of
lichen litmus formation (30) from orcinol (31) and ammonia in the
presence of oxygen [172, 173]. Included were investigations of
the reaction of the quinone (33) of 2,3,5-trihydroxytoluene (32)

with phenols (Fig. 5). These reactions involve either a 1,4 addition of the phenol to the hydroxytoluquinone or a reaction of two
radicals formed from the quinone and the hydroquinone. Reactions
of quinones with phenols were also noted under acidic conditions
[174-176]. Under the pronounced alkaline conditions necessary for
litmus formation a hydroxyl group of the diphenyl derivative exchanges with ammonia and forms an amino group. This amine reacts
with another hydroxyhydroquinone [173] to form indophenols and
phenoxazones that are intermediates in the litmus formation. Under
the relatively neutral pH conditions present during formation of
the fungal polymers indicated above, ammonia ions probably did not
link into the large molecules. The nitrogen content more probably
originated from amino acids or peptides that could be detected in
the culture solutions in relatively high concentrations during the
autolysis of the cells. The actual amount of nitrogenous substances
available for linkage into the fungal polymers depends upon the
source and amount of nitrogen available to the organisms during
growth [169].

Some of the possible reactions of quinones with amino acid
compounds have been compiled by Mason [177] and are discussed by
Haider et al. [178]. In a recent review, Haworth [179] stated that
in humic acids some hydrogen-bound protein may be attached to the
aromatic rings. However, Hayes [180], by differential thermoanaly-
sis of an oxidized lignin complex with casein, obtained thermograms
that resembled those for lignin and not those for humic acid. In
a further mechanism a more stable linkage could involve a reaction
of o-quinones with amino acids or peptides as a nucleophilic 1,4
addition. This latter mechanism was proposed by Trautner and
Roberts [181] (see Bremner [182]). According to this proposal
appreciable amounts of ammonia should be released from the amino
group by Schiff base formation of the amino acid-substituted quinone
with another molecule of the amino acid. Riemer [183] concluded
from polarographic studies that a reaction of the o-quinone with
only one amino acid molecule was more probable (Fig. 6).

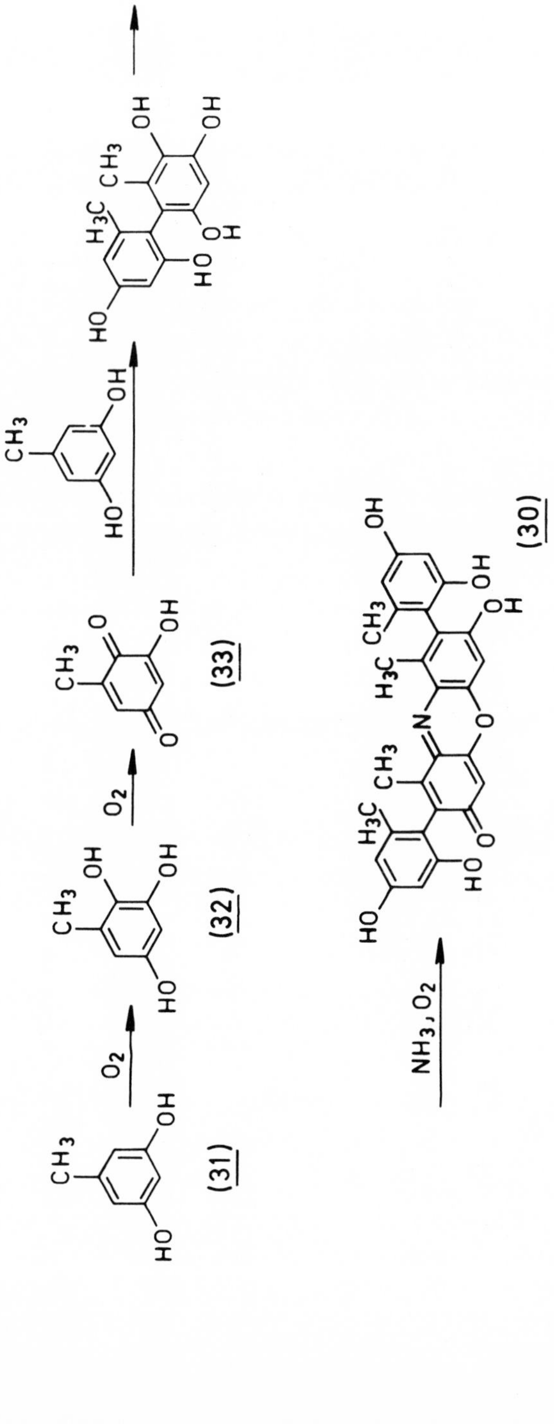

Fig. 5. Litmus formation from orcinol, oxygen, and ammonia [172].

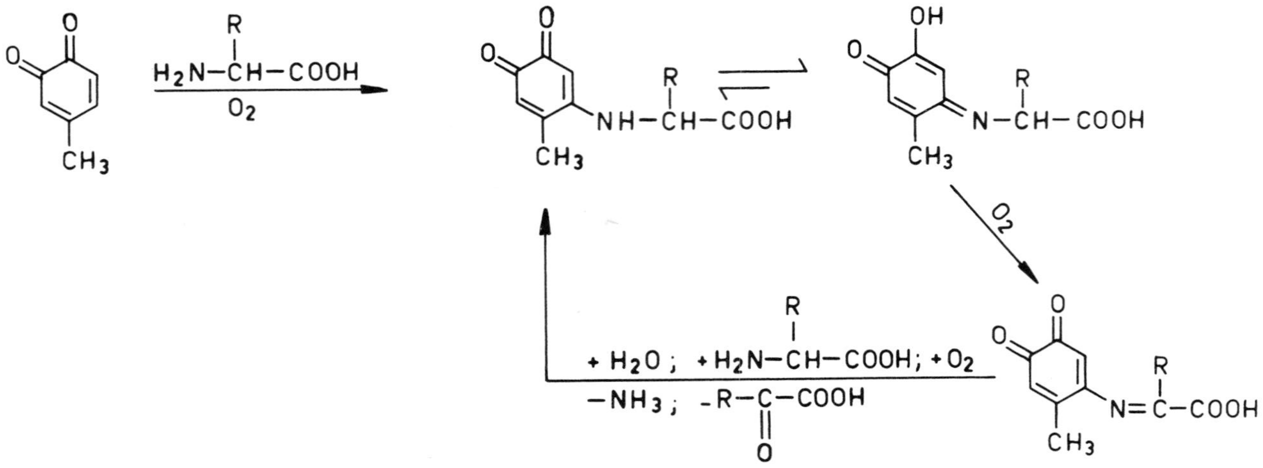

Fig. 6. Reaction of an o-quinone with amino acids under oxidizing conditions [183].

The quinone substituted by an amino acid is predominantly present in the p-quinoid imino stage and deaminates by shifting of the double bond and hydrolysis. Both the resulting amines and the quinones not substituted with amino acids are highly reactive compounds and polymerize either with themselves or with other phenols to form nitrogen-containing polymers. As long as the single quinone is substituted by the amino acid hydrolysis of the amino acid residue under acid conditions occurs. As polymerization progresses the residue becomes more and more resistant to hydrolysis [178].

Significant differences in the reactivity of various phenols were found when they were oxidized together with amino acids or peptides [93, 178]. For example, 2,3,5-trihydroxytoluene largely bound amino acids and peptides, whereas 2,4,5-trihydroxytoluene actively deaminated the amino acids and peptides. Riemer [183] and also Flaig and Riemer [184, 185] studied the reactions using polarographic techniques. They found that the amino acid-substituted 2-hydroxy-6-methylbenzoquinone-1,4 (*34*) was stabilized in the p-quinone form. The 2-hydroxy-5-methylbenzoquinone-1,4 (*35*), the oxidation product of 2,4,5-trihydroxytoluene, after the addition of the amino acid molecule was predominantly present in the o-quinone form and quickly disintegrated with the release of ammonia (Fig. 7).

Similarly the third possible isomer of the asymmetric trihydroxytoluenes, the 2,3,5-trihydroxytoluene, binds amino acid and undergoes deamination only to a minor extent because of its stabilization in the p-quinoid form.

Amino sugar units are present in soil humus and account for at least 5-10% of the soil nitrogen [182]. They are present in the fulvic acid fraction and have been isolated after 6 N HCl hydrolysis of humic acid [186, 187]. Some of these units may be associated with relatively resistant fungal cell wall debris [34, 141, 142] but most probably originate from numerous microbial polymers that have undergone various degrees of degradation and recombination. Webley and Jones [41] have suggested that more attention should be given to microbial cell wall polymers with respect to their role in soil humus formation.

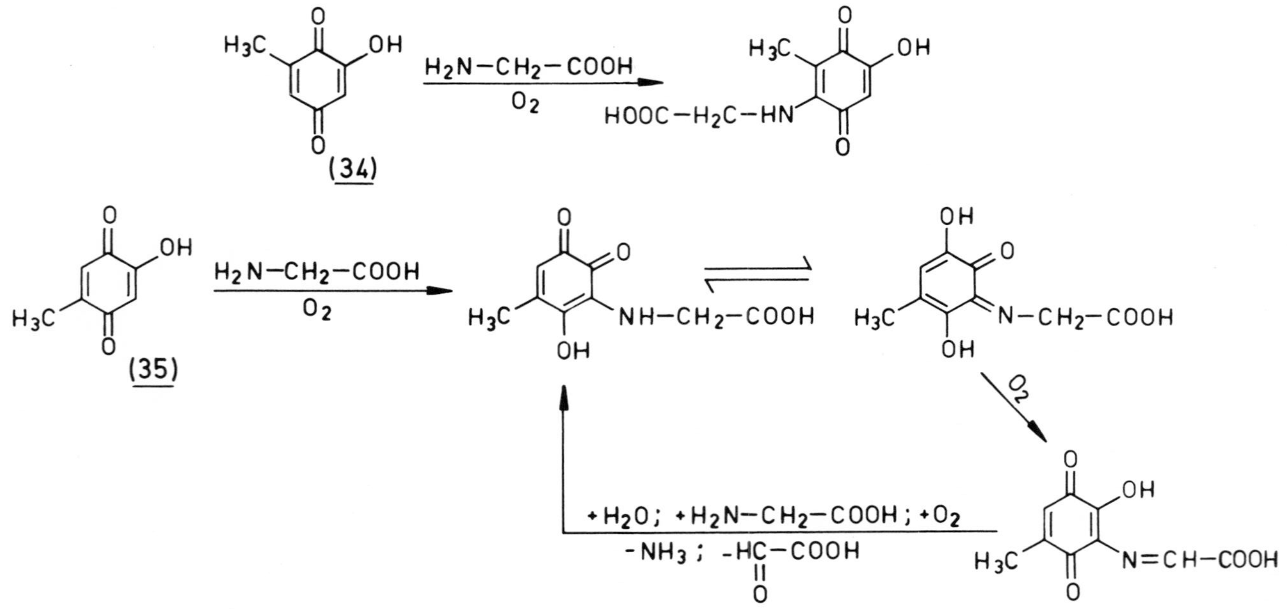

Fig. 7. Reaction of 2-hydroxy-6-methyl- and 2-hydroxy-5-methylbenzoquinone-1,4 with amino acids [184, 185].

Recently, Bondietti et al. [188] studied the linkage of ^{14}C-glucosamine and chitosan from *Mucor rouxii* into model phenolase and autoxidatively formed phenolic polymers using mixtures of phenols commonly synthesized by soil fungi. Respirometer studies showed an increased O_2 consumption with the addition of glucosamine or chitosan. Polymers formed in the presence of glucosamine contained up to one-third amino sugar units. Both the glucosamine and the chitosan were appreciably stabilized against microbial degradation in the soil through incorporation into the polymers. The study suggested that amino sugar units are good nucleophiles and may be linked through the amino group to phenols in the presence of phenolases or trihydroxyphenols, which readily autoxidase. In this manner numerous amino sugar-containing microbial polymers at different stages of degradation and recombination could be linked into soil humic polymers.

The participation of phenolase enzymes during the formation of the polymers is possibly of minor significance for most of the fungi listed in Table 2. The formation of the polymers appears to be laregly an autoxidative process. *Hendersonula toruloidea* is an exception, because an active phenolase concentrate can be obtained from the mycelium of this fungus [160] and polymer formation in the culture medium occurs at pH 4.5 and above.

The fungi that produce humic acid-type substances through phenol biosynthesis belong to the Imperfecti group and are common soil fungi [4, 167]. Most of the wood-destroying basidiomycetes, especially the white rot fungi, do not form similar phenols through biosynthesis and are more or less restricted to the biodegradation of phenolic polymers, such as lignin. The production of "humic acids" during their action on lignified plant material seems to be low; however, Schanel [189] reported the formation of a red pigment, which was present after the decomposition of sawdust by *Pleurotus ostreatus*. For brown rot fungi, however, biosynthesis of phenols has been reported. *Lentinus lepideus* [84, 190], for example, forms p-coumaric acid methyl ester. This compound is transformed to p-methoxycinnamic acid and to isoferulic acid and their methyl esters, respectively. Twelve different species of wood-destroying fungi described by Power et al. [191] synthesized p-hydroxybenzoic, p-coumaric, caffeic, and isoferulic acids from glucose through the shikimic acid pathway. Terphenyl derivatives, such as the polyporic acid, have been isolated from *Polyporus* spp. Reed et al. [192] concluded that these were synthesized by coupling of two phenylpropane units.

From the fruiting bodies of *Polyporus hispidus* and *P. schwein-itzii*, hispidin (36) (Fig. 8) was isolated by Bu'lock et al. [193, 194] and was oxidized by a highly active phenoloxidase present in the fruiting structures to form a lignin-like polymer that was bound to other cell constituents. This material did not have methoxy

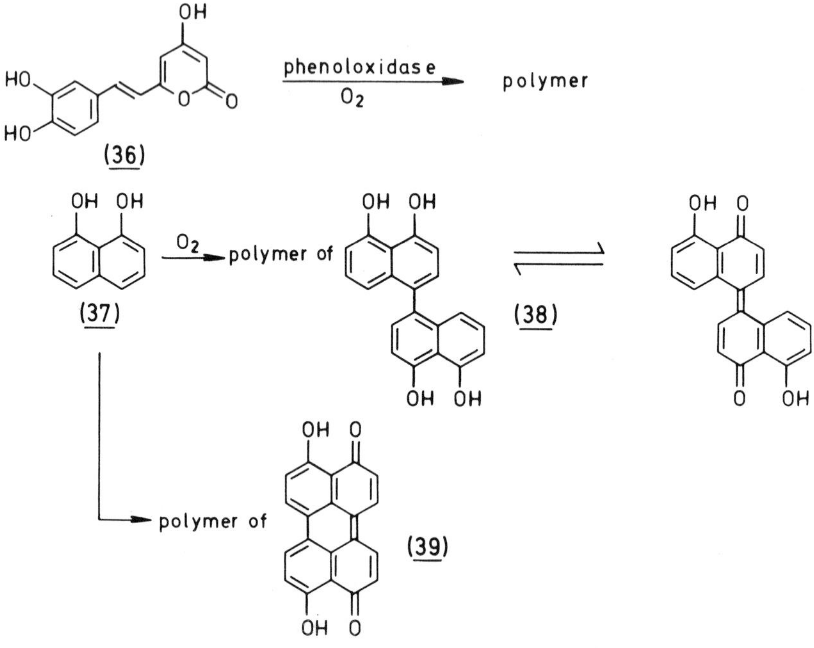

Fig. 8. Formation of polymers in *Polyporus hispidus* from his-pidin (36) and from naphthoquinone (37) in *Daldinia concentrica* (38) and *Aspergillus niger* (39).

groups but in terms of its function and mode of its formation it
was considered analogous to lignin. A similar substance is the
"Chagi" described by Loviagina et al. [195], which was isolated from
the fruiting sturctures of *Poria obliqua*. The polymer could be extracted with hot water and, according to Bu'Lock [196], it is a
phenolic polymer of lignin degradation products transported into
the fruiting bodies where they are repolymerized by the phenoloxidase. By degradation methods used in lignin chemistry, mixtures of
p-hydroxyphenyl, vanillyl, and sinapyl derivatives, mostly of the
C_6C_1 type, with lesser amounts of the C_6C_3 type, were obtained.
According to Loviagina et al. [195] Chagi is more similar to humic
acids than to lignin.

Condensed ring aromatic compounds formed by microbes may also
serve as structural units for soil humus formation. In this respect
the "P-type humic acids" isolated by Kumada and his co-workers [197-
199] and similar structures isolated from such ascomycetes as *Aspergillus niger* and from the fruiting bodies of *Daldinia concentrica*
are of interest. On alkali fusion, Nicolaus [166] and Bu'Lock [196]
obtained a mixture of 1,8-dihydroxynaphthalene (37) and catechol
from the *Daldinia* polymer. From the *Aspergillus* pigment only mel-
litic acid was isolated [196]. According to Anderson and Murray
[200] and Allport and Bu'Lock [201, 202] the *Daldinia* pigment is
probably a redox polymer of 1,8-naphthohydroquinone (38) (Fig. 8).
Lambert et al. [202a] extracted 69 mg of 2-methoxy-1,4-naphthoquinone
from 8 kg of a high-montmorillonite tropical soil.

Robertson and Whalley [203] and Bu'Lock [196] reported that the
Aspergillus pigment (39) is a derivative of perylenequinone, a structural type that is reported to occur in P-type humic acids [204],
and may originate from fungal metabolites [205]. Similar compounds
more related to anthraquinones have been obtained from many podzolic
soils [206] directly by extraction with organic solvents. Anthracene derivatives may also be synthesized by *Streptomyces aureus* [161].

Many condensed aromatic hydrocarbons are also obtained upon zinc
dust distillation of soil humic polymers. In this way naphthalene,

anthracene, benzofluorene, pyrene, benzopyrenes, perylene, and
others have been reported in small yields [143, 179, 207]. However,
some authors suggested the possibility that these products might be
formed from more simple phenols by the zinc dust treatment. However,
Mathur [208], by using cultures and enzyme preparation of *Poria
subacida*, obtained yields of 2-methyl-1,4-naphthoquinone up to 10%
of a podzol fulvic acid preparation that had been previously studied
by Hansen and Schnitzer [209].

For more details of the relationship between certain fungal
pigments and distinct soil constituents the reader is referred to
the reviews by Haworth [179], Hurst [210], and Kumada and Sato [211].

Most microbial pigments are formed by aromatization of aliphatic
carbohydrate degradation products. The aromatic structures originate from the so-called "secondary metabolism" of microorganisms.
Sometimes this metabolism is called "overflow metabolism" because
the total substrate energy is not used for the synthesis of the main
cell constituents but some of it is expended for the secondary metabolic processes through which a great variety of compounds are
synthesized. This biosynthesis is not a continuous activity of an
organism but occurs under certain conditions or at certain stages
of development. If dark colored microbial polymers are considered
as secondary metabolic products, environmental conditions will influence their formation. Jayasankar and Bhat [212] reported that
aeration exerted a pronounced effect on melanin production by *Micrococcus varians* in a culture solution containing phenols. Similarly,
Filip et al. [213] noted that *Epicoccum nigrum* formed smaller amounts
of polymer in vigorously aerated culture solutions than in stationary cultures.

The relationship between humification potentialities and oxidase activity of soil microorganisms have been frequently discussed.
Novak [214] theorized that by oxidative degradation of nutrients the
energy is furnished, whereas the anaerobic respiration furnishes the
metabolites for the formation of humic products. Bortels and colleagues [147, 147a] investigated the synthesis of dark pigments by

Azotobacter chroococcum. They concluded that the humification reactions are promoted when the oxidase activity is suppressed. Similar observations were reported by Sundman [148a]. With mixed bacterial populations selected for positive or negative reactions to
certain oxidase tests, it was found that the oxidase-negative bacteria were more active in producing humic substances from straw than
were the oxidase-positive organisms. The oxidase-negative inoculum
also significantly decreased the carbohydrate content of the straw.

In a study by Mann [148], the metabolic differences in melanin-
forming and melanin-free strains of *Pseudomonas aeruginosa* were investigated. The melanin formation occurred only in the presence of
tyrosin. The melanin-forming strains were not regarded as variants
containing tyrosinase but as strains lacking the enzyme for degrading
homogentisic acid, which is an intermediate in tyrosin degradation.
It was observed that this acid accumulates in melanin-forming strains
and is oxidized to the melanin (Fig. 9). The pigment is formed by
polymerization of homogentisic acid and the benzoquinone acetic
acid (40) and not by polymerization of dihydroxyphenlalanine (DOPA,
41). This observation is interesting in connection with some aspects of the browning reaction of freshly fallen leaves by *Pseudomonas* spp. [215].

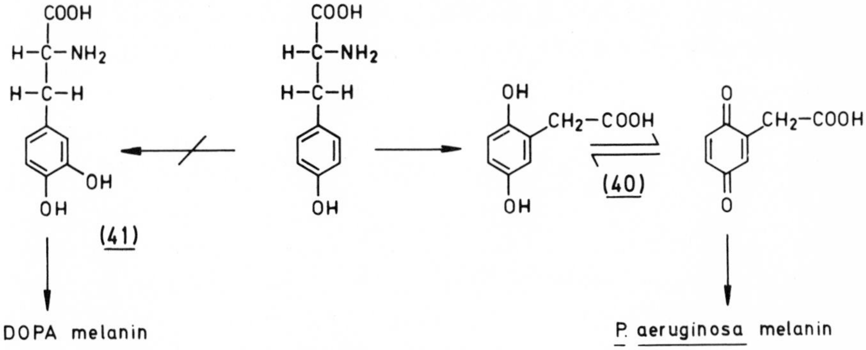

Fig. 9. Formation of *Pseudomonas aeruginosa* melanin from tyrosine through homogentisic acid (40).

IV. INFLUENCE OF CLAY MINERALS ON HUMUS-FORMING
PROCESSES BY SOIL MICROORGANISMS

As well as serving as a source of macro- and micronutrient elements, inorganic soil constituents influence microbial growth and
activity by adsorption phenomena [216]. The clay minerals are the
most active fractions and influence microbial communities and single
species by adsorption of organic and inorganic nutrients, of metabolic and autolytic products, or extracellular enzymes, and even of
the microbial cells [217-219]. These effects may sometimes increase
or decrease microbial growth and activity [213].

Inasmuch as humic substances are products of microbial activity,
clay minerals may presumably exert an effect on their synthesis.
This is implied by the well-known observation that the addition of
clays including allophane to sand or soil cultures decreases carbon
and nitrogen losses and increases humus formation [220-225]. Some
investigators have suggested that the enhanced humus formation may
be caused by a catalytic effect of the clay on the polymerization
process [226-229]. Scheffer and Kroll [230] reported an increased
polymerization of hydroquinone in the presence of finely ground
quartz. Kyuma and Kawaguchi [231] observed that allophane increased
oxygen uptake in a pyrogallol solution.

Several studies suggest that enhanced humus formation may be
related to a more direct effect of the clay minerals on the soil
microorganisms. Filip [232] found that bentonite additions to soil
or sand cultures increased the numbers of microbes and the formation
of humic substances. In further studies by Filip et al. [213, 233],
montmorillonite and other clay minerals in concentrations of 0.25-
1.0% were added to liquid cultures of *Epicoccum nigrum* and *Stachybotrys chartarum*; two fungi that form humic polymers from synthesized
phenols. Biomass formation and utilization of nutrients was greatly
accelerated or increased (Fig. 10). Autolysis commenced much earlier
and after 30 days the quantities of humic-type polymers found in
both the culture solutions and in the fungal cells were greater in

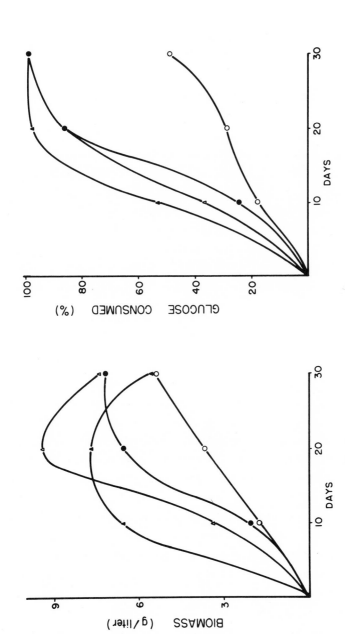

Fig. 10.   Influence of montmorillonite on biomass formation and glucose consumption by *E. nigrum.*

the cultures with clay additions (Table 3). These effects were
noted in shake or thin-layer stationary cultures. In poorly aerated
cultures the clays exerted little effect on growth processes or even
decreased growth at the higher concentrations.

TABLE 3

Influence of Montmorillonite on Phenolic Polymer Production
by *Epicoccum nigrum* and *Stachybotrys chartarum*[a]

| | | Montmorillonite (% w/v) | | | |
Fungus		Control	0.25	0.55	1.0
E. nigrum	HA$_1$[b]	0.12	0.38	0.57	0.98
	HA$_2$	0.10	0.73	0.78	0.47
S. chartarum	HA$_1$	0.49	0.86	1.31	1.62
	HA$_2$	3.61	4.00	4.60	4.55

[a]Reproduced from [213].

[b]Polymers formed (ash-free) in the solution (HA$_1$) and in the
cells (HA$_2$). Grams from 1 liter of culture solution after 30 days
in stationary cultures *(E. nigrum)* or after 15 days in shake cultures *(S. chartarum)*.

Bondietti et al. [169] studied the influence of clay and nitrogen source on growth and humic acid formation by *Hendersonula toruloidea*, *Aspergillus sydowi*, and *Stachybotrys* spp. The clays greatly
accelerated growth and humic-polymer formation. Without clay NaNO$_3$
was a poor N source for the *Stachybotrys* spp. The addition of montmorillonite or vermiculite greatly improved growth. In fact in the
presence of these minerals the NO$_3$-N was as good a N source as was
peptone in the cultures without clay. The clay additions did not
influence carbon or nitrogen content, exchange capacity, carboxyl
groups, hydroxyl groups, or the kinds of phenols released on reductive degradation of the polymers. The addition of clays did not
increase O$_2$ uptake in mixtures of fungus phenols with phenoloxidase
enzymes at pH 6.5 or under autoxidative conditions (pH 8.0). The
phenols formed by the fungi were adsorbed by the clays in slightly

acid solutions but not at neutral or slightly alkaline conditions. The adsorption of organic anions is associated with polyvalent metals at the clay surfaces [234]. By increasing the pH the adsorbed anions may be replaced.

The magnitude of the enhanced growth effect of the clays on the fungus cultures was related to the exchange capacity. Montmorillonite was more effective than vermiculite and vermiculite more effective than finely ground kaolinite or quartz. A direct contact of the clays with the fungal cells was not necessary for increased growth. When montmorillonite was enclosed in dialysis tubing, growth and metabolic activity were still enhanced, although to a slightly reduced degree.

V.   COMMENTS AND CONCLUSIONS

Aromatic plant constituents, especially lignins, are without doubt a very important source of constituent phenolic units for soil humus formation. Numerous degradative studies of soil organic polymers have always yielded phenols that are lignin derived. Recently, Mayaudon and Batistic [235] studied the decomposition of uniformly ^{14}C-labeled Klason lignin in soil. After 150 days unchanged lignin derived phenols were recovered upon nitrobenzene oxidation of the soil organic fraction. The quantity of unaltered lignin in most normal soils is very low, however, which indicates a relatively rapid change in the lignin after entering the soil [236].

Many aromatic or phenolic compounds not present in lignins have also been identified after various degradative procedures [66, 111, 207, 210]. Many of the additional phenols have been resorcinol derivatives and some investigators have suggested that they originate from plant flavonoids. Much evidence, however, is accumulating that microbial synthesis is an important source of phenolic units for soil humus polymer formation. In recent studies on microbial humic acid-type polymers predominantly resorcinol derivatives were found

on chemical degradation. Martin and Haider [66] found the same
phenols on Na-amalgam reduction of fungal humic acids as were found
in free form in culture solutions of the fungi. These and additional
aromatic structures were observed upon alkali fusion of soil and
Azotobacter humic acids by Robert-Gero et al. [237].

Recently, Fustec-Mathon et al. [238] incubated compost soil
with uniformly labeled glucose and degraded the radioactive humic
acids by Na-amalgam. After 5 days they obtained about 8-10% of the
humic acid radioactivity in the ether extracts of the acidified reduction mixtures. Upon separation on thin-layer plates this activity
was shown to be concentrated in several phenolic spots, whereas
others were inactive. Later on, the activity that could be extracted
with ether on Na-amalgam reduction decreased somewhat. Phenols that
were both lignin and microbially derived were found in the free state
in water extracts of the upper portions of manure accumulations in
cattle feed lots. In the deeper, more humified layers, the same
phenols were present in humic acid polymers and were released on reductive degradation [239]. Cheshire et al. [207] studied different
soil humic acids by KOH-fusion degradation. Phloroglucinol, resorcinol, and orcinol in addition to other phenols were obtained in
relatively high yields. The authors speculated that the resorcinol
compounds might have been secondary products of the reaction. Reductive degradation of peat and soil humic acids have yielded the
resorcinol-type phenols and these have been considered to be microbially derived [66, 210]. This conclusion was strengthened by
Grabbe and Haider [18], who found that the residues of white rot
fungi growing on straw yielded only lignin-derived phenols upon reductive degradation, whereas the residues from the same substrate
following incubation with phenol-synthesizing Fungi Imperfecti
yielded both lignin and fungal phenols.

Condensed aromatic structures isolated from soil humus should
receive more attention [205, 206, 211, 240, 241]. Although some
soil chemists have suggested that the methods used in their isolation
may have caused their formation, evidence is accumulating that they

may originate from microbial metabolism. Condensed aromatic structures have been found in various microbial pigments. Anthracene
and derivatives have recently been isolated from the humic acid-like
polymers from old cultures of *Streptomyces aureus* [161]. Additional
evidence of condensed aromatic structures has been obtained by
Mathur [209] who isolated 2-methyl-1,4-naphthoquinone in high yield
upon enzymatic degradation of a fulvic acid preparation.

   Soil and fungal humic acids contain nitrogen. As much as 40%
of this nitrogen can be recovered as α-amino nitrogen after hydrolysis of humic acid in 6 N HCl and another 5-10% may be recovered in
amino sugars. There is good evidence that the amino units are
linked into developing humic polymers through nucleophilic addition
of free amino groups in amino acids, peptides, amino sugars, and
polysaccharides containing amino sugar units to quinones formed
through enzymatic or autoxidative oxidation. The SH groups in certain peptides could also be involved in this type of reaction. It
is apparent, therefore, that the number and variety of constituents
for humic acid synthesis is tremendous and will depend on those
present in the microenvironment. Some of the humic acid polymers
found in microbial cells or new molecules formed during oxidative
reactions in the soil would undergo certain degrees of alterations
with time. Amino acid units in peptides [168] and sugar units in
polysaccharide chains some distance from the phenolic polymer linkage
could be more susceptible to microbial attack than those units closer
to the phenol. This may partly explain the greater susceptibility
of new humus to decomposition than the older humus polymers. Reactions of the molecules with metal ions or clays are also undoubtedly
involved in the stabilization process.

   Very little is known concerning the biochemistry of the formation of the polysaccharide fraction of soil humus. Most fractions
isolated by modern separation procedures contain ten or more major
constituent units [242-244]. Many investigators believe that these
fractions consist of a mixture of plant and microbial polysaccharides
and that the methods have failed to separate them. Recently, the

opinion has been expressed that in the soil environment, plant and microbial polysaccharides at all stages of decomposition may be re-combined to form very complex molecules and that those which are resistant to decomposition or become resistant through salt or com-plex formation with metal ions, clays, or phenolic polymers persist [48, 66].

Clay minerals exert a marked effect on growth of soil microbes and may accelerate or enhance humus formation. Enhanced humus for-mation may be related to a direct effect of the clays on microbial metabolism or a catalytic effect of the clays on the polymerization process.

For further possible chemical reactions involved in the forma-tion of soil humic polymers the reader is referred to reviews by Felbeck [245-247] and Flaig et al. [248].

Since this manuscript was prepared, a few additional references that should be briefly mentioned have come to the author's attention. Several deal with the microbial degradation of lignin in relation to soil humus formation [249, 250]. Harkin [251] and Kirk et al. [252] demonstrated the possibility of microbial depolymerization of lignin by phenoloxidase-catalyzed free-radical formation followed by oxi-dative cleavage of the alkylphenyl C-C bond of the lignin alcohol units with the release of the aliphatic three-carbon side chain. Studies by Trojanowsky [253] and Sundman [127] using an *Agrobacterium* sp. tend to support this view (Fig. 8). The accumulation of methoxy-aryl components may indicate a specific 0-demethylating enzyme of *Agro bacterium* sp. A specific vanillate 0-demethylase that cleaves 0-methy groups in the meta position to carboxyl groups has been demonstrated for *Pseudomonas fluorescen* [254, 255]. From another *Pseudomonas* sp. a specific p-anisate-0-demethylase was isolated that demethylates methoxyl groups in the para position to carboxyl groups [256].

Humification studies utilizing ^{14}C-labeled substrates continue to appear. After 20 to 30 days, 6-12% of the activity from ^{14}C-labeled glucose or cellulose was found in the hydrolyzable amino acid fraction [257]. From the amount remaining after another 6 years a half-life of 6 to 7 years was calculated for the carbon in this fraction. Investigations by Huntjens [258] demonstrated a marked influence of living plants on nitrogen transformations in grassland soil. The author theorized that microorganisms immobilize nitrogen by using root excretions and cells as carbon sources and that some of this nitrogen is stabilized in microbial products, such as the dark polymers formed by some streptomycetes.

Piper and Posner [259, 260] evaluated and improved the sodium amalgam method for degrading humic acid and applied the improved procedure to a large number of soil humic acids. They recovered a mixture of microbial and lignin-type hydroxyphenols and hydroxybenzoic acids. Seventeen were identified and accounted for approximately 12-32% of the original humic acid preparations.

REFERENCES

1. J. P. Martin, in *Organic Chemicals in the Soil Environment* (C. A. I. Goring and J. W. Hamaker, Eds.), p. 733, Dekker, New York, 1972.
2. D. J. Cosgrove, in *Soil Biochemistry* (A. D. McLaren and G. H. Peterson, Eds.), Vol. 1, p. 216, Dekker, New York, 1967.
3. J. R. Freney, in *Soil Biochemistry* (A. D. McLaren and G. H. Peterson, Eds.), Vol. 1, p. 229, Dekker, New York, 1967.
4. F. E. Clark and E. A. Paul, *Advan. Agron.*, *22*, 375 (1970).
5. B. A. Stewart, L. K. Porter, and F. G. Viets, *Soil Sci. Soc. Amer. Proc.*, *30*, 355, 453 (1966).
6. G. Minderman, *J. Ecol.*, *56*, 355 (1968).
7. M. H. B. Hayes, M. Stacey, and J. Standley, *Trans. 9th Int. Congr. Soil Sci.*, *3*, 247 (1968).
8. D. T. Parker, *Soil Sci. Soc. Amer. Proc.*, *26*, 559 (1962).
9. M. Witkamp and J. S. Olsen, *Oikos*, *14*, 138 (1963).
10. D. S. Jenkinson, *J. Soil Sci.*, *16*, 104 (1965).
11. D. S. Jenkinson, *Soil Sci.*, *111*, 64 (1971).
12. F. Führ and D. Sauerbeck, in *Isotopes and Radiation in Soil Organic Matter Studies*, p. 241, IAEA, Vienna 1968.
13. D. S. Jenkinson, in *Experimental Pedology*, p. 199, Butterworths, London, 1964.
14. S. L. Jansson and J. Persson, in *Isotopes and Radiation in Soil Organic Matter Studies*, p. 111, IAEA, Vienna 1968.
15. H. E. Oberländer and K. Roth, in *Isotopes and Radiation in Soil Organic Matter Studies*, p. 251, IAEA, Vienna 1968.
16. W. Flaig, U. Schobinger, and H. Deuel, *Chem. Ber.*, *92*, 1972 (1959).

17. K. Haider and K. H. Domsch, *Arch. Mikrobiol.*, *64*, 338 (1969).
18. K. Grabbe and K. Haider, *Z. Pflanzenernähr. Düng. Bodenk.*, *129*, 202 (1971).
19. J. Stotzky and J. L. Mortenson, *Soil Sci. Soc. Amer. Proc.*, *22*, 521 (1958).
20. H. Sörensen, *Soil Sci.*, *95*, 45 (1963).
21. D. S. Jenkinson, in *The Use of Isotopes in Soil Organic Matter Studies*, p. 187, FAO-IAEA, 1966.
22. F. E. Broadbent and A. G. Norman, *Soil Sci. Soc. Amer. Proc.*, *22*, 264 (1946).
23. J. Szolnoki, F. Kunc, J. Macura, and V. Vancura, *Folia Microbiol.*, *8*, 356 (1963).
24. D. Sauerbeck, Habilitationsschrift, Universität Bonn, 202 pp., 1966.
25. D. Sauerbeck, in *The Use of Isotopes in Soil Organic Matter Studies*, p. 209, FAO-IAEA 1966.
26. D. Sauerbeck, *Landw. Forsch.*, *21*, 91 (1968).
27. S. L. Jansson, *Trans. 7th Int. Congr. Soil Sci.*, *2*, 635 (1960).
28. H. E. Freytag and H. Igel, *Albrecht-Thaer Arch.*, *12*, 311, 327 (1968).
29. M. V. Cheshire, C. M. Mundie, and H. Shepherd, *Soil Biol. Biochem.*, *1*, 117 (1969).
30. B. Novák, *Zentbl. Bakter. Parasit. Infekt. Hyg. II. Abt.*, *125*, 71 (1970).
31. H. E. Freytag, in *Studies about Humus, Symp. Humus et Planta IV*, p. 46, Prague, 1967.
32. H. Igel, in *Studies about Humus, Symp. Humus et Planta V*, p. 103, Prague, 1971.
33. G. H. Wagner and V. K. Mutatkar, *Soil Sci. Soc. Amer. Proc.*, *32*, 683 (1968).
34. G. H. Wagner, in *Isotopes and Radiation in Soil Organic Matter Studies*, p. 197, IAEA, Vienna, 1968.
35. J. Mayaudon, in *Soil Biochemistry* (A. D. McLaren and J. Skujins, Ed.), Vol. 2, p. 202, Dekker, New York, 1971.
35a. J. Macura and Z. Kubátová, in *Studies about Humus, Symp. Humus et Planta V*, p. 161, Prague, 1971.
36. M. Haguchi and I. Uemura, *J. Gen. Appl. Microbiol. (Japan)*, *11*, 145 (1965).
37. M. Mandel and E. T. Reese, *J. Bacteriol.*, *79*, 816 (1960).
38. L. Jurasek, J. Ross Colvin, and D. R. Whitaker, *Advan. Appl. Microbiol.*, *9*, 131 (1967).
39. B. Norkrans, *Advan. Appl. Microbiol.*, *9*, 91 (1967).
40. E. T. Reese, in *Matière organique et fertilité du sol, Pontifica Academiae Scientiarum Scripta Varia*, *32*, 535 (1968).
41. D. M. Webley and D. Jones, in *Soil Biochemistry* (A. D. McLaren and J. Skujins, Eds.), Vol. 2, p. 446, Dekker, New York, 1971.
42. H. J. Potgieter and M. Alexander, *J. Bacteriol.*, *91*, 1526 (1966).
43. B. J. Bloomfield and M. Alexander, *J. Bacteriol.*, *93*, 1276 (1967).

44. M. Alexander, in *Saertryk af festskrift for Hans Laurits Jensen*, p. 41, 1968.
45. M. Alexander, in *Matière organique et fertilité du sol; Pontifica Academiae Scientiarum Scripta Varia*, *32*, 511 (1968).
46. R. M. Pengra, M. A. Cole, and M. Alexander, *J. Bacteriol.*, *97*, 1056 (1969).
47. P. Fynch, M. H. B. Hayes,and M. Stacey, in *Soil Biochemistry* (A. D. McLaren and J. Skujins, Eds.), Vol. 2, p. 257, Dekker, New York, 1971.
48. J. P. Martin, *Soil Biol. Biochem.*, *3*, 33 (1971).
49. J. P. Martin, J. O. Ervin, and R. Shepherd, *Soil Sci. Soc. Amer. Proc.*, *29*, 397 (1965).
50. J. P. Martin, J. O. Ervin, and R. Shepherd, *Soil Sci. Soc. Amer. Proc.*, *30*, 196 (1966).
51. J. P. Martin and S. J. Richards, *J. Bacteriol.*, *85*, 1288 (1963).
52. G. D. Swincer, J. M. Oades, and D. J. Greenland, *Advan. Agron.*, *21*, 195 (1969).
52a. D. J. Greenland, *Soils Fert.*, *28*, 415 (1965).
53. D. C. Lynch and L. J. Cotnoir, *Soil Sci. Soc. Amer. Proc.*, *20*, 367 (1956).
54. J. Mayaudon and P. Simonart, *Suppl. Ann. Inst. Pasteur (Paris)*, *109*, 224 (1965).
55. P. Simonart and J. Mayaudon, in *2e Symp. Int. sur les Sciences Nucléaires appliquées à la Pédologie*, p. 91, Gand, 1961.
56. J. Mayaudon, in *Isotopes and Radiation in Soil Organic Matter Studies*, p. 177, IAEA, Vienna, 1968.
57. P. Simonart, L. Batistic, and J. Mayaudon, *Plant Soil*, *27*, 153 (1967).
58. L. H. Sörensen, *Soil Sci.*, *104*, 234 (1967).
59. J. N. Ladd and P. G. Brisbane, *Austral. J. Soil Res.*, *5*, 161 (1967).
60. P. G. Brisbane and J. N. Ladd, *Trans. 9th Int. Congr. Soil Sci.* (Adelaide), *3*, 309 (1968).
60a. J. N. Ladd and H. J. A. Butler, *Austral. J. Soil Res.*, *7*, 241, 253 (1969).
61. J. Basaraba and R. L. Starkey, *Soil Sci.*, *101*, 17 (1966).
62. R. I. Davies, C. B. Coulson, and D. Lewis, *Proc. Roy. Dublin Soc.*, *Ser. A*, *1*, 183 (1960).
63. R. I. Davies, C. B. Coulson, and D. Lewis, *J. Soil Sci.*, *15*, 299 (1964).
64. R. I. Davies, C. B. Coulson, and D. Lewis, *J. Soil Sci.*, *15*, 310 (1964).
65. R. I. Davies, *Soil Sci.*, *111*, 80 (1971).
65a. F. E. Broadbent, in *Microbiology and Soil Fertility* (C. M. Gilmour and O. N. Allen, Eds.), p. 59, Oregon State Univ. Press, 1964.
66. J. P. Martin and K. Haider, *Soil Sci.*, *111*, 54 (1971).
67. S. Bruckert, F. Jaquin, and M. Metche, *Bull. Ecol. Natl. Sup. Agron. (Nancy)*, *9*, 73 (1967).
68. D. C. Whitehead, *Soil Fert.*, *26*, 217 (1963).
69. T. S. C. Wang, S-Y. Cheng, and H. Tung, *Soil Sci.*, *103*, 360 (1967).

70. T. S. C. Wang, T-K. Yang, and T-T Chuang, *Soil Sci.*, *103*, 239 (1967).
71. W. D. Guenzi and T. M. McCalla, *Soil Sci. Soc. Amer. Proc.*, *30*, 214 (1966).
72. T. M. McCalla, in *Biochemical Interactions among Plants*, p. 39, Natl. Acad. Sci., Washington, D.C., 1971.
73. M. Schnitzer and S. I. M. Skinner, *Soil Sci.*, *99*, 278 (1965).
74. G. Ogner and M. Schnitzer, *Can. J. Chem.*, *49*, 1053 (1971).
75. L. Batistic and J. Mayaudon, *Ann. Inst. Pasteur*, *118*, 199 (1970)
76. T. S. C. Wang, K-L. Yeh, S-Y. Cheng, and T-K. Yang, in *Biochemical Interactions among Plants*, p. 113, Natl. Acad. Sci., Washington, D.C., 1971.
76a. F. Kunc, *Folia Microbiol.*, *16*, 41 (1971).
77. S. Dagley, in *Soil Biochemistry* (A. D. McLaren and G. H. Peterson, Eds.), Vol. 2, p. 287, Dekker, New York, 1967.
78. W. C. Evans, in *Fermentation Advances* (D. Perlman, Ed.), p. 649, Academic, New York, London, 1969.
79. S. Dagley, in *Advances in Microbiology and Physiology* (A. H. Rose and Y. F. Wilkinson, Eds.), Vol. 6, Academic, New York, London, 1971.
80. O. Hayaishi, *Bacteriol. Rev.*, *30*, 720 (1966).
81. L. N. Ornston, *Bacteriol. Rev.*, *35*, 87 (1971).
82. J. Trojanowski, A. Leonowicz, and B. Hampel, *Acta Microbiol. Pol.*, *15*, 17 (1966).
83. H. Ishikawa, W. J. Schubert, and F. F. Nord, *Biochem. Zeitschr.*, *338*, 153 (1963).
84. W. J. Schubert, in *Lignin Biochemistry*, p. 131, Academic, New York, London, 1965.
85. H. Lyr and H. Ziegler, *Phytopathol. Z.*, *36*, 146 (1959).
86. J. Trojanowski, *Int. Biodetn. Bull.*, *5*, 119 (1969).
87. A. Leonowicz and J. Trojanowski, *Acta Microbiol. Pol.*, *14*, 55 (1965).
88. T. Fukuzumi, H. Takatuka, and K. Minami, *Arch. Biochem. Biophys.*, *129*, 396 (1969).
89. T. K. Kirk, J. M. Harkin, and E. B. Cowling, *Biochem. Biophys. Acta*, *165*, 145 (1968).
90. T. Fukuzumi and T. Shibamoto, *J. Jap. Wood Res. Soc.*, *11*, 248 (1965).
91. K. Haider, S. Lim and W. Flaig, *Holzforsch.*, *18*, 81 (1964).
92. K. Haider, *Zentbl. Bakter. Parasit. Infekt. Hyg. I.*, *198*, 308 (1965).
93. K. Haider and J. P. Martin, *Soil Sci. Soc. Amer. Proc.*, *31*, 766 (1967).
94. J. P. Martin and K. Haider, *Soil Sci.*, *107*, 260 (1969).
95. H. Börner, *Naturwissenschaften*, *6*, 1 (1958).
96. H. Börner, *Contr. Boyce Thompson Inst.*, *20*, 39 (1959).
97. W. Barz, *Z. Naturforsch.*, *24b*, 234 (1969).
98. H. Grisebach and H. Zilg, *Z. Naturforsch.*, *23b*, 494 (1968).
99. J. Holowczak, J. Kuć, and E. G. Williams, *Phytopathology*, *50*, 640 (1960).
100. S. Hattori and I. Noguchi, *Bot. Mag. (Tokyo*, *71*, 43 (1958).

101. S. Hattori and I. Noguchi, *Nature (London)*, *184*, 1145 (1959).
102. A. K. Chatterjee and L. N. Gibbins, *J. Bacteriol.*, *100*, 594 (1969).
103. D. W. S. Westlake, G. Talbot, E. R. Blakley, and F. J. Simpson, *Can. J. Microbiol.*, *5*, 621 (1959).
104. F. J. Simpson, G. Talbot, and D. W. S. Westlake, *Biochem. Biophys. Res. Commun.*, *2*, 15 (1960).
105. F. J. Simpson, *Can. J. Microbiol.*, *15*, 1365 (1969).
106. D. W. S. Westlake, J. M. Roxburgh, and G. Talbot, *Nature (London)*, *189*, 510 (1961).
107. H. P. Jayasankar, R. J. Bandoni, and G. H. N. Towers, *Phytochemistry*, *8*, 379 (1969).
108. W. Barz, *Phytochemistry*, *9*, 1745 (1970).
109. W. Barz, *Arch. Microbiol.*, *78*, 341 (1971).
110. R. T. Oglesby, R. F. Christman and C. H. Driver, *Advan. Appl. Microbiol.*, *9*, 171 (1967).
111. H. M. Hurst and N. A. Burges, in *Soil Biochemistry* (A. D. McLaren and G. H. Peterson, Eds.), Vol. 1, p. 260, Dekker, New York, 1967.
111a. R. F. Christman and R. T. Oglesby, in *Lignins* (K. V. Sarkanen and C. H. Ludwig, Eds.), p. 769, Wiley-Interscience, New York, 1971.
112. K. Kawase, *J. Fac. Agri. Hokkaido Univ.(Japan)*, *52*, 187 (1962).
113. W. Bavendamm, *Z. Pflanzenkrankh.*, *38*, 257 (1928).
114. T. K. Kirk and A. Kelman, *Phytopathology*, *55*, 739 (1965).
115. V. Sundman and L. Näse, *Paperi Ja Puu*, *2*, 67 (1971).
116. K. Seifert, *Holz Roh- und Werkst.*, *24*, 185 (1966).
117. J. G. Savory, *J. Appl. Bact.*, *17*, 213 (1954).
118. J. G. Savory, *Ann. Appl. Biol.*, *41*, 336 (1954).
119. C. F. Duncan, USDA Forest Product Laboratory, Madison, Rep. No. 2173, 1960.
120. K. Haider, *Holzforsch.*, in press (1972).
121. K. Freudenberg, *Science* (Washington), *148*, 595 (1965).
122. H. Nimz, *Chem. Ber.*, *102*, 799 (1969).
123. H. Nimz, *Chem. Ber.*, *104*, 1871 and 2359 (1971).
124. T. K. Kirk, S. Larsson, and G. E. Miksche, *Acta Chem. Scand.*, *24*, 1470 (1970).
125. V. Sundman, T. Kuusi, S. Kuhanen, S. Kilpi, and H. Sederholm, *Finska Kemists Medd.*, *77*, 2 (1968).
126. H. Jaschhof, *Geochim. Cosmochim. Acta*, *28*, 1623 (1964).
127. V. Sundman and K. Haro, *Finska Kemists Medd.*, *75*, 111 (1966).
128. A. A. Loman, *Can. J. Bot.*, *48*, 737 (1970).
129. V. Sundman, *J. Gen. Microbiol.*, *36*, 185 (1964).
130. M. M. Kononova, in *Matière organique et fertilité du sol*, *Pontifica Academiae Scientiarum Scripta Varia*, *37*, 361 (1968).
131. E. A. Paul, C. A. Campbell, D. A. Rennie, and K. J. McCallum, *Trans. 8th Int. Cong. Soil Sci.*, *2*, 44 (1964).
132. R. M. S. Perrin, E. H. Willis, and C. A. H. Hodge, *Nature (London)*, *202*, 165 (1964).
133. C. O. Tamm and H. G. Östlund, *Nature (London)*, *185*, 706 (1960).

134. J. Mayaudon and P. Simonart, *Plant Soil*, *9*, 381 (1958).
135. J. Mayaudon and P. Simonart, *Plant Soil*, *9*, 376 (1958).
136. J. Mayaudon and P. Simonart, in *The Ecology of Soil Fungi*, p. 257, Liverpool Univ. Press, Liverpool, 1961.
137. P. Simonart and J. Mayaudon, in *The Use of Isotopes in Soil Organic Matter Studies*, p. 245, FAO-IAEA, 1966.
138. R. J. Swaby and J. N. Ladd, in *The Use of Isotopes in Soil Organic Matter Studies*, p. 153, FAO-IAEA, 1966.
139. K. S. Chahal and G. H. Wagner, *Soil Sci.*, *100*, 96 (1965).
140. V. K. Mutatkar and G. H. Wagner, *Soil Sci. Soc. Amer. Proc.*, *31*, 66 (1967).
141. H. M. Hurst and G. H. Wagner, *Soil Sci. Soc. Amer. Proc.*, *33*, 707 (1969).
142. G. H. Wagner and H. Medynska-Rabinska, in *Studies about Humus*, Symp. Humus et Planta V, p. 27, Prague, 1971.
143. J. R. Wright and M. Schnitzer, *Nature (London)*, *190*, 703 (1961).
144. J. H. Warcup, in *Ecology of Soil Fungi* (K. Parkinson and J. S. Waid, Eds.), pp. 3-21, Liverpool Univ. Press, Liverpool, 1969.
145. D. P. Nicholas, D. Parkinson, and N. A. Burges, *J. Soil Sci.*, *16*, 258 (1965).
146. H. J. Kutzner, *Landw. Forsch.*, *21*, 48 (1968).
147. H. Bortels and J. Olivares, *Arch. Mikrobiol.*, *58*, 6 (1967).
147a. H. Bortels and H. G. Henkel, *Arch. Mikrobiol.*, *60*, 99 (1968).
148. S. Mann, *Arch. Mikrobiol.*, *65*, 359 (1969).
148a. V. Sundman, *Arch. Mikrobiol.*, *72*, 27 (1970).
149. S. A. Visser, *W. A. J. Appl. Chem.*, *10*, 31 (1968).
149a. I. V. Aleksandrova, *Pochvovedenie*, *6*, 23 (195), Transl. in *Soils Fert.*, *16*, 448 (1953).
150. J. P. Martin, J. O. Ervin, and R. A. Shepherd, *Soil Sci. Soc. Amer. Proc.*, *23*, 717 (1959).
151. J. J. Skujins, H. J. Potgieter, and M. Alexander, *Arch. Biochem. Biophys.*, *111*, 358 (1965).
152. M. J. Kuo and M. Alexander, *J. Bacteriol.*, *94*, 624 (1967).
153. K. S. Kang and G. T. Felbeck, *Soil Sci.*, *99*, 175 (1965).
154. G. Müller and D. Kleinhempel, *Zentbl. Bakter. Parasit. Infekt. Hyg. II*, *120*, 576 (1966).
155. F. O. Scheffer, O. v. Plotho, and W. Welte, *Landw. Forsch.*, *1*, 81 (1950).
156. W. Flaig, E. Küster, G. Segler-Holzweissig, and H. Beutelspacher, *Z. Pflanzenernähr. Düng. Bodenk.*, *57*, 42 (1952).
157. E. Küster, *Z. Pflanzenernähr. Düng. Bodenk.*, *69*, 137 (1955).
158. O. Plotho, *Z. Pflanzenernähr. Düng. Bodenk.*, *51*, 212 (1950), and *53*, 151 (1951).
159. W. Laatsch, L. Hoops, and I. Bauer, *Z. Pflanzenernähr. Düng. Bodenk.*, *53*, 20 (1951).
160. J. P. Martin, K. Haider, and D. Wolf, *Soil Sci. Soc. Amer. Proc.*, *36*, 311 (1972).
161. K. Steinbrenner and J. Matschke, in *Studies about Humus*, Symp. Humus et Planta V, p. 111, Prague, 1971.

162. M. Piatelli, E. Fatorusso, S. Magno, and R. A. Nicolaus, *Tetrahedron, 19,* 2061 (1963).
163. M. Piatelli, E. Fatorusso, S. Magno, and R. A. Nicolaus, *Tetrahedron Letters, 15,* 997 (1963).
164. R. A. Nicolaus, M. Piatelli, and E. Fatorusso, *Tetrahedron, 20,* 1163 (1964).
165. R. A. Nicolaus and M. Piatelli, *Estratto dal Rend. dell Academic di Scienze Fisiche Matematiche (Napoli) Ser. 4, 32,* 1 (1965).
166. R. A. Nicolaus, in *Melanins,* p. 127, Hermann, Paris, 1968.
167. K. H. Domsch and W. Gams, in *Pilze aus Agrarböden,* p. 222, G. Fischer, Stuttgart, 1970.
168. K. Haider and J. P. Martin, *Soil Biol. Biochem., 2,* 145 (1970).
169. E. Bondietti, J. P. Martin, and K. Haider, *Soil Sci. Soc. Amer. Proc., 35,* 917 (1971).
170. J. P. Martin, S. J. Richards, and K. Haider, *Soil Sci. Soc. Amer. Proc., 31,* 657 (1967).
171. W. A. Burges, H. M. Hurst, and B. Walkden, *Geochim. Cosmochim. Acta, 28,* 1547 (1964).
172. H. Beeken, U. v. Gizyki, E. M. Gottschalk, H. Krämer, D. Maassen, H. G. Matthies, H. Musso, C. Rathjen, and U. I. Záhorszky, *Angew, Chem. Int. Ed., 2,* 723 (1963).
173. H. Musso and U. I. Záhorzky, *Chem. Ber., 98,* 3964 (1965).
174. H. Erdtman, *Acta Chem. Scand., 13,* 653 (1959).
175. H. Musso, U. v. Gizycki, H. Krämer, and H. Döpp, *Chem. Ber., 98,* 3952 (1965).
176. H. Musso, in *Oxidative Coupling of Phenols* (W. I. Taylor and A. R. Battersby, Eds.), pp. 1-84, Dekker, New York, 1967.
177. H. S. Mason, *Advan. Enzymol., 16,* 105 (1955).
178. K. Haider, L. R. Frederick, and W. Flaig, *Plant Soil, 22,* 49 (1965).
179. R. D. Haworth, *Soil Sci., 111,* 71 (1971).
180. M. H. B. Hayes, Ph.D. Thesis, Ohio State University, 1960.
181. E. M. Trautner and E. A. H. Roberts, *Austral. J. Soil Res. Ser. B, 3,* 356 (1950).
182. J. M. Bremner, in *Soil Biochemistry* (A. D. McLaren and G. H. Peterson, Eds.), Vol. 1, p. 19, Dekker, New York, 1967.
183. H. Riemer, Ph.D. Thesis, Techn. University Braunschweig, Germany, 1970.
184. W. Flaig and H. Riemer, *Liebigs Ann. Chem., 746,* 81 (1971).
185. W. Flaig and H. Riemer, in *Studies about Humus,* Symp. Humus et Planta V, p. 519, Prague, 1971.
186. F. J. Stevenson, *Soil Sci. Soc. Amer. Proc., 24,* 472 (1960).
187. T. J. Piper and A. M. Posner, *Soil Sci., 106,* 188 (1968).
188. E. Bondietti, J. P. Martin, and K. Haider, *Soil Sci. Soc. Amer. Proc., 36,* 597 (1972).
189. L. Schánel, in *Studies about Humus,* Symp. Humus et Planta IV, p. 73, Prague, 1967.
190. H. Shimazono and F. F. Nord., *Arch. Biochem. Biophys., 78,* 263 (1958); *87,* 140 (1960).

191. D. M. Power, G. H. N. Towers, and A. C. Neish, *Can. J. Bio-chem.*, *43*, 1397 (1965).
192. G. Reed, L. C. Vining, and R. H. Haskins, *Can. J. Chem.*, *40*, 2357 (1962).
193. J. D. Bu'Lock, P. R. Leeming, and H. G. Smith, *Experientia*, *17*, 553 (1961).
194. J. D. Bu'Lock and H. G. Smith, *J. Chem. Soc.*, *1962*, 2085.
195. E. V. Loviagina, A. N. Schivrina, and E. G. Platonova, *Biokhymia*, *25*, 640 (1960).
196. J. D. Bu'Lock, Essays in *Biosynthesis and Microbial Develop-ment*, p. 71, Wiley, New York, 1967.
197. K. Kumada and O. Sato, *Soil Sci. Plant Nutr.*, *8*, 31 (1962).
198. K. Kumada, *Soil Sci. Plant Nutr.*, *11*, 151 (1965).
199. K. Kumada and O. Sato, *J. Soc. Soil Manure (Japan)*, *36*, 373 (1965).
200. A. Anderson and J. Murray, *Chem. Ind. (London)*, *1956*, 376.
201. J. D. Bu'Lock and D. C. Allport, *J. Chem. Soc.*, *1958*, 4090.
202. D. C. Allport and J. D. Bu'Lock, *J. Chem. Soc.*, *1960*, 654.
202a. E. N. Lambert, C. E. Seaworth, and N. Ahmad, *Soil Sci. Soc. Amer. Proc.*, *35*, 463 (1971).
203. A. Robertson and W. B. Whalley, *J. Chem. Soc.*, *1953*, 2434.
204. O. Sato and K. Kumada, *Soil Sci. Plant Nutr.*, *13*, 121 (1967).
205. K. Kumada and H. M. Hurst, *Nature (London)*, *214*, 631 (1967).
206. D. McGrath, *Nature (London)*, *215*, 1414 (1967).
207. M. V. Cheshire, P. A. Cranwell, and R. D. Haworth, *Tetrahedron*, *24*, 5155 (1968).
208. E. H. Hansen and M. Schnitzer, *Soil Sci. Soc. Amer. Proc.*, *33*, 29 (1967).
209. S. P. Mathur, *Soil Sci.*, *111*, 147 (1971).
210. H. M. Hurst, in *Studies about Humus*, Symp. Humus et Planta IV, p. 28, Prague, 1967.
211. K. Kumada and O. Sato, in *Studies about Humus*, Symp. Humus et Planta IV, p. 131, Prague, 1967.
212. N. P. Jayasankar and J. V. Bhat, *Can. J. Microbiol.*, *12*, 1031 (1966).
213. Z. Filip, K. Haider, and J. P. Martin, *Soil Biol. Biochem.*, *4*, 135 (1972).
214. B. Novak, *For. Social Agri. Sci. (Prague)*, *12*, 201 (1963).
215. F. Mangenot, in *Studies about Humus*, Symp. Humus et Planta V, p. 37, Prague, 1971.
216. K. C. Marshall, in *Soil Biochemistry* (A. D. McLaren and J. J. Skujins, Eds.), Vol. 2, p. 409, Dekker, New York, 1971.
217. M. Alexander, *Ann. Rev. Microbiol.*, *18*, 217 (1964).
218. T. M. McCalla, *J. Bact.*, *40*, 33 (1940).
219. G. Stotzky, *Trans. N.Y. Acad. Sci. (Ser. II)*, *30*, 11 (1967).
220. J. Kobus and A. Strezelcowa, *Rocz. Glebozn.*, *18*, 115 (1967).
221. J. Kobus and T. Pacewiczowa, *Rocz. Glebozn.*, *16*, 53 (1966).
222. Z. Filip, *Pochvovedeniye*, *9*, 55 (1968).
223. R. H. Jackman, *New Zealand J. Agri. Res.*, *7*, 445 (1964).
224. F. E. Broadbent and R. H. Jackman, *Soil Sci.*, *98*, 118 (1964).

225. D. L. Lynch, L. M. Wright and L. J. Cotnoir, *Soil Sci. Soc. Amer. Proc.*, *20*, 6 (1956).
226. C. Hess, Ph.D. Thesis, University of Göttingen, Germany, 1965.
227. S. Singh, *J. Soil Sci.*, *7*, 43 (1956).
228. E. R. Turner, *J. Soil Sci.*, *6*, 319 (1955).
229. S. A. Visser, *Nature (London)*, *196*, 1211 (1962).
230. F. Scheffer and W. Kroll, *Agrochim.*, *4*, 97 (1960).
231. K. Kyuma and K. Kawaguchi, *Soil Sci. Soc. Amer. Proc.*, *28*, 371 (1964).
232. Z. Filip, *Rostlinna Vyroba (Prague)*, *14*, 209 and 963 (1968).
233. Z. Filip, K. Haider, and J. P. Martin, *Soil Biol. Biochem.*, *4*, 147 (1972).
234. D. J. Greenland, *Soil Sci.*, *111*, 34 (1971).
235. J. Mayaudon and L. Batistic, *Ann. Inst. Pasteur*, *118*, 191 (1970).
236. J. M. Bremner, *J. Soil Sci.*, *6*, 214 (1954).
237. M. Robert-Gero, G. Vidal, C. Hardisson, L. Le Borgue, and J. Pochon, in *Studies about Humus*, Symp. Humus et Planta IV, p. 39, Prague, 1967.
238. E. Fustec-Mathon, K. Haider, and J. P. Martin, *C. R. Acad. Sci. Paris, Ser. D*, *276*, 929 (1973).
239. A. R. Mosier, K. Haider, and F. E. Clark, *J. Environ. Quality*, *1*, 320 (1972).
240. J. H. A. Butler, D. T. Downing, and R. J. Swaby, *Austral. J. Chem.*, *17*, 817 (1964).
241. M. H. B. Hayes, *Residue Rev.*, *32*, 131 (1970).
242. S. A. Barker, M. H. B. Hayes, R. G. Simmonds, and M. Stacey, *Carbohydr. Res.*, *5*, 13 (1967).
243. N. C. Metha, P. Dubach, and H. Deuel, *Advan. Carbohyd. Chem.*, *16*, 335 (1961).
244. G. D. Swincer, J. M. Oades, and D. J. Greenland, *Advan. Agron.*, *21*, 195 (1969).
245. G. T. Felbeck, in *Soil Biochemistry* (A. D. McLaren and J. Skujins, Eds.), Vol. 2, p.   , Dekker, New York, 1971.
246. G. T. Felbeck, *Advan. Agron.*, *17*, 327 (1965).
247. G. T. Felbeck, *Soil Sci.*, *111*, 42 (1971).
248. W. Flaig, H. Beutelspacher, and E. Rietz, in *Soil Science Monographs*, in press, Springer Verlag, New York, 1974.
249. Higuchi, *Advan. Enzymol.*, *34*, 207 (1971).
250. V. Sundman and L. Näse, *Arch. Microbiol.*, *86*, 339 (1972).
251. J. M. Harkin, in *Oxidative Coupling of Phenols* (W. I. Taylor and A. R. Battersby, Eds.), p. 243, Dekker, New York, 1967.
252. T. K. Kirk, J. M. Harkin, and E. B. Cowling, *Biochim. Biophys. Acta*, *165*, 134 and 145 (1968).
253. J. Trojanowski, M. Woytas-Wassilewska, and B. Junosza-Wolska, *Acta Microbiol. Pol. Ser. B*, *2*, 13 (1970).
254. N. J. Cartwright and A. R. Smith, *Biochem. J.*, *102*, 826 (1967).
255. N. J. Cartwright and J. A. Buswell, *Biochem. J.*, *105*, 767 (1967).
256. F. H. Bernhardt, H. J. Staudinger, and V. Ullrich, *Hoppe-Seyler's Z. Physiol. Chem.*, *351*, 467 (1970).

257. L. H. Sörensen, *Soil Biol. Biochem.*, *4*, 245 (1972).
258. J. L. M. Huntjens, *Soil Biol. Biochem.*, *4*, 339, 347 (1972).
259. T. J. Piper and A. M. Posner, *Soil Biol. Biochem.*, *4*, in press (1972).
260. T. J. Piper and A. M. Posner, *Soil Biol. Biochem.*, *4*, in press (1972).

AUTHOR INDEX

Numbers in brackets are reference numbers and indicate that an author's work is referred to although his name is not cited in the text. Underlined numbers give the page on which the complete reference is listed.

A

Abramovici, C., 51[80], 62
Acree, F., Jr., 120[194], 123, 139
Adams, A. F. R., 42[40], 55, 57[40, 105], 61, 63
Adams, R. S., 109[33], 113[91, 94], 134, 136
Adel, A., 9[43, 44], 27
Aebi, H., 118[154], 119[154], 138
Aelbers, E., 111[55], 135
Agundis, O., 125[203], 139
Agustin, W., 165[192], 166[192], 167[192], 192
Ahlrichs, J. L., 118[156], 138
Ahmad, N., 225[202a], 242
Akino, M., 160[99-101], 161, 189
Albergina, F., 160, 189
Albert, A., 85[187], 100
Albu-Weissenberg, M., 165[143], 167[143], 169[143], 171[143], 172[143], 176[143], 177[143], 179[143], 180[143], 191
Aldrete, J. S., 92[217], 101
Aleksandrova, I. V., 212[149a], 240
Alexander, B., 165[170], 189
Alexander, M., 70[42], 91[42, 203-206], 95, 100, 128, 141, 161, 192, 199[42-46], 212[42, 43, 151, 152], 228[217], 236, 237, 240, 242
Allen, E. K., 8[24], 26

Allen, E. R., 8[35], 10[74], 26, 28
Allen, O. N., 8[24], 26
Alley, H. P., 123[189], 139
Allport, D. C., 225, 242
Alumot, E., 160, 189
Amato, M., 144[26], 187
Ambroz, Z., 144[12], 187
Ancajas, R., 10[66], 27
Anderegg, G., 78[123], 85[123], 98
Anderson, A., 225, 242
Anderson, G., 32[3], 36[3, 9, 10], 37[3, 15, 22, 47], 38[3, 19, 21, 22], 39[3], 40[3, 27], 41[3, 32], 42[21], 43, 44[19, 22, 47], 45, 46[3], 47[63], 48[64, 66], 49[47, 70], 52[3], 60, 61, 62
Anderson, W. P., 116[136], 137
Anglade, P., 71[60, 61], 96
Anke, H., 79, 80[133], 98
Anslow, W. R., 74[96], 97
Antoine, A. D., 86[188], 87[193], 100
Aomine, S., 144[11], 187
Aoyagi, T., 92[212], 100
Applegate, H. G., 109[36], 121[36], 127[36], 134
Arceneaux, J. L., 75[112], 97
Arlidge, E. Z., 48[66], 62
Armstrong, D. E., 58[116, 117], 59[118, 119], 63, 109[27, 28, 32], 116[27, 32], 119[27, 163], 134, 138

245

SUBJECT INDEX

A

Acetohydroxamic acid, 91
Acetylphosphate, 35
Actinomycetes, 120
Actinonin, 72
Adenosine triphosphate (ATP),
  35, 59
  accumulation, 46
  assays, 45-46
  concentrations, 45-46
Aerobacter, 128
Aerobacter aerogenes (Enterobacter aerogenes), 47, 75
Aerobactin, 75-76
Agrobacterium, 234
Albomycin, 82
Albumin, reaction with chlorogenoquinone, 154
Alcohol dehydrogenase, inhibition
  of, 159
Aldolase, effect of humic acid
  on, 161
Alnus
  crispa, 6
  glutenosa, 6
Amiben, 108
Amines, in the atmosphere, 10
Amino acids, reactions with
  phenols and quinones, 151-152
Amino compounds, degradation
  of, 200-201
Amino sugars, 221
Ammonia
  in the atmosphere, 10
  formation by bacteria, 156
  phytotoxic concentrations,
  92-94
Amylase, effect of humic acid on,
  160-161

Anaerobic microenvironments, 125
Anthraquinones, in podzolic
  soil, 225
Arthrobacter
  flavescens, 83
  pascens, 76, 83
  simplex, 81
  terregens, 83, 87
Arthrobactin, 76, 83
Aspergillic acid, 68
Aspergillus sp., 204
  flavus, 68, 70, 204
  niger, 204
  sydowi, 214-215, 230
ATP, *see* Adenosine triphosphate
Atrazine, 71-72, 108

B

Bacillus, 128
  cereus, 74
  megaterium, 75, 83
  subtilis, 74, 161
p-Benzoquinone, effect of humic
  acid on, 153, 162
Benzoxazin, 70-72
Biomass, in ecosystems, 20
Bonds
  covalent, 33, 144, 146, 152-153, 156, 161, 164, 181
  electrostatic, 146, 161
  hydrogen, 144, 146, 152-153,
  155-156, 158-159, 164,
  181
  ionic, 144, 158, 164, 181
  peptide, 155, 181

C

Caffeic acid, synthesis of, 224

271